Get organ-ised for Biology with CGP...

There's a lot to learn in GCSE Biology, that's for sure. Luckily, this CGP book explains all the facts, theory and practical skills you'll need — with practice questions on each page to test you on what you've learned.

How to access your free Online Edition

This book includes a free Online Edition to read on your PC, Mac or tablet.
To access it, just go to **cgpbooks.co.uk/extras** and enter this code...

1216 2513 0082 4539

By the way, this code only works for one person. If somebody else has used this book before you, they might have already claimed the Online Edition.

Contents

Topic B6 — Global Challenges

Topic B7 — Practical Skills

Published by CGP
From original material by Richard Parsons

Editors: Christopher Lindle, Claire Plowman, Rachael Rogers, Camilla Simson
Contributor: Paddy Gannon

ISBN: 978 1 78294 566 6

With thanks to Katherine Faudemer and Jonathan Schofield for the proofreading

Printed by Elanders Ltd, Newcastle upon Tyne.
Clipart from Corel®

0800 1712 712 • www.cgpbooks.co.uk

The Scientific Method

This section isn't about how to 'do' science — but it does show you the way most scientists work.

Scientists Come Up With Hypotheses — Then Test Them

1) Scientists try to explain things. They start by observing something they don't understand.
2) They then come up with a hypothesis — a possible explanation for what they've observed.
3) The next step is to test whether the hypothesis might be right or not. This involves making a prediction based on the hypothesis and testing it by gathering evidence (i.e. data) from investigations. If evidence from experiments backs up a prediction, you're a step closer to figuring out if the hypothesis is true.

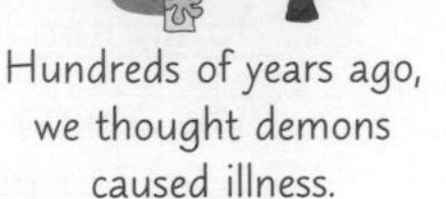

Hundreds of years ago, we thought demons caused illness.

Several Scientists Will Test a Hypothesis

1) Normally, scientists share their findings in peer-reviewed journals, or at conferences.
2) Peer-review is where other scientists check results and scientific explanations to make sure they're 'scientific' (e.g. that experiments have been done in a sensible way) before they're published. It helps to detect false claims, but it doesn't mean that findings are correct — just that they're not wrong in any obvious way.
3) Once other scientists have found out about a hypothesis, they'll start basing their own predictions on it and carry out their own experiments. They'll also try to reproduce the original experiments to check the results — and if all the experiments in the world back up the hypothesis, then scientists start to think the hypothesis is true.
4) However, if a scientist does an experiment that doesn't fit with the hypothesis (and other scientists can reproduce the results) then the hypothesis may need to be modified or scrapped altogether.

Then we thought it was caused by 'bad blood' (and treated it with leeches).

If All the Evidence Supports a Hypothesis, It's Accepted — For Now

1) Accepted hypotheses are often referred to as theories. Our currently accepted theories are the ones that have survived this 'trial by evidence' — they've been tested many times over the years and survived.
2) However, theories never become totally indisputable fact. If new evidence comes along that can't be explained using the existing theory, then the hypothesising and testing is likely to start all over again.

Now we've collected more evidence, we know that illnesses that can be spread between people are due to microorganisms.

Theories Can Involve Different Types of Models

1) A representational model is a simplified description or picture of what's going on in real life. Like all models, it can be used to explain observations and make predictions. E.g. the lock and key hypothesis of enzyme action is a simplified way of showing how enzymes work (see p.17). It can be used to explain why enzymes only catalyse particular reactions.
2) Computational models use computers to make simulations of complex real-life processes, such as climate change. They're used when there are a lot of different variables (factors that change) to consider, and because you can easily change their design to take into account new data.
3) All models have limitations on what they can explain or predict. Climate change models have several limitations — for example, it's hard to take into account all the biological and chemical processes that influence climate. It can also be difficult to include regional variations in climate.

Scientists test models by carrying out experiments to check that the predictions made by the model happen as expected.

I'm off to the zoo to test my hippo-thesis...

The scientific method has developed over time, and many people have helped to develop it. From Aristotle to modern day scientists, lots of people have contributed. And many more are likely to contribute in the future.

Communication & Issues Created by Science

Scientific developments can be great, but they can sometimes raise more questions than they answer...

It's Important to Communicate Scientific Discoveries to the General Public

Some scientific discoveries show that people should change their habits, or they might provide ideas that could be developed into new technology. So scientists need to tell the world about their discoveries.

Gene technologies are used in genetic engineering to produce genetically modified crops. Information about these crops needs to be communicated to farmers who might benefit from growing them and to the general public, so they can make informed decisions about the food they buy and eat.

Scientific Evidence can be Presented in a Biased Way

1) Reports about scientific discoveries in the media (e.g. newspapers or television) aren't peer-reviewed.
2) This means that, even though news stories are often based on data that has been peer-reviewed, the data might be presented in a way that is over-simplified or inaccurate, making it open to misinterpretation.
3) People who want to make a point can sometimes present data in a biased way. (Sometimes without knowing they're doing it.) For example, a scientist might overemphasise a relationship in the data, or a newspaper article might describe details of data supporting an idea without giving any evidence against it.

Scientific Developments are Great, but they can Raise Issues

Scientific knowledge is increased by doing experiments. And this knowledge leads to scientific developments, e.g. new technologies or new advice. These developments can create issues though. For example:

Economic issues: Society can't always afford to do things scientists recommend (e.g. investing in alternative energy sources) without cutting back elsewhere.

Social issues: Decisions based on scientific evidence affect people — e.g. should alcohol be banned (to prevent health problems)? Would the effect on people's lifestyles be acceptable...?

Personal issues: Some decisions will affect individuals. For example, someone might support alternative energy, but object if a wind farm is built next to their house.

Environmental issues: Human activity often affects the natural environment — e.g. genetically modified crops may help us to produce more food — but some people think they could cause environmental problems (see p.90).

Science Can't Answer Every Question — Especially Ethical Ones

1) We don't understand everything. We're always finding out more, but we'll never know all the answers.
2) In order to answer scientific questions, scientists need data to provide evidence for their hypotheses.
3) Some questions can't be answered yet because the data can't currently be collected, or because there's not enough data to support a theory.
4) Eventually, as we get more evidence, we'll answer some of the questions that currently can't be answered, e.g. what the impact of global warming on sea levels will be. But there will always be the "Should we be doing this at all?"-type questions that experiments can't help us to answer...

Think about new drugs which can be taken to boost your 'brain power'.

- Some people think they're good as they could improve concentration or memory. New drugs could let people think in ways beyond the powers of normal brains.
- Other people say they're bad — they could give you an unfair advantage in exams. And people might be pressured into taking them so that they could work more effectively, and for longer hours.

Tea to milk or milk to tea? — Totally unanswerable by science...

Science can't tell you whether or not you should do something. That's for you and society to decide. But there are tons of questions science might be able to answer, like where life came from and where my superhero socks are.

Risk

By reading this page you are agreeing to the risk of a paper cut or severe drowsiness...

Nothing is Completely Risk-Free

1) A hazard is something that could potentially cause harm.
2) All hazards have a risk attached to them — this is the chance that the hazard will cause harm.
3) The risks of some things seem pretty obvious, or we've known about them for a while, like the risk of causing acid rain by polluting the atmosphere, or of having a car accident when you're travelling in a car.
4) New technology arising from scientific advances can bring new risks, e.g. scientists are unsure whether nanoparticles that are being used in cosmetics and suncream might be harming the cells in our bodies. These risks need to be considered alongside the benefits of the technology, e.g. improved sun protection.
5) You can estimate the size of a risk based on how many times something happens in a big sample (e.g. 100 000 people) over a given period (e.g. a year). For example, you could assess the risk of a driver crashing by recording how many people in a group of 100 000 drivers crashed their cars over a year.
6) To make decisions about activities that involve hazards, we need to take into account the chance of the hazard causing harm, and how serious the consequences would be if it did. If an activity involves a hazard that's very likely to cause harm, with serious consequences if it does, it's considered high risk.

People Make Their Own Decisions About Risk

1) Not all risks have the same consequences, e.g. if you chop veg with a sharp knife you risk cutting your finger, but if you go scuba-diving you risk death. You're much more likely to cut your finger during half an hour of chopping than to die during half an hour of scuba-diving. But most people are happier to accept a higher probability of an accident if the consequences are short-lived and fairly minor.
2) People tend to be more willing to accept a risk if they choose to do something (e.g. go scuba diving), compared to having the risk imposed on them (e.g. having a nuclear power station built next door).
3) People's perception of risk (how risky they think something is) isn't always accurate. They tend to view familiar activities as low-risk and unfamiliar activities as high-risk — even if that's not the case. For example, cycling on roads is often high-risk, but many people are happy to do it because it's a familiar activity. Air travel is actually pretty safe, but a lot of people perceive it as high-risk.
4) People may over-estimate the risk of things with long-term or invisible effects, e.g. ionising radiation.

Investigations Can be Hazardous

1) Hazards from science experiments might include:
   - Microorganisms, e.g. some bacteria can make you ill.
   - Chemicals, e.g. sulfuric acid can burn your skin and alcohols catch fire easily.
   - Fire, e.g. an unattended Bunsen burner is a fire hazard.
   - Electricity, e.g. faulty electrical equipment could give you a shock.

Hmm... Where did my bacteria sample go?

2) Part of planning an investigation is making sure that it's safe.
3) You should always make sure that you identify all the hazards that you might encounter. Then you should think of ways of reducing the risks from the hazards you've identified. For example:
   - If you're working with sulfuric acid, always wear gloves and safety goggles. This will reduce the risk of the acid coming into contact with your skin and eyes.
   - If you're using a Bunsen burner, stand it on a heat proof mat. This will reduce the risk of starting a fire.

You can find out about potential hazards by looking in textbooks, doing some internet research, or asking your teacher.

Not revising — an unacceptable exam hazard...

The world's a dangerous place, but if you can recognise hazards, decide how to reduce their risks, and be happy to accept some risks, you can still have fun. Just maybe don't go skydiving with a great white shark on Friday 13th.

Designing Investigations

Dig out your lab coat and dust down your badly-scratched safety goggles... it's investigation time.

Investigations Produce Evidence to Support or Disprove a Hypothesis

1) Scientists observe things and come up with hypotheses to explain them (see p.2). You need to be able to do the same. For example:

> Observation: People have big feet and spots. Hypothesis: Having big feet causes spots.

2) To determine whether or not a hypothesis is right, you need to do an investigation to gather evidence. To do this, you need to use your hypothesis to make a prediction — something you think will happen that you can test. E.g. people who have bigger feet will have more spots.
3) Investigations are used to see if there are patterns or relationships between two variables, e.g. to see if there's a pattern or relationship between the variables 'number of spots' and 'size of feet'.

Evidence Needs to be Repeatable, Reproducible and Valid

Investigations include experiments and studies.

1) Repeatable means that if the same person does an experiment again using the same methods and equipment, they'll get similar results.
2) Reproducible means that if someone else does the experiment, or a different method or piece of equipment is used, the results will still be similar.

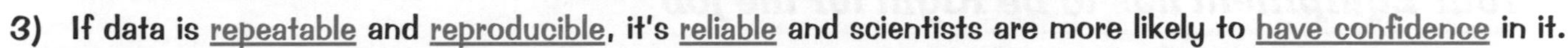

3) If data is repeatable and reproducible, it's reliable and scientists are more likely to have confidence in it.
4) Valid results are both repeatable and reproducible AND they answer the original question. They come from experiments that were designed to be a FAIR TEST...

To Make an Investigation a Fair Test You Have to Control the Variables

1) In a lab experiment you usually change one variable and measure how it affects another variable.
2) To make it a fair test, everything else that could affect the results should stay the same — otherwise you can't tell if the thing you're changing is causing the results or not.
3) The variable you CHANGE is called the INDEPENDENT variable.
4) The variable you MEASURE when you change the independent variable is the DEPENDENT variable.
5) The variables that you KEEP THE SAME are called CONTROL variables.

> You could find how temperature affects the rate of an enzyme-controlled reaction. The independent variable is the temperature. The dependent variable is the rate of reaction. Control variables include the concentration and amounts of reactants, pH, the time period you measure, etc.

6) Because you can't always control all the variables, you often need to use a control experiment. This is an experiment that's kept under the same conditions as the rest of the investigation, but doesn't have anything done to it. This is so that you can see what happens when you don't change anything at all.

The Bigger the Sample Size the Better

1) Data based on small samples isn't as good as data based on large samples. A sample should represent the whole population (i.e. it should share as many of the characteristics in the population as possible) — a small sample can't do that as well. It's also harder to spot anomalies if your sample size is too small.
2) The bigger the sample size the better, but scientists have to be realistic when choosing how big. For example, if you were studying how lifestyle affects people's weight it'd be great to study everyone in the UK (a huge sample), but it'd take ages and cost a bomb. It's more realistic to study a thousand people, with a mixture of ages, gender and race.

This is no high street survey — it's a designer investigation...

Not only do you need to be able to plan your own investigations, you should also be able to look at someone else's plan and decide whether or not it needs improving. Those examiners aren't half demanding.

Collecting Data

You've designed the perfect investigation — now it's time to get your hands mucky and collect some data.

Your Data Should be Repeatable, Reproducible, Accurate and Precise

1) To check repeatability you need to repeat the readings and check that the results are similar. You need to repeat each reading at least three times.
2) To make sure your results are reproducible you can cross check them by taking a second set of readings with another instrument (or a different observer).
3) Your data also needs to be ACCURATE. Really accurate results are those that are really close to the true answer. The accuracy of your results usually depends on your method — you need to make sure you're measuring the right thing and that you don't miss anything that should be included in the measurements. E.g. estimating the amount of gas released from a reaction by counting the bubbles isn't very accurate because you might miss some of the bubbles and they might have different volumes. It's more accurate to measure the volume of gas released using a gas syringe (see p.110).
4) Your data also needs to be PRECISE. Precise results are ones where the data is all really close to the mean (average) of your repeated results (i.e. not spread out).

Brian's result was a curate.

Repeat	Data set 1	Data set 2
1	12	11
2	14	17
3	13	14
Mean	13	14

Data set 1 is more precise than data set 2.

Your Equipment has to be Right for the Job

1) The measuring equipment you use has to be sensitive enough to measure the changes you're looking for. For example, if you need to measure changes of 1 cm^3 you need to use a measuring cylinder that can measure in 1 cm^3 steps — it'd be no good trying with one that only measures in 10 cm^3 steps.
2) The smallest change a measuring instrument can detect is called its RESOLUTION. E.g. some mass balances have a resolution of 1 g, some have a resolution of 0.1 g, and some are even more sensitive.
3) Also, equipment needs to be calibrated by measuring a known value. If there's a difference between the measured and known value, you can use this to correct the inaccuracy of the equipment.

You Need to Look out for Errors and Anomalous Results

1) The results of your experiment will always vary a bit because of RANDOM ERRORS — unpredictable differences caused by things like human errors in measuring. E.g. the errors you make when reading from a measuring cylinder are random. You have to estimate or round the level when it's between two marks — so sometimes your figure will be a bit above the real one, and sometimes it will be a bit below.
2) You can reduce the effect of random errors by taking repeat readings and finding the mean. This will make your results more precise.
3) If a measurement is wrong by the same amount every time, it's called a SYSTEMATIC ERROR. For example, if you measured from the very end of your ruler instead of from the 0 cm mark every time, all your measurements would be a bit small. Repeating the experiment in the exact same way and calculating a mean won't correct a systematic error.
4) Just to make things more complicated, if a systematic error is caused by using equipment that isn't zeroed properly, it's called a ZERO ERROR. For example, if a mass balance always reads 1 gram before you put anything on it, all your measurements will be 1 gram too heavy.
5) You can compensate for some systematic errors if you know about them though, e.g. if your mass balance always reads 1 gram before you put anything on it you can subtract 1 gram from all your results.
6) Sometimes you get a result that doesn't fit in with the rest at all. This is called an ANOMALOUS RESULT. You should investigate it and try to work out what happened. If you can work out what happened (e.g. you measured something totally wrong) you can ignore it when processing your results.

If there's no systematic error, then doing repeats and calculating a mean can make your results more accurate.

Watch what you say to that mass balance — it's very sensitive...

Weirdly, data can be really precise but not very accurate. For example, a fancy piece of lab equipment might give results that are really precise, but if it's not been calibrated properly those results won't be accurate.

Processing and Presenting Data

Processing your data means doing some calculations with it to make it more useful. Once you've done that, you can present your results in a nice chart or graph to help you spot any patterns in your data.

Data Needs to be Organised

Tables are dead useful for organising data. When you draw a table use a ruler and make sure each column has a heading (including the units).

You Might Have to Process Your Data

1) When you've done repeats of an experiment you should always calculate the mean (a type of average). To do this add together all the data values and divide by the total number of values in the sample.
2) You might also need to calculate the range (how spread out the data is). To do this find the largest number and subtract the smallest number from it.

Ignore anomalous results when calculating these.

EXAMPLE: The results of an experiment to find the volume of gas produced in an enzyme-controlled reaction are shown below. Calculate the mean volume and the range.

Repeat 1 (cm^3)	Repeat 2 (cm^3)	Repeat 3 (cm^3)	Mean (cm^3)	Range (cm^3)
28	37	32	$(28 + 37 + 32) \div 3 = 32$	$37 - 28 = 9$

3) You might also need to calculate the median or mode (two more types of average). To calculate the median, put all your data in numerical order — the median is the middle value. The number that appears most often in a data set is the mode.

E.g. If you have the data set: 1 2 1 1 3 4 2
The median is: 1 1 1 2 2 3 4. The mode is 1 because 1 appears most often.

If you have an even number of values, the median is halfway between the middle two values.

Round to the Lowest Number of Significant Figures

The first significant figure of a number is the first digit that's not zero. The second and third significant figures come straight after (even if they're zeros). You should be aware of significant figures in calculations.

1) In any calculation, you should round the answer to the lowest number of significant figures (s.f.) given.
2) Remember to write down how many significant figures you've rounded to after your answer.
3) If your calculation has multiple steps, only round the final answer, or it won't be as accurate.

EXAMPLE: A plant produces 10.2 cm^3 of oxygen in 6.5 minutes whilst photosynthesising. Calculate the rate of photosynthesis.

rate = 10.2 cm^3 ÷ 6.5 min = 1.5692... = 1.6 cm^3/min (2 s.f.) — Final answer should be rounded to 2 s.f.

(10.2: 3 s.f.; 6.5: 2 s.f.)

If Your Data Comes in Categories, Present It in a Bar Chart

1) If the independent variable is categoric (comes in distinct categories, e.g. flower colour, blood group) you should use a bar chart to display the data.
2) You also use them if the independent variable is discrete (the data can be counted in chunks, where there's no in-between value, e.g. number of bacteria is discrete because you can't have half a bacterium).
3) There are some golden rules you need to follow for drawing bar charts:

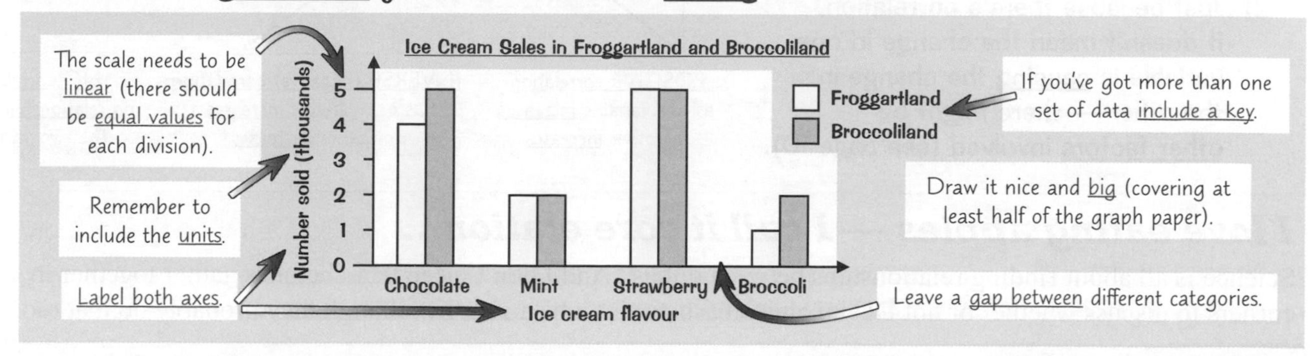

If Your Data is Continuous, Plot a Graph

If both variables are continuous (numerical data that can have any value within a range, e.g. length, volume, temperature) you should use a graph to display the data.

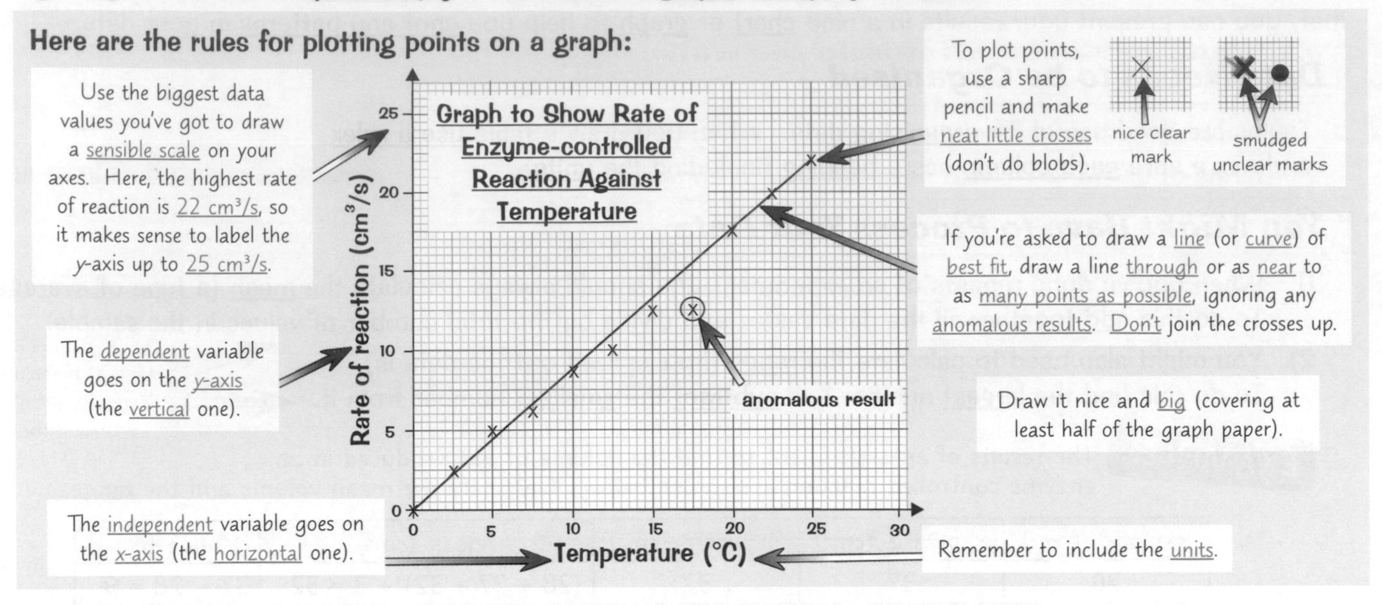

Graphs Can Give You a Lot of Information About Your Data

1) The gradient (slope) of a graph tells you how quickly the dependent variable changes if you change the independent variable.

$$\text{gradient} = \frac{\text{change in } y}{\text{change in } x}$$

This graph shows the volume of gas produced in a reaction against time. The graph is linear (it's a straight line graph), so you can simply calculate the gradient of the line to find out the rate of reaction.

1) To calculate the gradient, pick two points on the line that are easy to read and a good distance apart.
2) Draw a line down from one of the points and a line across from the other to make a triangle. The line drawn down the side of the triangle is the change in y and the line across the bottom is the change in x.

Volume of gas (cm³) — Time (s) — change in y — change in x

Change in y = 6.8 – 2.0 = 4.8 cm³   Change in x = 5.2 – 1.6 = 3.6 s

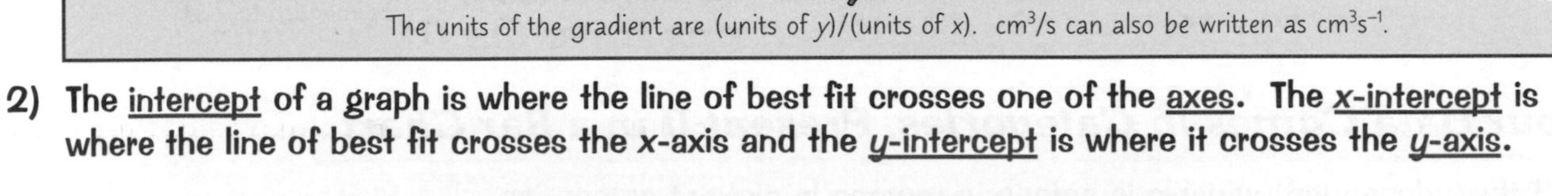

$$\text{Rate} = \text{gradient} = \frac{\text{change in } y}{\text{change in } x} = \frac{4.8 \text{ cm}^3}{3.6 \text{ s}} = 1.3 \text{ cm}^3\text{/s or } 1.3 \text{ cm}^3\text{s}^{-1}$$

The units of the gradient are (units of y)/(units of x). cm³/s can also be written as cm³s⁻¹.

You can use this method to calculate other rates from a graph, not just the rate of a reaction. Just remember that a rate is how much something changes over time, so x needs to be the time.

2) The intercept of a graph is where the line of best fit crosses one of the axes. The x-intercept is where the line of best fit crosses the x-axis and the y-intercept is where it crosses the y-axis.

Graphs Show the Relationship Between Two Variables

1) You can get three types of correlation (relationship) between variables:
2) Just because there's correlation, it doesn't mean the change in one variable is causing the change in the other — there might be other factors involved (see page 10).

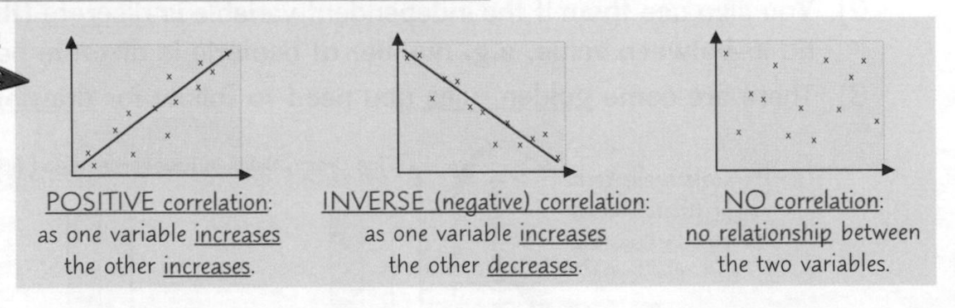

POSITIVE correlation: as one variable increases the other increases.

INVERSE (negative) correlation: as one variable increases the other decreases.

NO correlation: no relationship between the two variables.

I love eating apples — I call it core elation...

Science is all about finding relationships between things. And I don't mean that chemists gather together in corners to discuss whether or not Devini and Sebastian might be a couple... though they probably do that too.

Units and Equations

Graphs and maths skills are all very well, but the numbers don't mean much if you can't get the units right.

S.I. Units Are Used All Round the World

1) It wouldn't be all that useful if I defined volume in terms of bath tubs, you defined it in terms of egg-cups and my pal Sarwat defined it in terms of balloons — we'd never be able to compare our data.
2) To stop this happening, scientists have come up with a set of standard units, called S.I. units, that all scientists use to measure their data. Here are some S.I. units you'll see in biology:

Quantity	S.I. Base Unit
mass	kilogram, kg
length	metre, m
time	second, s

Scaling Prefixes Can Be Used for Large and Small Quantities

1) Quantities come in a huge range of sizes. For example, the volume of a swimming pool might be around 2 000 000 000 cm^3, while the volume of a cup is around 250 cm^3
2) To make the size of numbers more manageable, larger or smaller units are used. These are the S.I. base unit (e.g. metres) with a prefix in front:

prefix	tera (T)	giga (G)	mega (M)	kilo (k)	deci (d)	centi (c)	milli (m)	micro (μ)	nano (n)
multiple of unit	10^{12}	10^{9}	1 000 000 (10^{6})	1000	0.1	0.01	0.001	0.000001 (10^{-6})	10^{-9}

3) These prefixes tell you how much bigger or smaller a unit is than the base unit. So one kilometre is one thousand metres.

The conversion factor is the number of times the smaller unit goes into the larger unit.

4) To swap from one unit to another, all you need to know is what number you have to divide or multiply by to get from the original unit to the new unit — this is called the conversion factor.

- To go from a bigger unit (like m) to a smaller unit (like cm), you multiply by the conversion factor.
- To go from a smaller unit (like g) to a bigger unit (like kg), you divide by the conversion factor.

5) Here are some conversions that'll be useful for GCSE biology:

Mass can have units of kg and g.

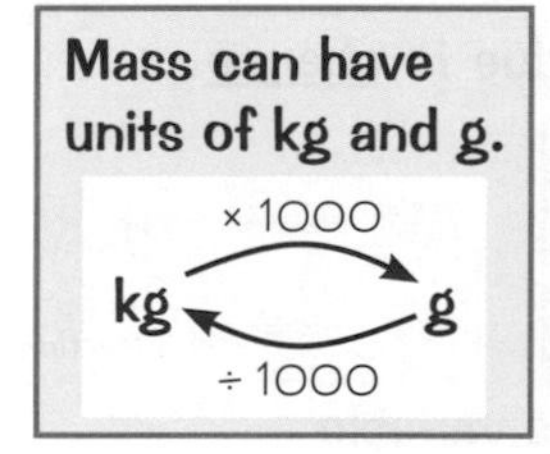

Length can have lots of units, including mm, μm and nm.

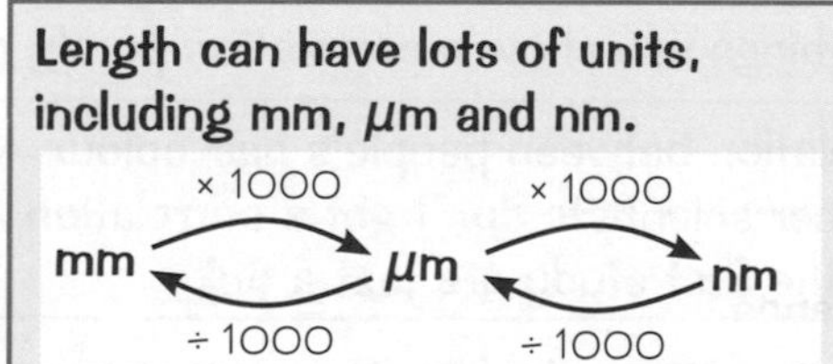

Time can have units of min and s.

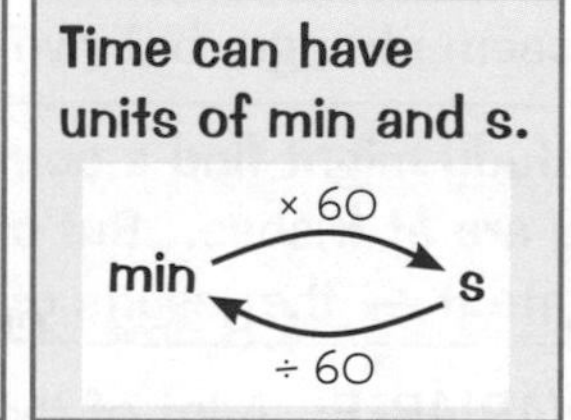

Volume can have units of m^3, dm^3 and cm^3.

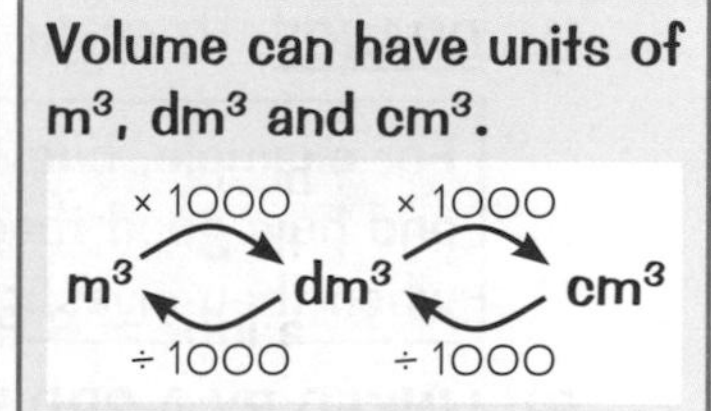

Always Check The Values Used in Equations Have the Right Units

1) Formulas and equations show relationships between variables.
2) To rearrange an equation, make sure that whatever you do to one side of the equation you also do to the other side.

You can find the magnification of something using the equation: magnification = image size ÷ real size (see p.14). You can rearrange this equation to find the image size by multiplying each side by the real size: image size = magnification × real size.

3) To use a formula, you need to know the values of all but one of the variables. Substitute the values you do know into the formula, and do the calculation to work out the final variable.
4) Always make sure the values you put into an equation or formula have the right units. For example, if you're calculating the magnification of something, but your image size is in mm and the real size is in μm, you'll have to convert both measurements into the same unit (either mm or μm) before you start.
5) To make sure your units are correct, it can help to write down the units on each line of your calculation.

I wasn't sure I liked units, but now I'm converted...

It's easy to get in a muddle when converting between units, but there's a handy way to check you've done it right. If you're moving from a smaller unit to a larger unit (e.g. g to kg) the number should get smaller, and vice versa.

Drawing Conclusions

Congratulations — you're nearly at the end of a gruelling investigation, time to draw conclusions.

You Can Only Conclude What the Data Shows and NO MORE

1) Drawing conclusions might seem pretty straightforward — you just look at your data and say what pattern or relationship you see between the dependent and independent variables.

The table on the right shows the heights of pea plant seedlings grown for three weeks with different fertilisers.

Fertiliser	Mean growth / mm
A	13.5
B	19.5
No fertiliser	5.5

CONCLUSION: Fertiliser B makes pea plant seedlings grow taller over a three week period than fertiliser A.

2) But you've got to be really careful that your conclusion matches the data you've got and doesn't go any further.

   You can't conclude that fertiliser B makes any other type of plant grow taller than fertiliser A — the results could be totally different.

3) You also need to be able to use your results to justify your conclusion (i.e. back up your conclusion with some specific data).

   Over the three week period, fertiliser B made the pea plants grow 6 mm more on average than fertiliser A.

4) When writing a conclusion you need to refer back to the original hypothesis and say whether the data supports it or not:

   The hypothesis for this experiment might have been that adding fertiliser would increase the growth of plants and that different types of fertiliser would affect growth by different amounts. If so, the data supports the hypothesis.

Correlation DOES NOT Mean Cause

If two things are correlated (i.e. there's a relationship between them) it doesn't necessarily mean a change in one variable is causing the change in the other — this is REALLY IMPORTANT — DON'T FORGET IT. There are three possible reasons for a correlation:

1) CHANCE: It might seem strange, but two things can show a correlation purely due to chance.

   For example, one study might find a correlation between people's hair colour and how good they are at frisbee. But other scientists don't get a correlation when they investigate it — the results of the first study are just a fluke.

2) LINKED BY A 3RD VARIABLE: A lot of the time it may look as if a change in one variable is causing a change in the other, but it isn't — a third variable links the two things.

   For example, there's a correlation between water temperature and shark attacks. This isn't because warmer water makes sharks crazy. Instead, they're linked by a third variable — the number of people swimming (more people swim when the water's hotter, and with more people in the water you get more shark attacks).

3) CAUSE: Sometimes a change in one variable does cause a change in the other. You can only conclude that a correlation is due to cause when you've controlled all the variables that could, just could, be affecting the result.

   For example, there's a correlation between smoking and lung cancer. This is because chemicals in tobacco smoke cause lung cancer. This conclusion was only made once other variables (such as age and exposure to other things that cause cancer) had been controlled and shown not to affect people's risk of getting lung cancer.

I conclude that this page is a bit dull...

...although, just because I find it dull doesn't mean that I can conclude it's dull (you might think it's the most interesting thing since that kid got his head stuck in the railings near school). In the exams you could be given a conclusion and asked whether some data supports it — so make sure you understand how far conclusions can go.

Uncertainties and Evaluations

Hurrah! The end of another investigation. Well, now you have to work out all the things you did wrong.

Uncertainty is the Amount of Error Your Measurements Might Have

1) When you repeat a measurement, you often get a slightly different figure each time you do it due to random error. This means that each result has some uncertainty to it.
2) The measurements you make will also have some uncertainty in them due to limits in the resolution of the equipment you use (see page 6).
3) This all means that the mean of a set of results will also have some uncertainty to it. You can calculate the uncertainty of a mean result using the equation:
4) The larger the range, the less precise your results are and the more uncertainty there will be in your results. Uncertainties are shown using the '±' symbol.

The range is the largest value minus the smallest value (p.7).

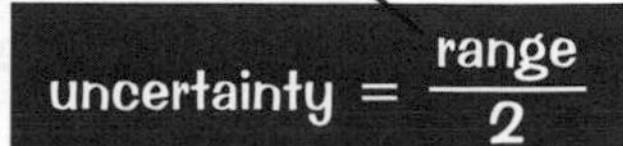

The table below shows the results of a respiration experiment to determine the volume of carbon dioxide produced. Calculate the uncertainty of the mean.

Repeat	1	2	3	mean
Volume of CO_2 produced (cm^3)	20.2	19.8	20.0	20.0

1) First work out the range:
Range = 20.2 − 19.8
= 0.4 cm^3

2) Use the range to find the uncertainty:
Uncertainty = range ÷ 2 = 0.4 ÷ 2 = 0.2 cm^3.

So the uncertainty of the mean = 20.0 ± 0.2 cm^3

5) Measuring a greater amount of something helps to reduce uncertainty. For example, in a rate of reaction experiment, measuring the amount of product formed over a longer period compared to a shorter period will reduce the percentage uncertainty in your results.

Evaluations — Describe How it Could be Improved

An evaluation is a critical analysis of the whole investigation.

1) You should comment on the method — was it valid? Did you control all the other variables to make it a fair test?
2) Comment on the quality of the results — was there enough evidence to reach a valid conclusion? Were the results repeatable, reproducible, accurate and precise?
3) Were there any anomalous results? If there were none then say so. If there were any, try to explain them — were they caused by errors in measurement? Were there any other variables that could have affected the results? You should comment on the level of uncertainty in your results too.

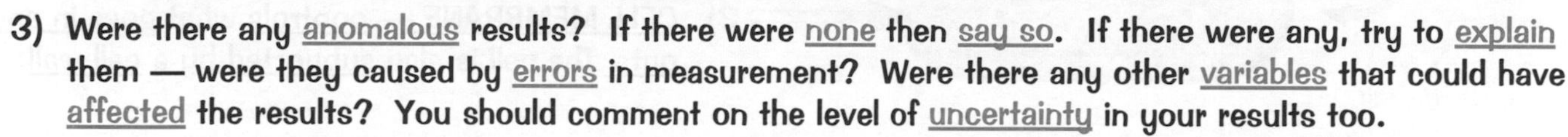

4) All this analysis will allow you to say how confident you are that your conclusion is right.
5) Then you can suggest any changes to the method that would improve the quality of the results, so that you could have more confidence in your conclusion. For example, you might suggest changing the way you controlled a variable, or increasing the number of measurements you took. Taking more measurements at narrower intervals could give you a more accurate result. For example:

> Enzymes have an optimum temperature (a temperature at which they work best). Say you do an experiment to find an enzyme's optimum temperature and take measurements at 10 °C, 20 °C, 30 °C, 40 °C and 50 °C. The results of this experiment tell you the optimum is 40 °C. You could then repeat the experiment, taking more measurements around 40 °C to a get a more accurate value for the optimum.

6) You could also make more predictions based on your conclusion, then further experiments could be carried out to test them.

When suggesting improvements to the investigation, always make sure that you say why you think this would make the results better.

Evaluation — next time, I'll make sure I don't burn the lab down...

So there you have it — Working Scientifically. Make sure you know this stuff like the back of your hand. It's not just in the lab that you'll need to know how to work scientifically. You can be asked about it in the exams as well.

Cells and Microscopy

Biology's all about living stuff. And all living stuff contains cells. So let's make a start with cells...

Organisms can be Eukaryotes or Prokaryotes

1) Eukaryotes (e.g. all animals and plants) are made from complex cells called eukaryotic cells.
2) Prokaryotes (e.g. bacteria) are smaller and simpler cells called prokaryotic cells.
3) Both types of cells contain sub-cellular structures — parts of cells that each have a specific function.

You Need to Learn the Structures Within Eukaryotic Cells...

ANIMAL CELL

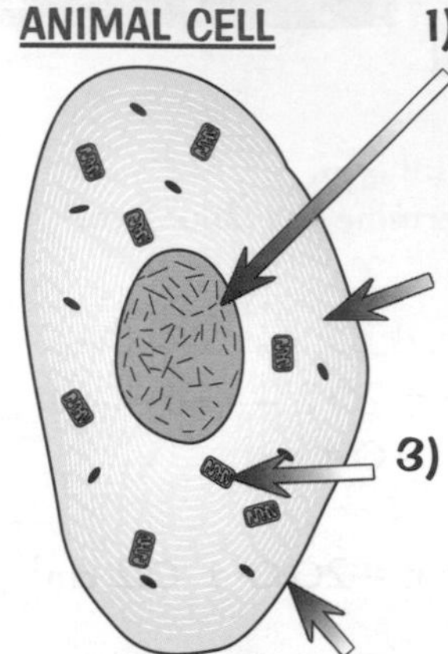

1) NUCLEUS — contains DNA (genetic material) in the form of chromosomes (see p.15) that controls the cell's activities.
2) CYTOPLASM — gel-like substance where most of the chemical reactions happen.
3) MITOCHONDRIA — these are the site of cellular respiration (see p.20) and contain the enzymes needed for the reactions involved.
4) CELL MEMBRANE — holds the cell together and controls what goes in and out by providing a selective barrier (see p.30). They also contain receptor molecules that are used for cell communication, e.g. by hormones.

PLANT CELL — plant cells include everything animal cells have as well as these extras:

1) RIGID CELL WALL — made of cellulose, gives support for the cell.
2) CHLOROPLASTS — where photosynthesis occurs (see p.25). They contain a green substance called chlorophyll.

...and Within Prokaryotic Cells

1) CHROMOSOMAL DNA — (one long circular chromosome) controls the cell's activities and replication. It floats free in the cytoplasm (not in a nucleus).
2) PLASMIDS — small loops of extra DNA that aren't part of the chromosome. Plasmids contain genes for things like drug resistance, and can be passed between bacteria.
3) CELL MEMBRANE — controls what goes in and out. The cell is also supported by a cell wall.

A bacterial cell

Cells are Studied Using Microscopes

There's loads more on light microscopes coming up on the next two pages.

1) Microscopes use lenses to magnify images (make them look bigger).
2) They also increase the resolution of an image. This means they increase the detail you can see. Resolution is how well a microscope distinguishes between two points that are close together.
3) Light microscopes were invented in the 1590s. They let us see things like nuclei and chloroplasts.
4) Electron microscopes were invented in the 1930s. They let us see much smaller things in more detail like the internal structure of mitochondria. This has allowed us to have a much greater understanding of sub-cellular structures. Only electron microscopes will let us see things as tiny as plasmids or viruses.
5) Transmission electron microscopes (TEMs) have a higher magnification and resolution than light microscopes but they're not portable, they're expensive and it's a complicated process to prepare specimens for use (which means they can't be used to look at living tissue, unlike light microscopes).

Cell structures — become an estate agent...

The number of some sub-cellular structures will depend on the cell's function, e.g. muscle cells, which respire lots, will have more mitochondria than other cells, and plant cells that don't get any light won't have chloroplasts.

Q1 Give two functions of the cell membrane in an animal cell. [2 marks]

Light Microscopy

PRACTICAL

Ah, the light microscope — that great scientific invention that has enabled us to get up close and personal with the humble cell (and other really small things). Here's how to use one...

You Need to Be Familiar with the Parts of a Light Microscope

Here are the main parts of a light microscope and what they do:

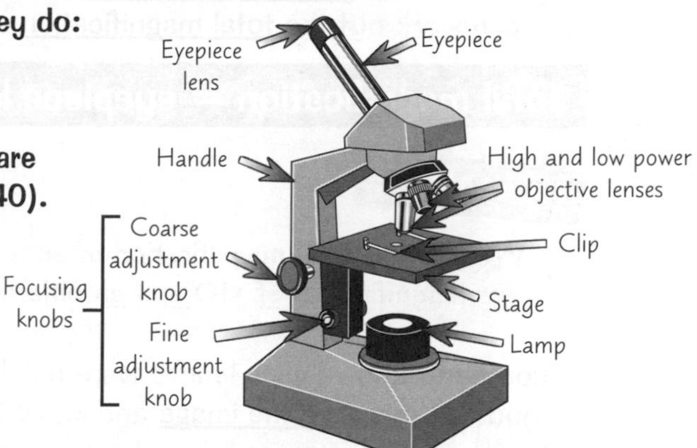

- Eyepiece lens — looked through to see the image and also magnifies the image.
- Objective lens — magnifies the image. Usually there are three different objective lenses (e.g. ×4, ×10 and ×40).
- Stage — supports the slide (see below).
- Clip — holds the slide in place.
- Handle — to carry the microscope with.
- Lamp — shines light through the slide so the image can be seen more easily.
- Focusing knobs — move the stage up and down to bring the image into focus.

Specimens Need to be Prepared Before Investigation...

1) Your specimen (the sample you're looking at) needs to let light through it for you to be able to see it clearly — if you've got quite a thick specimen, you'll need to take a thin slice of it to start with.
2) Next, take a clean slide (a strip of clear glass or plastic) and use a pipette to put one drop of water or mountant (a clear, gloopy liquid) in the middle of it — this will secure the specimen in place.
3) Use tweezers to place your specimen on the slide.
4) Add a drop of stain if needed — if your specimen is completely transparent or colourless, a drop of stain is added to make the specimen easier to see. Different stains are used to highlight different structures or tissues. For example, eosin is used to stain cytoplasm and methylene blue stains DNA.
5) Place a cover slip (a square of thin, transparent plastic or glass) at one end of the specimen, holding it at an angle with a mounted needle.
6) Carefully lower the cover slip onto the slide. Press it down gently with the needle so that no air bubbles are trapped under it.

mounted needle
cover slip
slide
specimen and water/mountant

... Then You're Ready for Viewing

1) Start by clipping the slide containing your specimen onto the stage.
2) Select the lowest-powered objective lens (i.e. the one that produces the lowest magnification).
3) Use the coarse adjustment knob to move the stage up to just below the objective lens. Then, looking down the eyepiece, move the stage downwards (so you don't accidently crash the slide into the lens) until the specimen is just about in focus.
4) Then, still looking down the eyepiece, adjust the focus with the fine adjustment knob, until you get a clear image of your specimen.
5) If you need to see your specimen with greater magnification, swap to a higher-powered objective lens and refocus.

A higher magnification isn't always a good thing — if your specimen is relatively big you might not be able to see the whole thing. It can also be difficult to focus at high magnifications.

Once you're happy with what you can see, you can produce a scientific drawing of your specimen (see p.111).

Mi-cros-copy — when my twin gets annoyed...

Yowch. Sorry. Anyway, there's some important stuff about using microscopes here, so get learning.

Q1 A scientist wants to use a light microscope to view the cell walls of a colourless sample of plant tissue. Describe how she could prepare a slide containing the tissue, where the cell walls are visible. [4 marks]

More on Light Microscopy

Sometimes you need to do a bit of maths with microscope images. It's time to get your numbers head on...

Magnification is How Many Times Bigger the Image is than its Real Size

1) If you know the power of the lenses used by a microscope to view an image, you can work out the total magnification of the image using this simple formula:

total magnification = eyepiece lens magnification × objective lens magnification

EXAMPLE:

What is the total magnification of an image viewed with an eyepiece lens magnification of ×10 and an objective lens magnification of ×40?

10 × 40 = 400, so the total magnification is ×400

2) If you don't know which lenses were used, you can still work out the magnification of an image as long as you can measure the image and know the real size of the specimen. This is the formula you need:

$$\text{magnification} = \frac{\text{image size}}{\text{real size}}$$

Both measurements should have the same units. If they don't, you'll need to convert them first (see p.9).

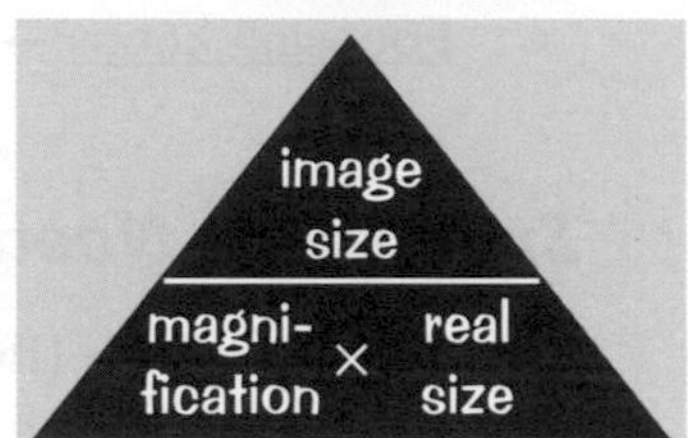

If you want to work out the image size or the real size of the object, you can rearrange the equation using the formula triangle. Cover up the thing you're trying to find. The parts you can still see are the formula you need to use.

EXAMPLE: A specimen is 50 μm wide. Calculate the width of the image of the specimen under a magnification of ×100. Give your answer in mm.

1) Rearrange the magnification formula. image size = magnification × real size
2) Fill in the values you know. image size = 100 × 50
3) Remember the units in your answer. = 5000 μm
4) Convert the units. = 5 mm

Remember, to convert from micrometres (μm) to millimetres (mm), you need to divide by 1000 (see p.9).

You Need to Know How to Work With Numbers in Standard Form

1) Because microscopes can see such tiny objects sometimes it's useful to write numbers in standard form.
2) This is where you change very big or small numbers with lots of zeros into something more manageable, e.g. 0.017 can be written 1.7×10^{-2}.
3) To do this you just need to move the decimal point left or right.
4) The number of places the decimal point moves is then represented by a power of 10 — this is positive if the decimal point's moved to the left, and negative if it's moved to the right.

EXAMPLE: A mitochondrion is approximately 0.0025 mm long. Write this figure in standard form.

1) The first number needs to be between 1 and 10 so the decimal point needs to move after the '2'.

0.0025

2) Count how many places the decimal point has moved — this is the power of 10. Don't forget the minus sign because the decimal point has moved right.

2.5×10^{-3}

You can put standard form numbers into your calculator using the 'EXP' or the '$\times 10^x$' button. E.g. enter 2.67×10^{15} by pressing 2.67 then 'EXP' then 15.

Gather your microscopes, comrades — it's the bio resolution...

Congratulations — you've made it to the end of the microscopy pages. If the whole concept of microscopy has yet to swim into focus, go back and have another read through. Then make yourself a nice cup of tea.

Q1 Calculate the magnification of images viewed with an eyepiece lens magnification of ×8 and an objective lens magnification of ×15. [1 mark]

DNA

DNA is a big, big deal in biology, but the mystery of its structure was only solved relatively recently. Luckily, you get to learn all about it, so pen at the ready, thinking cap on... woah there, we nearly forgot the biscuits...

DNA — a Double Helix of Paired Bases

DNA contains all of an organism's genetic material — the chemical instructions it needs to grow and develop. DNA is arranged into chromosomes.

1) Chromosomes are long molecules of coiled up DNA. The DNA is divided up into short sections called genes (see next page).
2) DNA is a double helix (a double-stranded spiral). Each of the two DNA strands is made up of lots of nucleotides joined together in a long chain — this makes DNA a polymer (see below).
3) Each nucleotide contains a small molecule called a "base". DNA has just four different bases.
4) The bases are A (adenine), C (cytosine), G (guanine) and T (thymine).
5) Each base forms cross links to a base on the other strand. This keeps the two DNA strands tightly wound together.
6) A always pairs up with T, and C always pairs up with G. This is called complementary base-pairing.

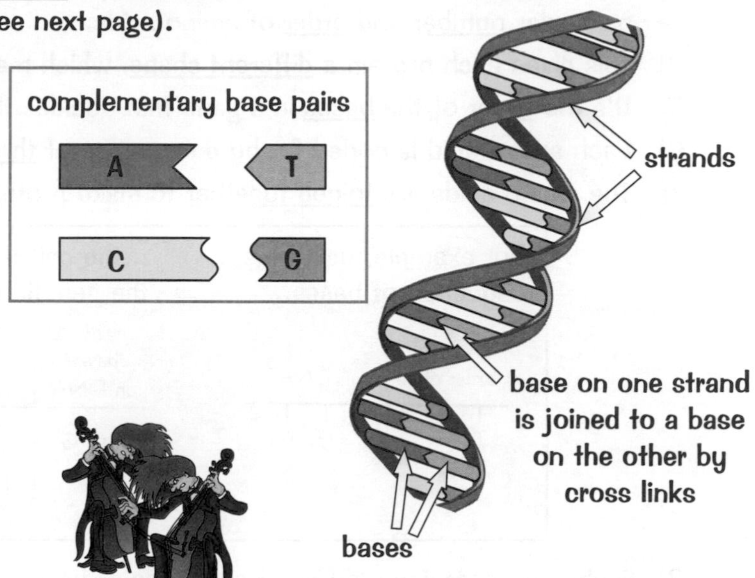

Nucleotides Contain a Sugar, a Phosphate Group and a Base

1) Each DNA nucleotide has the same sugar and a phosphate group. The base on each nucleotide is the only part of the molecule that varies (i.e. it's either A, C, G or T).
2) The base is attached to the sugar.

DNA nucleotide

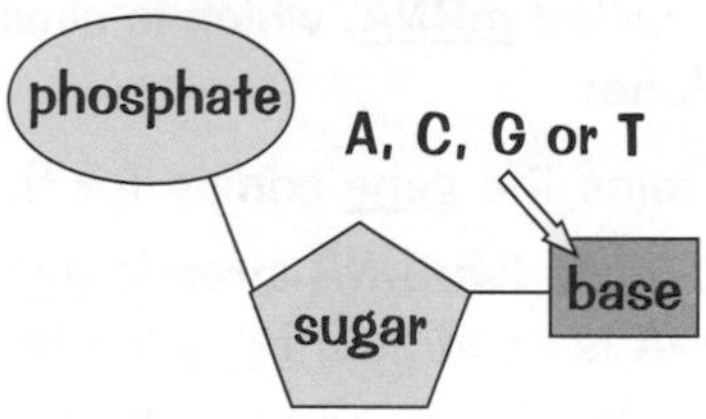

phosphate

A, C, G or T

base

sugar

DNA is a Polymer

1) Polymers are large, complex molecules composed of long chains of monomers joined together.
2) Monomers are small, basic molecular units.
3) DNA is a polymer made up of nucleotide monomers.

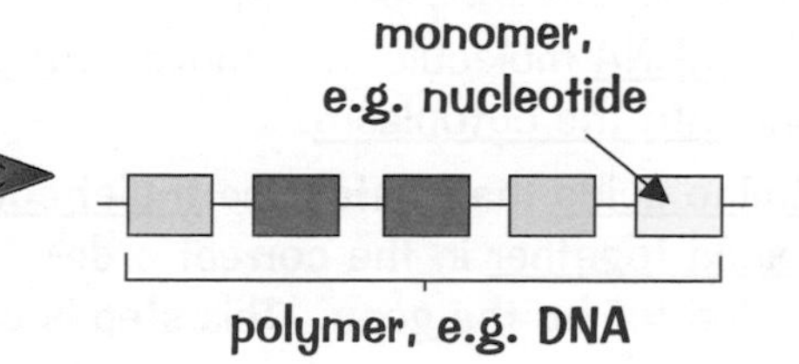

Complementary base pairs — oh A, darling, you are stunning...

The complementary base-pairing thing is mega important in protein synthesis (see next page) so make sure you've got your head around it. Then you can treat yourself to some twisty crisps and imagine you're eating DNA.

Q1 Why can DNA be described as a polymer? [1 mark]

Q2 a) Which base does 'C' pair with in DNA? [1 mark]

b) Explain the effect of base-pairing on the structure of DNA. [2 marks]

Protein Synthesis

So here's how life works — DNA molecules contain a genetic code that determines which proteins are built. The proteins determine how all the cells in the body function. Simple, eh.

Proteins are Made by Reading the Code in DNA

1) DNA controls the production of proteins (protein synthesis) in a cell.
2) A section of DNA that codes for a particular protein is called a gene.
3) Proteins are made up of chains of molecules called amino acids. Each different protein has its own particular number and order of amino acids.
4) This gives each protein a different shape, which means each protein can have a different function.
5) It's the order of the bases in a gene that decides the order of amino acids in a protein.
6) Each amino acid is coded for by a sequence of three bases in the gene — this is called a triplet code.
7) The amino acids are joined together to make proteins, following the order of the bases in the gene.

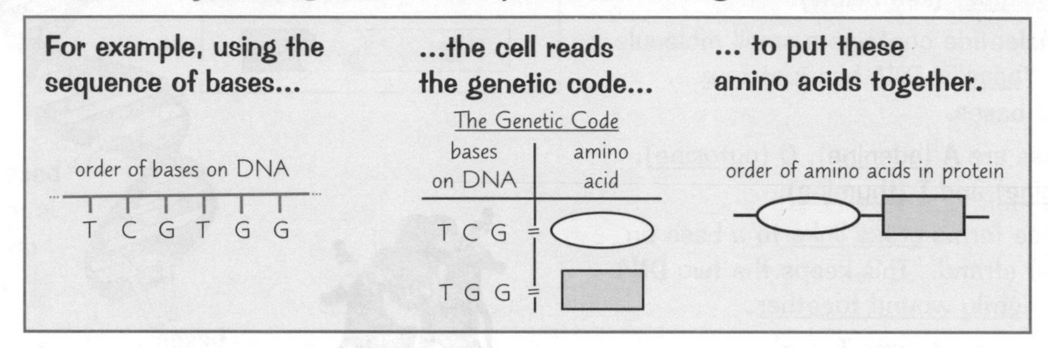

8) Each gene contains a different sequence of bases — which is what allows it to code for a particular protein.

Proteins are Synthesised in the Cytoplasm

DNA is found in the cell nucleus and can't move out of it because it's really big. The cell needs to get the information from the DNA to the cell cytoplasm where proteins are synthesised. This is done using a molecule called mRNA, which is similar to DNA, but it's shorter and only a single strand. Here's how it's done:

1) The DNA contains the gene coding for the protein.
2) In the nucleus, the two DNA strands unzip around the gene. The DNA is used as a template to make the mRNA. Base pairing ensures it's complementary (it matches the opposite strand). This step is called transcription.
3) The mRNA molecule then moves out of the nucleus and into the cytoplasm.
4) Amino acids that match the triplet codes on the mRNA are joined together in the correct order. This makes the protein coded for by the gene. This step is called translation.

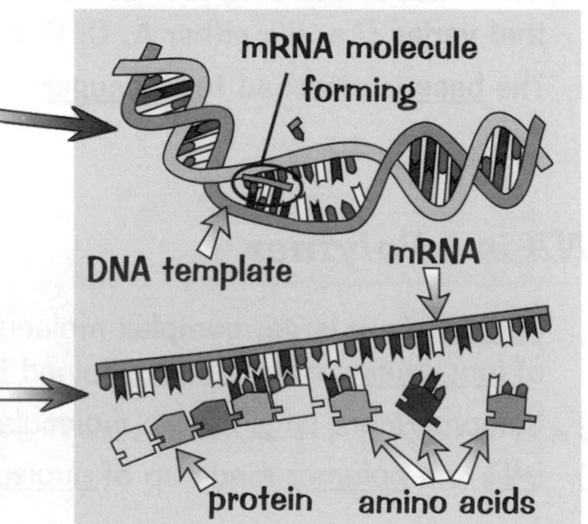

A triplet of bases — three-tiered cheesecake anyone...

Definitely been watching too much Bake Off. Remember — the order of bases in the DNA is copied to create mRNA, which moves to the cytoplasm. Then a chain of amino acids is built up according to the order of the bases.

Q1 Explain how a gene can code for a particular protein. [2 marks]

Q2 Explain why mRNA is described as 'complementary' to a DNA strand during protein synthesis. [2 marks]

Q3 Describe what happens during the translation stage of protein synthesis. [3 marks]

Enzymes

Enzymes are the magicians of the protein world — they make reactions happen faster without being changed themselves. Surely that's not possible without a little bit of magic... though here's what science says...

Enzymes Control Cell Reactions

1) Cells have thousands of different chemical reactions going on inside them all the time — like respiration, photosynthesis and protein synthesis. Together these make up the cell's metabolism.
2) These reactions need to be carefully controlled — to get the right amounts of substances and keep the organism working properly.
3) You can usually make a reaction happen more quickly by raising the temperature. This would speed up the useful reactions but also the unwanted ones too... not good. There's also a limit to how far you can raise the temperature inside a living creature before its cells start getting damaged.
4) So living things produce enzymes, which act as biological catalysts. A catalyst is a substance that speeds up a reaction, without being changed or used up in the reaction itself.
5) Enzymes reduce the need for high temperatures and we only have enzymes to speed up the useful chemical reactions in the body.
6) Every different biological reaction has its own enzyme especially for it.
7) Each enzyme is a protein coded for by a different gene, and has a unique shape which it needs to do its job.

Enzymes are Very Specific

1) Chemical reactions usually involve things either being split apart or joined together.
2) The substrate is the molecule changed in the reaction.
3) Every enzyme has an active site — the part where it joins on to its substrate to catalyse the reaction.
4) Enzymes are really picky — they usually only work with one substrate. The posh way of saying this is that enzymes have a high specificity for their substrate.
5) This is because, for the enzyme to work, the substrate has to fit into the active site. If the substrate's shape doesn't match the active site's shape, then the reaction won't be catalysed. This is called the 'lock and key' hypothesis, because the substrate fits into the enzyme just like a key fits into a lock.

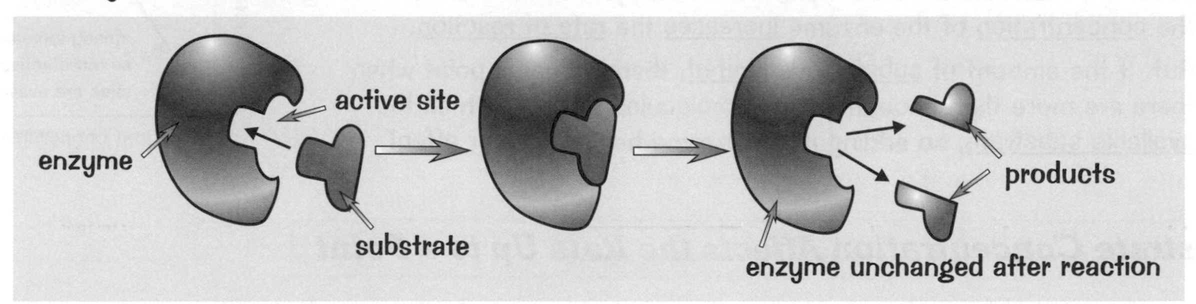

If the lock and key mechanism fails, there's always the window...

Enzymes aren't just useful for controlling chemical reactions in the body — we even put them in things like biological washing powders to catalyse the breakdown of nasty stains (like tomato ketchup). Useful, eh?

Q1 Which statement best describes the role of enzymes in the body?

A Enzymes speed up the rate of all the body's reactions.

B Enzymes raise the temperature allowing reactions to happen faster.

C Enzymes speed up specific reactions without being used up themselves.

D Each enzyme can speed up of lots of different chemical reactions. [1 mark]

Q2 Enzymes are described as having a 'high specificity' for their substrate. What is meant by this? [3 marks]

More on Enzymes

Enzymes are fussy little blighters — they like just the right temperature, pH, concentration...

Enzymes Like it Warm but Not Too Hot

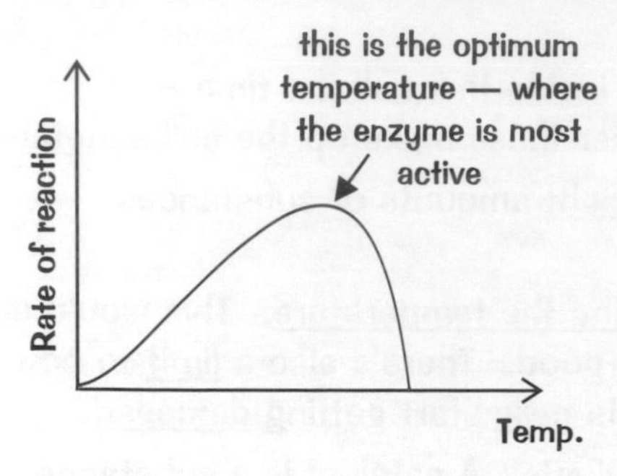

1) Changing the temperature changes the rate of an enzyme-controlled reaction.
2) Like with any reaction, a higher temperature increases the rate at first. The enzymes and the substrate move about more, so they're more likely to meet up and react. But if it gets too hot, some of the bonds holding the enzyme together break. This makes the enzyme become denatured — it loses its shape and the substrate doesn't fit the active site any more. This means the enzyme can't catalyse the reaction and the reaction stops. The enzyme is denatured irreversibly — it won't go back to its normal shape if things cool down again.
3) Each enzyme has its own optimum temperature when the reaction goes fastest. This is the temperature just before it gets too hot and starts to denature. The optimum temperature for the most important human enzymes is about 37 °C — the same temperature as our bodies. Lucky for us.

Enzymes Like it the Right pH Too

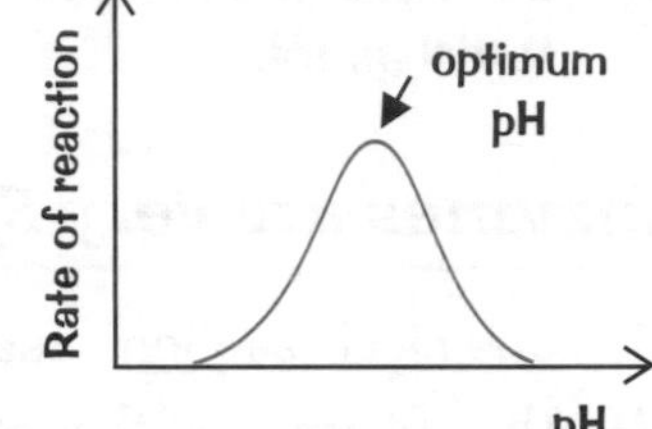

1) The pH also has an effect on enzymes. If it's too high or too low, it interferes with the bonds holding the enzyme together. This changes the shape of the active site and can irreversibly denature the enzyme.
2) All enzymes have an optimum pH that they work best at. It's often neutral pH 7, but not always. For example, pepsin is an enzyme used to break down proteins in the stomach. It works best at pH 2, which means it's well-suited to the acidic conditions in the stomach.

Enzyme Concentration Affects the Rate of Reaction

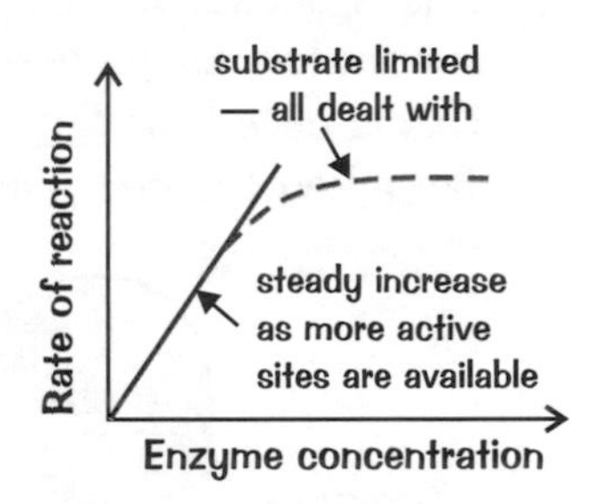

1) The more enzyme molecules there are in a solution, the more likely a substrate molecule will meet up with one and join with it. So increasing the concentration of the enzyme increases the rate of reaction.
2) But, if the amount of substrate is limited, there comes a point when there are more than enough enzyme molecules to deal with all the available substrate, so adding more enzyme has no further effect.

Substrate Concentration Affects the Rate Up to a Point

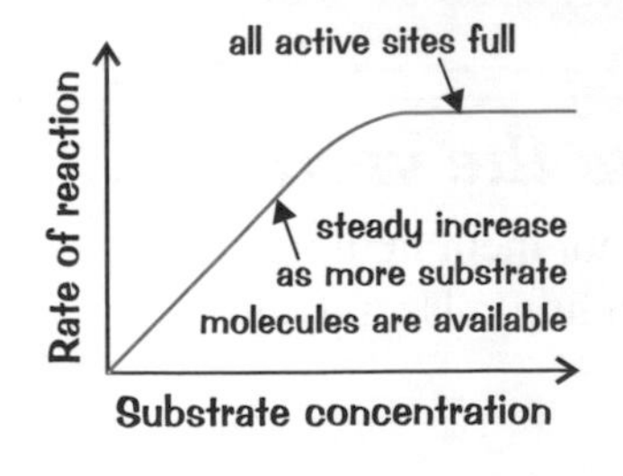

1) The higher the substrate concentration, the faster the reaction — it's more likely the enzyme will meet up and react with a substrate molecule.
2) This is only true up to a point though. After that, there are so many substrate molecules that the enzymes have about as much as they can cope with (all the active sites are full), and adding more makes no difference.

My concentration — affects rate of revision up to a point...

With enzymes it's all about the active sites. Anything that changes their shape stops the reaction. Simple.

Q1 Enzyme A's optimum pH is 4. Explain what might happen to enzyme A's activity in conditions above pH 4. [5 marks]

Investigating Enzyme Activity

You'll soon know how to investigate the effect of a variable on the rate of enzyme activity... I bet you're thrilled.

You Can Investigate How Temperature Affects Enzyme Activity

There are a couple of different ways to investigate how temperature affects enzyme activity. You can also adapt these experiments to measure variables other than temperature. For example:

1) To investigate the effect of pH, add a buffer solution with a different pH level to a series of different tubes containing the enzyme-substrate mixture.
2) Vary the initial concentrations of the substrate to investigate the effect of substrate concentration.
3) Vary the initial concentrations of the enzyme to investigate the effect of enzyme concentration.

You Can Measure How Fast a Product Appears...

PRACTICAL

1) The enzyme catalase catalyses the breakdown of hydrogen peroxide into water and oxygen.
2) You can collect the oxygen and measure how much is produced in a set time.
3) Use a pipette to add a set amount of hydrogen peroxide to a boiling tube. Put the tube in a water bath at 10 °C.
4) Set up the rest of the apparatus as shown. Add a source of catalase (e.g. 1 cm^3 of potato) to the hydrogen peroxide and quickly attach the bung.

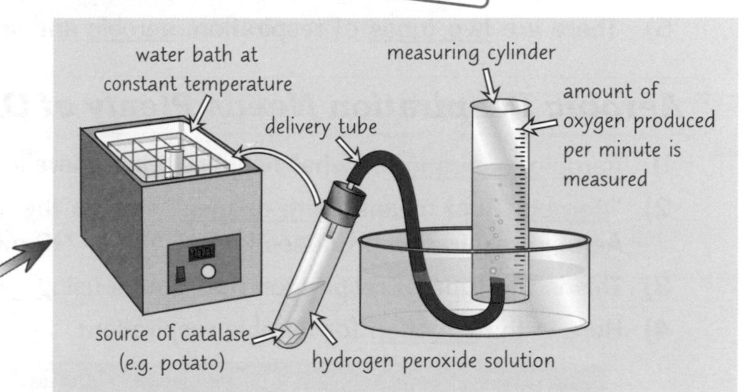

5) Record how much oxygen is produced in the first minute. Repeat three times and calculate the mean.
6) Repeat at 20 °C, 30 °C and 40 °C.
7) Control any variables (e.g. pH, the potato used, the size of potato pieces, etc.) to make it a fair test.
8) Calculate the mean rate of reaction at each temperature by dividing the mean volume of oxygen produced (in cm^3) by the time taken (i.e. 60 s). The units will be cm^3/second.

...Or How Fast a Substrate Disappears

PRACTICAL

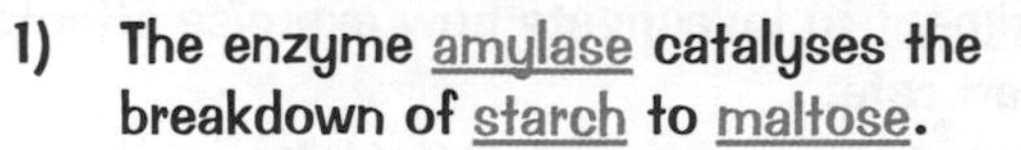

1) The enzyme amylase catalyses the breakdown of starch to maltose.

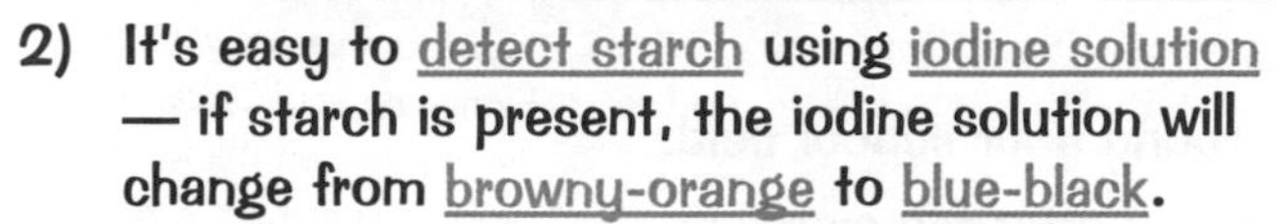

2) It's easy to detect starch using iodine solution — if starch is present, the iodine solution will change from browny-orange to blue-black.
3) Set up the apparatus as in the diagram. Put a drop of iodine solution into each well on the spotting tile. Every ten seconds, drop a sample of the mixture into a well using a pipette. When the iodine solution remains browny-orange (i.e. starch is no longer present) record the total time taken.

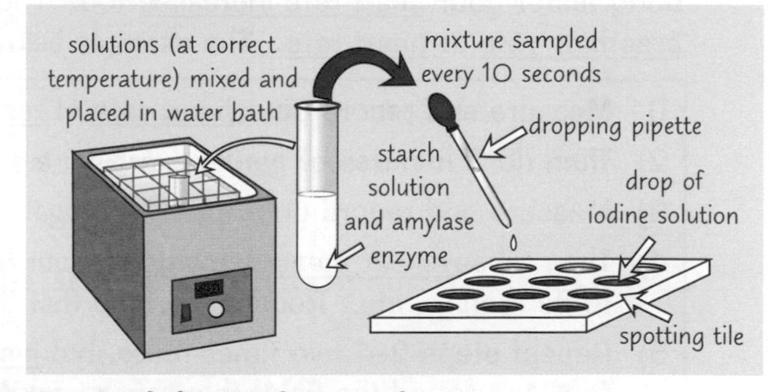

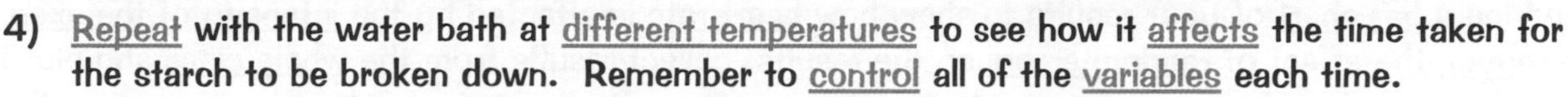

4) Repeat with the water bath at different temperatures to see how it affects the time taken for the starch to be broken down. Remember to control all of the variables each time.

You could improve the accuracy of this experiment by using a colorimeter — a piece of electronic equipment that measures the strength of a coloured solution so measurements aren't just based on somebody's judgement of when the colour has changed.

Mad scientists — they're experi-mental...

The key thing with experiments is to only change the thing you're testing — and absolutely nothing else. Sorted.

Q1 An enzyme-controlled reaction was carried out at 25 °C. After 60 seconds, 33 cm^3 of product had been released. Calculate the rate of reaction in cm^3/second. [1 mark]

Respiration

You need energy to keep your body going. Energy comes from food, and it's transferred by respiration.

Respiration is NOT "Breathing In and Out"

1) Respiration is the process of transferring energy from the breakdown of glucose (a sugar). It goes on in every cell in all living organisms, all the time — it's a universal chemical process.
2) The energy transferred by respiration can't be used directly by cells — so it's used to make a substance called ATP. ATP stores the energy needed for many cell processes.

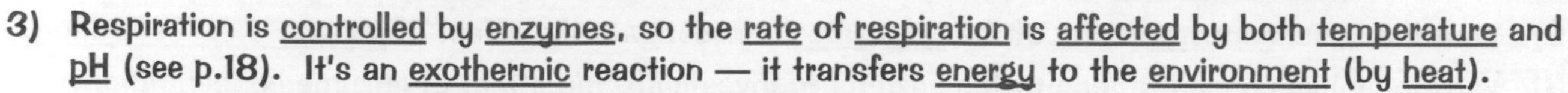

3) Respiration is controlled by enzymes, so the rate of respiration is affected by both temperature and pH (see p.18). It's an exothermic reaction — it transfers energy to the environment (by heat).
4) Cells can respire using glucose as a substrate, but organisms can also break down other organic molecules (such as other carbohydrates, proteins and lipids) to use as substrates for respiration.
5) There are two types of respiration, aerobic and anaerobic.

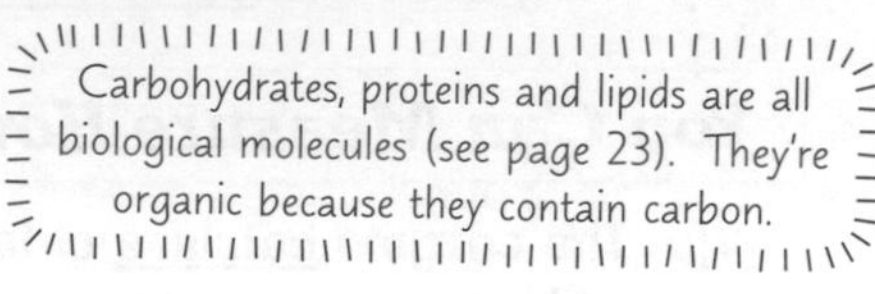

Carbohydrates, proteins and lipids are all biological molecules (see page 23). They're organic because they contain carbon.

Aerobic Respiration Needs Plenty of Oxygen

In eukaryotic cells, respiration takes place in the mitochondria.

1) Aerobic respiration is what happens when there's plenty of oxygen available.
2) "Aerobic" just means "with oxygen" and it's the most efficient way to transfer energy from glucose. Aerobic respiration produces lots of ATP — 32 molecules per molecule of glucose.
3) This is the type of respiration that you're using most of the time.
4) Here is the equation for aerobic respiration:

$$\text{glucose} + \text{oxygen} \longrightarrow \text{carbon dioxide} + \text{water}$$
$$C_6H_{12}O_6 + 6O_2 \longrightarrow 6CO_2 + 6H_2O$$

In chemical equations, the substances before the arrow are the reactants and those after the arrow are the products.

You Can Investigate The Effect of Exercise on Heart Rate

PRACTICAL

When you exercise, more energy is needed by your muscles to allow them to contract more. This means your rate of respiration increases, so you need to get more oxygen into your cells. Your breathing rate (ventilation rate) increases to get more oxygen into the blood, and to get this oxygenated blood around the body faster your heart rate increases too. You can do an experiment to investigate how exercise affects breathing rate or heart rate. The example below investigates heart rate:

You can measure your heart rate by finding your pulse rate — put two fingers on the inside of your wrist or your neck and count the number of pulses in 1 minute.

1) Measure and record your heart rate at rest.
2) Then do 3 minutes of gentle exercise, e.g. walk around your school field.
3) Measure and record your heart rate again immediately after the exercise.
4) Then take regular measurements of your heart rate until it has returned to its resting rate. Record the time that this takes — this is called the recovery time.
5) Repeat steps 2-4 two times more, but increase the intensity of the exercise each time (e.g. jog round the field, then run round it).
6) Produce a bar chart of your results to show how heart rate is affected by the intensity of the exercise. To reduce the effect of random errors on the results, collect results from the whole class and plot the average percentage change in heart rate for each exercise. Do the same to show how recovery time is affected by the intensity of exercise.
7) Remember to control any variables during the experiment, e.g. if you're using results from the whole class, make sure everyone's done the same exercise activities and for the same length of time.

Respiration transfers energy — but this page has worn me out...

Thank goodness for respiration — transferring the energy stored in my tea and biscuits to my brain cells. Great.

Q1 Give the word equation for aerobic respiration. [2 marks]

Anaerobic Respiration

Now on to the second type of respiration — anaerobic respiration. If you've ever really felt 'the burn' while you're exercising you're about to find out why. See, biology can actually be really interesting...

Anaerobic Respiration Doesn't Use Oxygen At All

"Anaerobic" just means "without oxygen". It's not the best way to transfer energy from glucose because it transfers much less energy per glucose molecule than aerobic respiration — just 2 molecules of ATP are produced. The process of anaerobic respiration is slightly different in different organisms:

Animals Produce Lactic Acid

1) When you do really vigorous exercise your body can't supply enough oxygen to your muscles for aerobic respiration — even though your heart rate and breathing rate increase as much as they can. Your muscles have to start respiring anaerobically as well.
2) In anaerobic respiration, the glucose is only partially broken down, and lactic acid is also produced. All animals that respire anaerobically produce lactic acid by the same process.
   This is the word equation for anaerobic respiration in animals:

glucose ⟶ lactic acid

3) The lactic acid builds up in the muscles, which gets painful and makes your muscles fatigued.
4) The advantage is that at least you can keep on using your muscles.
5) After resorting to anaerobic respiration, when you stop exercising you'll have an oxygen debt. Basically you need extra oxygen to break down all the lactic acid that's built up and to allow aerobic respiration to begin again. So you need to keep breathing hard for a while.

Plants and Fungi Produce Ethanol and Carbon Dioxide

1) Under certain conditions plants may also have to resort to anaerobic respiration, e.g. in waterlogged soil (where there is little or no oxygen) plant root cells respire anaerobically.
2) Some fungi (such as yeast) can respire anaerobically too.
3) Anaerobic respiration in plants and fungi produces ethanol and carbon dioxide instead of lactic acid. This is the word equation:

Anaerobic respiration in yeast is known as fermentation.

glucose ⟶ ethanol + carbon dioxide

You Need to Compare Aerobic and Anaerobic Respiration

This handy table shows the differences and similarities between aerobic and anaerobic respiration.

	Aerobic	Anaerobic
Conditions	Oxygen present	Not enough oxygen present, e.g. during vigorous exercise, in waterlogged soils
Substrate	Glucose (or another organic molecule)	
Products	Carbon dioxide and water	In animals — lactic acid In plants and some fungi (e.g. yeast) — ethanol and carbon dioxide
Energy transferred	Lots — 32 ATP made	Much less — 2 ATP made

My friend Anne O'Robic is rather odd — I only see her at the gym...

Make sure you know those word equations and can compare the processes of aerobic and anaerobic respiration.

Q1 Name the product(s) of anaerobic respiration in plants. [1 mark]

Q2 Why is it advantageous for organisms to respire aerobically rather than anaerobically? [1 mark]

PRACTICAL Respiration Experiments

Ready to see that carbon dioxide (CO_2) is produced and energy is transferred by heat during respiration? Good.

Carbon Dioxide Production can be Detected

Hydrogen-carbonate solution is an indicator — a substance that visibly indicates the presence of another chemical, usually by changing colour.

1) You can use hydrogen-carbonate solution to show that living organisms produce CO_2 as they respire. Normally this solution is red, but it changes to a lovely yellow when there's plenty of CO_2 present.
2) Here's how you can set up an experiment to demonstrate CO_2 production by some beans:

First, soak some dried beans in water for a day or two. They will start to germinate (you should see little sprouts coming out of them). Germinating beans will respire.
Boil a similar-sized, second bunch of dried beans. This will kill the beans and make sure they can't respire. The dead beans will act as your control.
Now, set up the experiment as shown on the right:

- Put some hydrogen-carbonate indicator into two test tubes.
- Place a platform made of gauze into each test tube and place the beans on this.
- Seal the test tubes with a rubber bung.
- Leave the apparatus for a set period of time (e.g. an hour).
- During that time the CO_2 produced by the germinating beans should have had an effect on the hydrogen-carbonate indicator — it will have turned yellow.

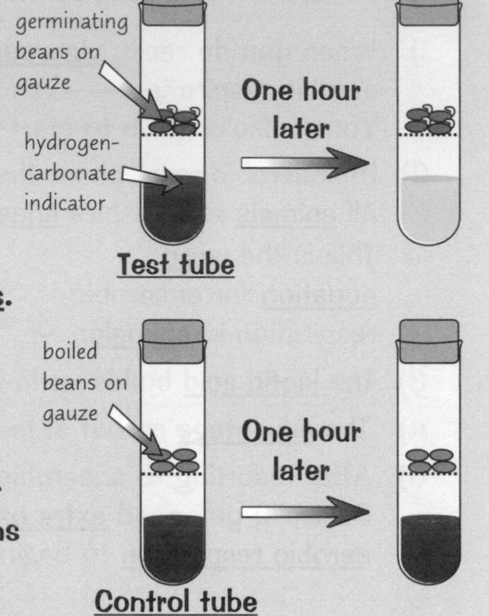

3) You could also carry out this experiment with small organisms like woodlice or maggots (the control for these would be glass beads though and you'd need to make sure you didn't leave the organisms in the sealed tube for too long).
4) You could extend the experiment by timing how long it takes the hydrogen-carbonate indicator to turn yellow for different organisms — in this way you could investigate the rate of respiration.

The Energy Transferred by Heat During Respiration can be Measured

On page 20, I said that respiration transfers energy to the environment by heat — well here's an experiment to measure that transferred energy. You'll be glad to know it uses more dried beans.

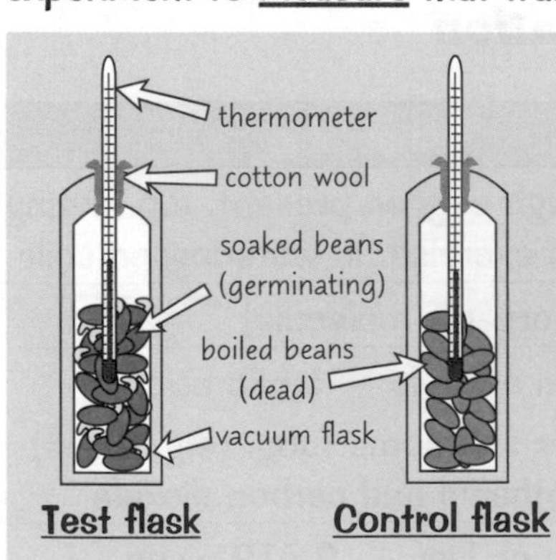

- Firstly, prepare two sets of beans as described in the experiment above.
- Add each set of beans to a vacuum flask, making sure there's some air left in the flasks (so the beans can respire aerobically).
- Place a thermometer into each flask and seal the top with cotton wool.
- Record the temperature of each flask daily for a week.
- The beans are well-insulated in the flasks, so when the germinating beans respire and transfer energy to their surroundings by heat, the test flask's temperature will increase compared to the control flask.

My beans keep disappearing from the lab — must be runner beans...

Controls are important in experiments — they're used to check the thing you're changing (the independent variable) is what's affecting the results and nothing else. You can't go round killing woodlice though. It's just not ethical.

Q1 A student carried out an experiment to measure the energy transferred by respiration using germinating beans in a vacuum flask. What should the student use as a control? [1 mark]

Biological Molecules

Biological molecules are molecules found in living organisms — things like carbohydrates, proteins and lipids. They're generally long, complex molecules made up from smaller basic units.

Biological Molecules Can be Broken Down to Fuel Respiration

As you may remember from page 20, carbohydrates, proteins and lipids can be broken down so that energy can be transferred to ATP through respiration — the energy stored in ATP is then available for the cell to use. You need to know how the structures of these biological molecules are formed from their basic units:

Carbohydrates are Made up of Simple Sugars

1) Carbohydrate molecules contain the elements carbon, hydrogen and oxygen.
2) The smallest units, monomers (see page 15), are simple sugars, e.g. glucose or fructose molecules.
3) These can be joined together in long chains, polymers, to make large, complex carbohydrates, e.g. starch and glycogen.
4) The polymer molecules can be broken down back into sugars again when the chemical bonds between the monomers are broken.
5) In the body, carbohydrates are broken down (digested) by enzymes in the mouth and small intestine.

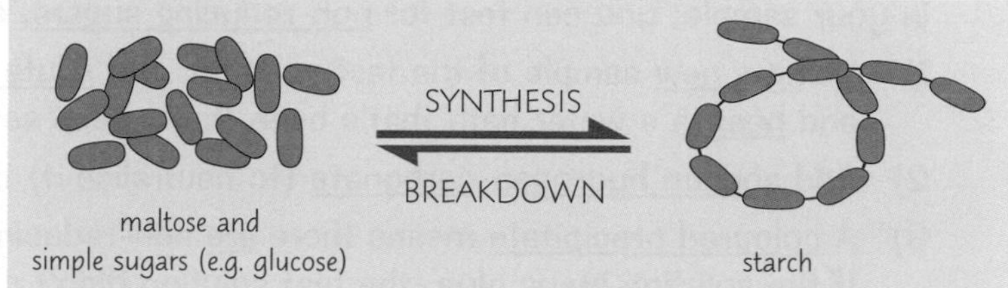

Proteins are Made Up of Amino Acids

1) Proteins are polymers that are made up of long chains of monomers called amino acids (see page 16).
2) Amino acids all contain carbon, nitrogen, hydrogen and oxygen atoms.
3) In the body, proteins are broken down by enzymes in the stomach and small intestine.

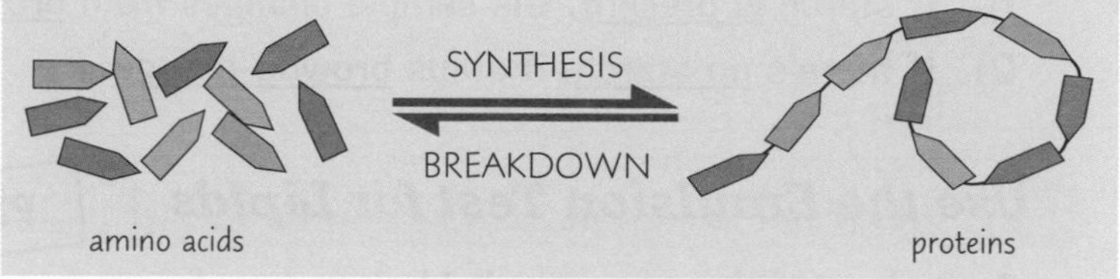

Lipids are Made Up of Fatty Acids and Glycerol

1) Lipids (fats and oils) are made from glycerol and three fatty acids.
2) Unlike carbohydrates and proteins they are NOT polymers because they don't form a long chain of repeating units.
3) Lipids contain carbon, hydrogen and oxygen atoms.
4) In the body, lipids are broken down by enzymes in the small intestine.

When lipids are broken down, the fatty acids will make the solution they are in more acidic (it will have a lower pH).

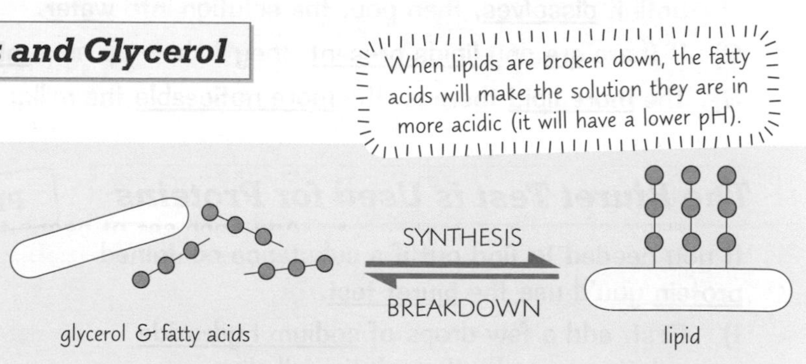

What do you call an acid that's eaten all the pies...

This page isn't too bad really, once you've got the whole monomer/polymer thing sorted. But you still need to make sure you learn it properly. So look, cover and scribble 'til you can do the whole lot standing on your head.

Q1 Name the monomers that result from the breakdown of:
a) carbohydrates, b) proteins. [2 marks]

Q2 Give one reason why it's important for the body to be able to break down large, complex molecules, such as starch. [1 mark]

Testing for Biological Molecules

There might come a day when you have a <u>sample of food</u> and you're just desperate to know what <u>biological molecules</u> it contains. Well, just make sure your sample's all <u>liquidy</u>, keep <u>this page open</u>, then <u>off you go</u>...

You Can Test for Sugars Using Benedict's Reagent

PRACTICAL

<u>REDUCING SUGARS</u> — Reducing sugars include simple sugars made from just <u>one unit</u>, e.g. glucose, and a few made from two units joined together, e.g. maltose. Here's how you can test for them:

1) Add <u>Benedict's reagent</u> (which is <u>blue</u>) to a sample and <u>heat</u> it in a water bath that's been set at <u>75 °C</u>. If the test's <u>positive</u> it will form a <u>coloured precipitate</u> (solid particles suspended in the solution).
2) The <u>higher</u> the <u>concentration</u> of reducing sugar, the <u>further</u> the colour change goes — you can use this to <u>compare</u> the amount of reducing sugar in different solutions.

The colour of the precipitate changes from:

blue → green → yellow → orange → brick red

<u>NON-REDUCING SUGARS</u> — If there <u>aren't</u> any reducing sugars in your sample, you can test for <u>non-reducing sugars</u>, e.g. sucrose.

1) Using a <u>new</u> sample of the test solution, add <u>dilute hydrochloric acid</u> and <u>heat</u> in a water bath that's been that's been set at <u>75 °C</u>.
2) Add <u>sodium hydrogen-carbonate</u> (to neutralise it) then carry out the <u>Benedict's test</u> as above.

3) A <u>coloured precipitate</u> means there <u>are</u> non-reducing sugars present. If the solution <u>stays blue</u>, the test solution <u>didn't</u> contain any <u>sugar</u> at all.

Starch is Tested for with Iodine

PRACTICAL

Iodine solution is iodine dissolved in potassium iodide solution.

Just add <u>iodine solution</u> to the test sample.

1) If starch <u>is present</u>, the sample changes from <u>browny-orange</u> to a dark, <u>blue-black</u> colour.
2) If there's <u>no starch</u>, it stays <u>browny-orange</u>.

Use the Emulsion Test for Lipids

PRACTICAL

To find out if there are any <u>lipids</u> in a sample:

1) <u>Shake</u> the test substance with <u>ethanol</u> for about a minute until it <u>dissolves</u>, then pour the solution into <u>water</u>.
2) If there <u>are</u> any <u>lipids present</u>, they'll show up as a <u>milky emulsion</u>.
3) The <u>more lipid</u> there is, the <u>more noticeable</u> the milky colour will be.

Test substance and ethanol → Shake → Add to water → Milky colour indicates lipid

An emulsion is when one liquid doesn't dissolve in another — it just forms little droplets.

The Biuret Test is Used for Proteins

PRACTICAL

If you needed to find out if a substance contained <u>protein</u> you'd use the <u>biuret test</u>.

1) First, add a few drops of <u>sodium hydroxide</u> solution to make the solution <u>alkaline</u>.
2) Then add some <u>copper(II) sulfate</u> solution (which is <u>bright blue</u>).
   - If there's <u>no protein</u>, the solution will stay <u>blue</u>.
   - If protein <u>is present</u>, the solution will turn <u>purple</u>.

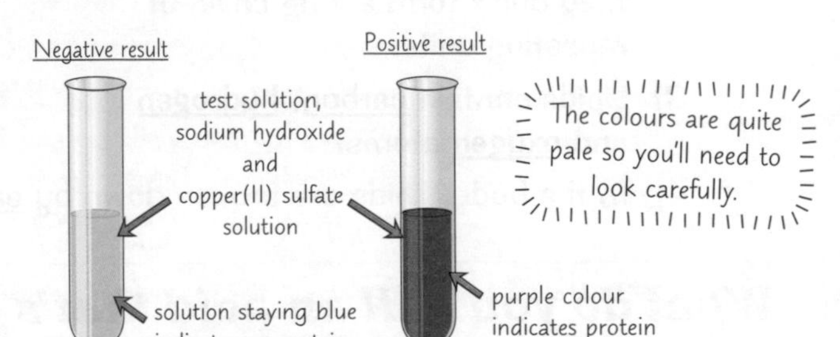

The colours are quite pale so you'll need to look carefully.

The Anger Test — annoy test subject. Red face = anger present...

OK, so this stuff isn't thrilling but learning it is better than being dissolved in a giant vat of vinegar. Yowch.

Q1 A solution that has been mixed with sodium hydroxide and copper(II) sulfate solution turns purple. What conclusion would you draw from this test? [1 mark]

Photosynthesis

You don't know photosynthesis 'til you know its equation. It's in a nice green box so you can't possibly miss it.

Plants are Able to Make Their Own Food by Photosynthesis

1) During photosynthesis, photosynthetic organisms, such as green plants and algae, use energy from the Sun or an artificial source to make glucose.
2) Some of the glucose is used to make larger, complex molecules that the plants or algae need to grow. These make up the organism's biomass — the mass of living material.
3) The energy stored in the organisms' biomass then works its way through the food chain as animals eat them and each other. So ultimately, photosynthetic organisms support nearly all life on Earth.
4) Photosynthesis happens inside chloroplasts — they contain chlorophyll which absorbs light. Energy is transferred to the chloroplasts from the environment by light. This is the equation for photosynthesis:

$$\text{carbon dioxide} + \text{water} \xrightarrow[\text{chlorophyll}]{\text{LIGHT}} \text{glucose} + \text{oxygen}$$

$$6CO_2 + 6H_2O \xrightarrow[\text{chlorophyll}]{\text{LIGHT}} C_6H_{12}O_6 + 6O_2$$

5) Photosynthesis is an endothermic reaction — energy is transferred from the environment during it.
6) Photosynthesis actually happens in two main stages. First, energy transferred by light is used to split water into oxygen gas and hydrogen ions.
7) Carbon dioxide gas then combines with the hydrogen ions to make glucose.

Oxygen Production Shows the Rate of Photosynthesis

PRACTICAL

1) The rate of photosynthesis is affected by light intensity, concentration of CO_2 and temperature. Any of these three factors can become the limiting factor. This just means that it's stopping photosynthesis from happening any faster.
2) You can investigate how each of the different factors affect the rate of photosynthesis. A classic way to do this is to use pondweed and to measure oxygen production.
3) The rate at which the pondweed produces oxygen corresponds to the rate at which it's photosynthesising — the faster the rate of oxygen production, the faster the rate of photosynthesis.
4) The box below describes the basic method you could use — the ways in which you could alter the experiment to test the different factors are described on the next page.

> 1) The experiment is set up as shown in the diagram.
> 2) The pondweed is left to photosynthesise for a set amount of time. As it photosynthesises, the oxygen released will collect in the capillary tube.
> 3) At the end of the experiment, the syringe is used to draw the gas bubble in the tube up alongside a ruler and the length of the gas bubble is measured. This is proportional to the volume of O_2 produced.
> 4) The experiment is then repeated to test a range of values for the factor being investigated, e.g. a range of different temperatures.
> 5) Variables other than the one being investigated should be kept the same, e.g. the other limiting factors, the time the pondweed is left for.

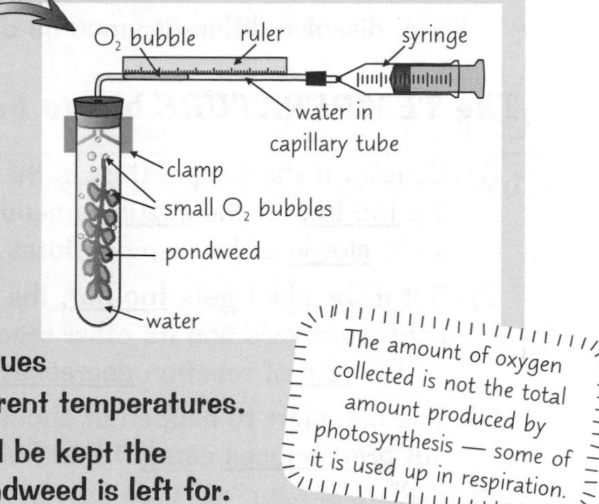

The amount of oxygen collected is not the total amount produced by photosynthesis — some of it is used up in respiration.

I'm working on sunshine — woah oh...

You could also measure how much oxygen's produced by counting the bubbles — fun, but it's not as accurate.

Q1 Explain how photosynthesis contributes to a plant's biomass. [2 marks]

The Rate of Photosynthesis

Before you start on this page, make sure you've read the photosynthesis experiment from the last page. OK...

Three Important Graphs for Rate of Photosynthesis

Not Enough LIGHT Slows Down the Rate of Photosynthesis

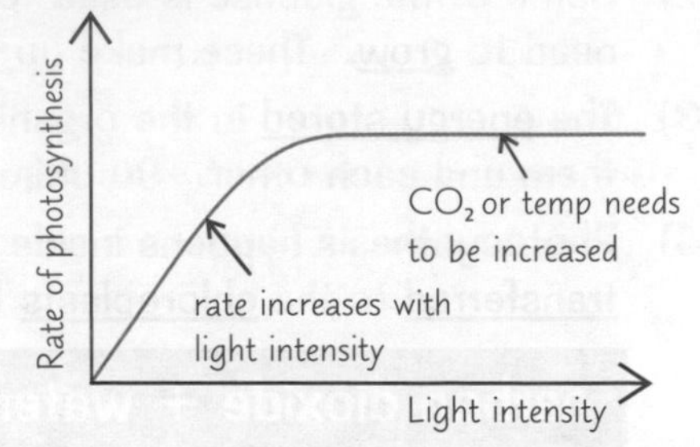

1) Light transfers the energy needed for photosynthesis.
2) As the light level is raised, the rate of photosynthesis increases steadily — but only up to a certain point.
3) Beyond that, it won't make any difference — it'll be either the temperature or the CO_2 level which is the limiting factor.
4) In the lab you can investigate light intensity by moving a lamp closer to or further away from your plant.
5) But if you just plot the rate of photosynthesis against "distance of lamp from the plant", you get a weird-shaped graph. To get a graph like the one above you either need to measure the light intensity at the plant using a light meter or do a bit of nifty maths with your results. Here's why:

The distance from the lamp and light intensity are inversely proportional to each other — this means that as the distance increases, the light intensity decreases. However, light intensity decreases in proportion to the square of the distance. This is called the inverse square law and is written like this:

Putting one over the distance shows the inverse.

$$\text{light intensity (i)} \propto \frac{1}{\text{distance (d)}^2}$$

Halving the distance → intensity is 2×2 = 4 times greater
Tripling the distance → intensity is 3×3 = 9 times smaller

Too Little CARBON DIOXIDE Also Slows it Down

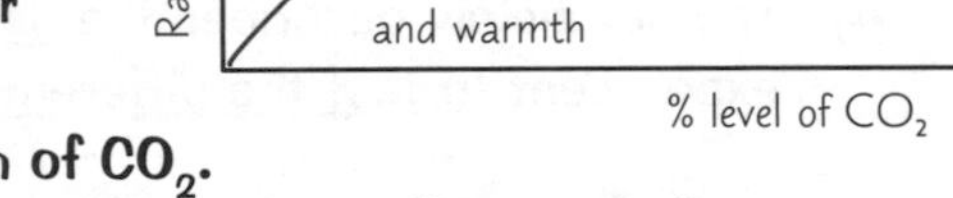

1) CO_2 is one of the raw materials needed for photosynthesis.
2) As with light intensity the concentration of CO_2 will only increase the rate of photosynthesis up to a point. After this the graph flattens out showing that CO_2 is no longer the limiting factor.
3) As long as light and CO_2 are in plentiful supply then the factor limiting photosynthesis must be temperature.
4) There are loads of different ways to control the concentration of CO_2. E.g. dissolve different amounts of sodium hydrogen-carbonate (which gives off CO_2) in the water.

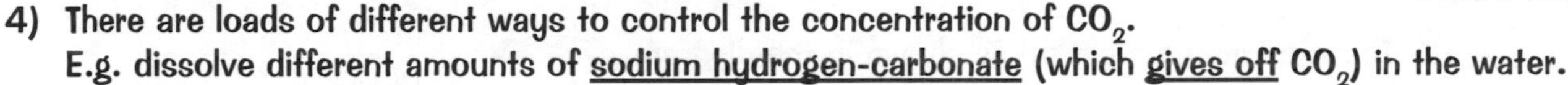

The TEMPERATURE has to be Just Right

See page 18 for more on the effect of temperature on enzymes.

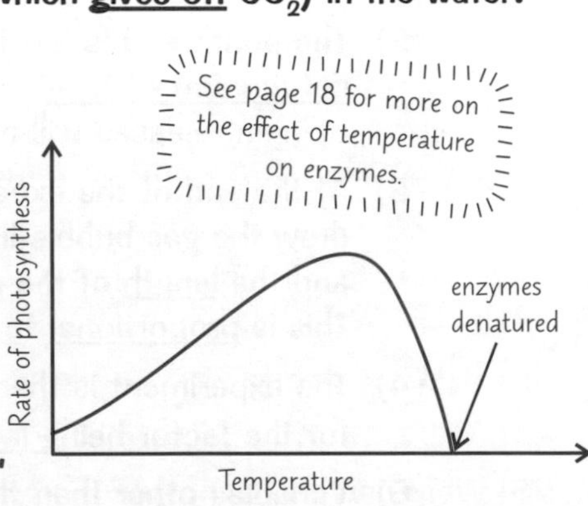

1) Usually, if the temperature is the limiting factor it's because it's too low — the enzymes needed for photosynthesis work more slowly at low temperatures.
2) But if the plant gets too hot, the enzymes it needs for photosynthesis and its other reactions will be denatured — the rate of reaction decreases dramatically.
3) This can start to happen at about 45 °C (pretty hot for outdoors, but greenhouses can get that hot if you're not careful).
4) Experimentally, the best way to control the temperature of a boiling tube is to put it in a water bath.

Don't blame it on the sunshine, don't blame it on the CO_2...

...don't blame it on the temperature, blame it on the plant. And now you'll never forget these three limiting factors. in photosynthesis. No... well, make sure you read these pages over and over again 'til you're sure you won't.

Q1 Explain the effect of increasing temperature on the rate of photosynthesis. [4 marks]

Revision Questions for Topic B1

Well, that's Topic B1 covered — time to see how much stayed in and didn't go in one eye and out the other.

- Try these questions and tick off each one when you get it right.
- When you've done all the questions under a heading and are completely happy with it, tick it off.

Cells and Microscopy (p12-14)

1) List four features that animal and plant cells have in common.
2) Give two sub-cellular structures that are present in prokaryotic cells but not eukaryotic cells.
3) How have electron microscopes been able to increase our understanding of sub-cellular structures?
4) Why is it important to take a thin slice of a sample before viewing it under a light microscope?
5) How can you calculate the magnification of an image if you don't know which lenses were used?

DNA and Protein Synthesis (p15-16)

6) Give the initials of the four bases present in DNA.
7) Describe the structure of a nucleotide.
8) What is a gene?
9) What is a triplet code?
10) What is the process of making mRNA from DNA called?
11) In what part of a cell are amino acids joined together to form a protein?

Enzymes (p17-19)

12) Draw a diagram to show how the 'lock and key' mechanism of enzymes works.
13) What does it mean when an enzyme has been 'denatured'?
14) Sketch a graph to show how substrate concentration affects the rate of an enzyme-controlled reaction.
15) Give two things that you could measure when investigating the rate of an enzyme-controlled reaction.
16) Give two variables that need controlling when investigating the effect of pH on an enzyme-controlled reaction.

Respiration (p20-22)

17) What is respiration?
18) Is respiration an exothermic or an endothermic reaction?
19) Name the type of respiration that requires oxygen.
20) Give an example of when lactic acid would be produced as a product of respiration.
21) Which form of respiration transfers more energy per glucose molecule?
22) Briefly describe an experiment to show that carbon dioxide is a product of respiration.

Biological Molecules (p23-24)

23) What type of polymer do you get when you join together simple sugars?
24) Name the basic units that lipids are made from.
25) What can you conclude if a test sample turns a blue-black colour when iodine is added?
26) How would you test for lipids in a sample solution?

Photosynthesis (p25-26)

27) In what part of a cell does photosynthesis take place?
28) Give three factors that can limit the rate of photosynthesis.
29) Describe how you could investigate the effect of CO_2 concentration on the rate of photosynthesis.

The Cell Cycle and Mitosis

Your cells have to be able to divide for your body to grow. And that means your DNA has to be copied...

New Cells are Needed for Growth and Repair

The cells of your body divide to produce more cells, so your body can grow and replace damaged cells. Cells grow and divide over and over again — this is called the cell cycle. Of course, cell division doesn't just happen in humans — animals and plants do it too. There are two main parts:

First the cell physically grows and replicates its contents...

The period of cell growth and replication of its contents is divided up into three separate growth stages.

These are called G_1, S and G_2:

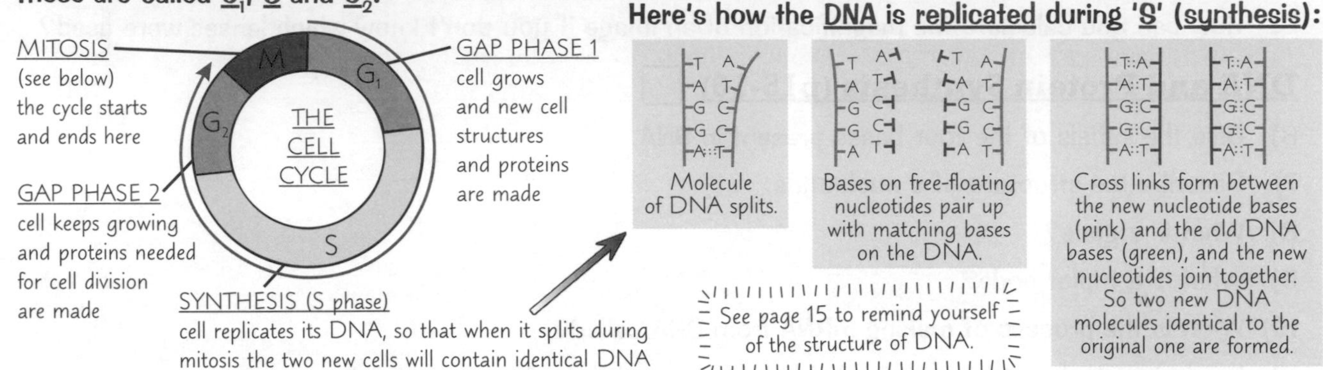

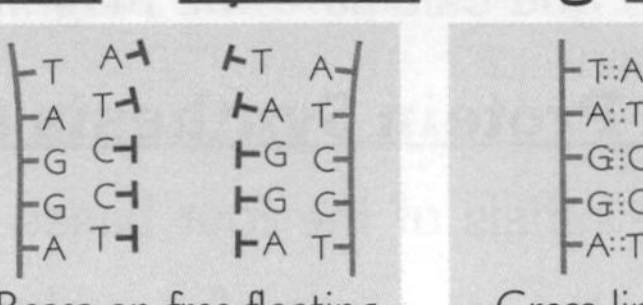

See page 15 to remind yourself of the structure of DNA.

...then it splits into two by Mitosis

Mitosis is when a cell reproduces itself by splitting to form two identical offspring.

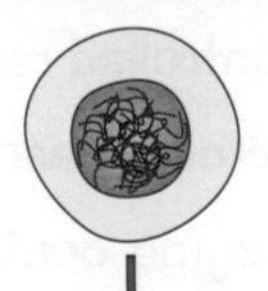

The cell has two copies of its DNA all spread out in long strings.

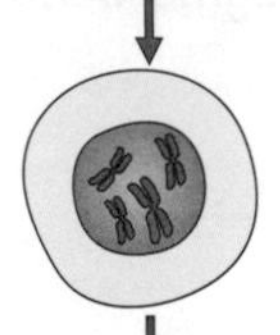

Before the cell divides, the DNA forms X-shaped chromosomes. Each 'arm' of a chromosome is an exact copy of the other.

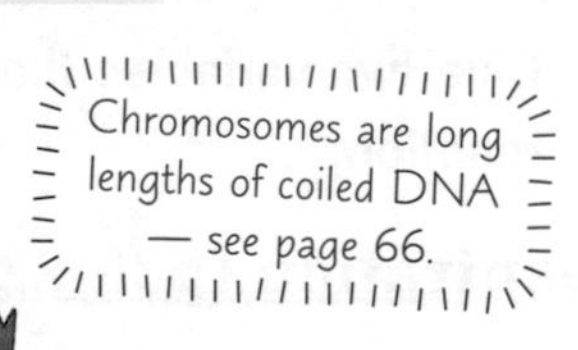

Chromosomes are long lengths of coiled DNA — see page 66.

The chromosomes then line up at the centre of the cell and cell fibres pull them apart. The two arms of each chromosome go to opposite ends of the cell.

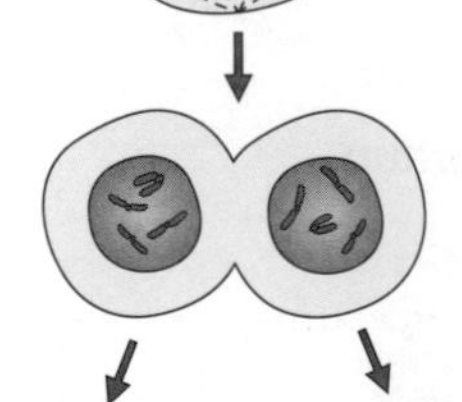

Membranes form around each of the sets of chromosomes. These become the nuclei of the two new cells.

Lastly, the cytoplasm divides.

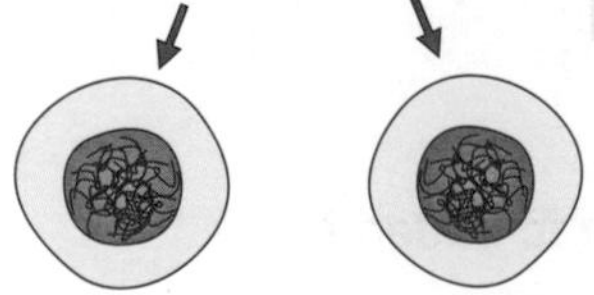

You now have two new cells containing exactly the same DNA — they're genetically identical to each other and to the parent cell.

A cell's favourite computer game — divide and conquer...

This can seem tricky at first. But don't worry — just go through it slowly, one step at a time and it'll soon sink in.

Q1 Explain why a cell's DNA is replicated during the cell cycle. [1 mark]

Q2 What is mitosis? [1 mark]

Cell Differentiation and Stem Cells

Multicellular organisms have lots of cells — most of these cells are specialised to do a particular job...

Most Cells are Specialised for a Specific Job

1) Differentiation is the process by which a cell changes to become specialised for its job.
2) In most animal cells, the ability to differentiate is lost at an early stage, but lots of plant cells don't ever lose this ability.
3) Having specialised cells is important — it allows organisms to work more efficiently.
4) Most cells are specialised to carry out a particular job. For example:

PALISADE LEAF CELLS

Palisade leaf cells do most of the photosynthesis in plants, so they are packed with chloroplasts (see p.12). Their tall shape means they have a lot of surface area exposed down the side for absorbing CO_2 from the air in the leaf, and their thin shape means that you can fit loads of them in at the top of a leaf, so they're nearer the light.

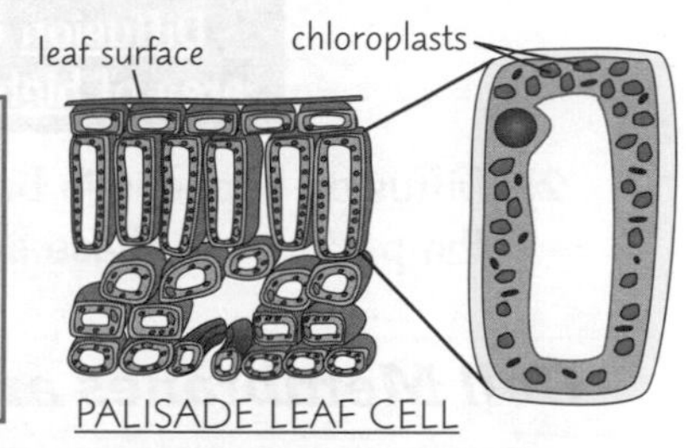

PALISADE LEAF CELL

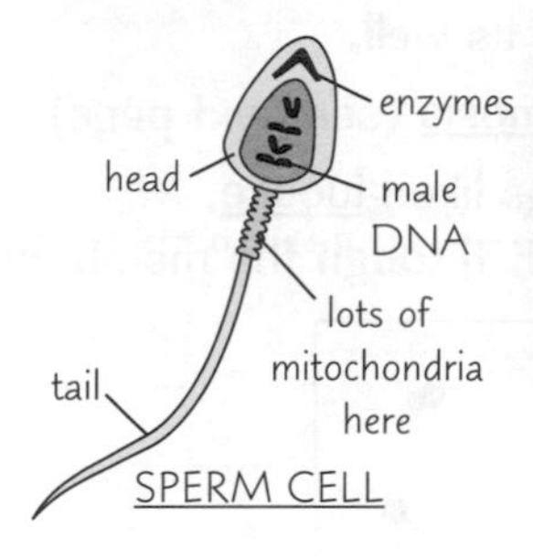

SPERM CELL

SPERM

The function of sperm is basically to get the male DNA to the female DNA during reproduction (see page 68). Sperm have long tails and streamlined heads to help them swim, they contain lots of mitochondria to provide them with energy, and they have enzymes in their heads to digest through the egg cell membrane.

5) In multicellular organisms, specialised cells are grouped together to form tissues — groups of cells working together to perform a particular function. Different tissues work together to form organs. Different organs make up an organ system.

Stem Cells can Differentiate into Different Types of Cells

1) Stem cells are undifferentiated. Depending on what instructions they're given, they can divide by mitosis to become new cells, which then differentiate.
2) Embryonic stem cells are found in early human embryos. They have the potential to turn into any kind of cell at all. This makes sense if you think about it — all the different types of cell found in a human being have to come from those few cells in the early embryo.
3) This means stem cells are really important for the growth and development of organisms.
4) Adults also have stem cells, but they're only found in certain places, like bone marrow. These aren't as versatile as embryonic stem cells — they can't turn into any cell type at all, only certain ones from the tissue they originally came from.
5) In animals, adult stem cells are used to replace damaged cells, e.g. to make new skin or blood cells.

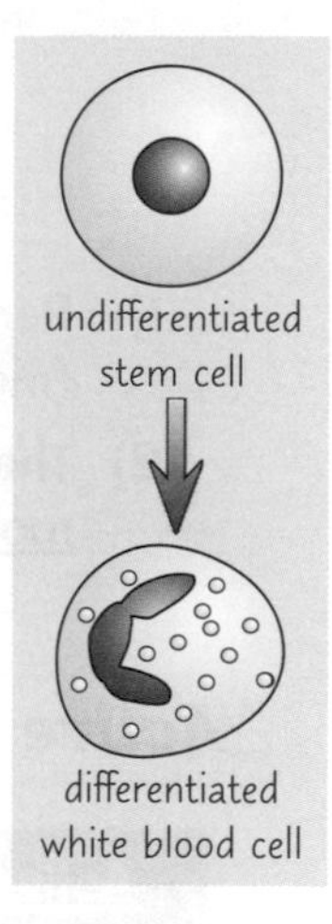

Meristems Contain Plant Stem Cells

1) In plants, the only cells that divide by mitosis are found in plant tissues called meristems.
2) Meristem tissue is found in the areas of a plant that are growing — such as the roots and shoots.
3) Meristems produce unspecialised cells that are able to divide and form any cell type in the plant — they act like embryonic stem cells. But unlike human stem cells, these cells can divide to generate any type of cell for as long as the plant lives.
4) The unspecialised cells can become specialised and form tissues like xylem and phloem (see page 39).

Cheery cells, those merry-stems...

Turns out stem cells are pretty nifty. Now, let's see if you're specialised to answer this question...

Q1 What is differentiation? [1 mark]

Diffusion and Active Transport

Substances need to move in and out of cells, through the cell membrane. Diffusion and active transport are two of the ways that this can happen. There's also osmosis too — see the next page.

Diffusion is the Movement of Particles from Higher to Lower Concentration

1) Diffusion is simple. It's just the gradual movement of particles from places where there are lots of them to places where there are fewer of them. That's all it is — just the natural tendency for stuff to spread out. Here's the fancy definition:

> Diffusion is the net (overall) movement of particles from an area of higher concentration to an area of lower concentration.

If something moves from an area of higher concentration to an area of lower concentration it is said to have moved down its concentration gradient.

2) Diffusion happens in both liquids and gases — that's because the particles in these substances are free to move about randomly.

Cell Membranes are Pretty Clever

1) They're clever because they hold the cell together but they let stuff in and out as well.
2) Substances can move in and out of cells by diffusion, active transport and osmosis (see next page).
3) Only very small molecules can diffuse through cell membranes though — things like glucose, amino acids, water and oxygen. Big molecules like starch and proteins can't fit through the membrane.

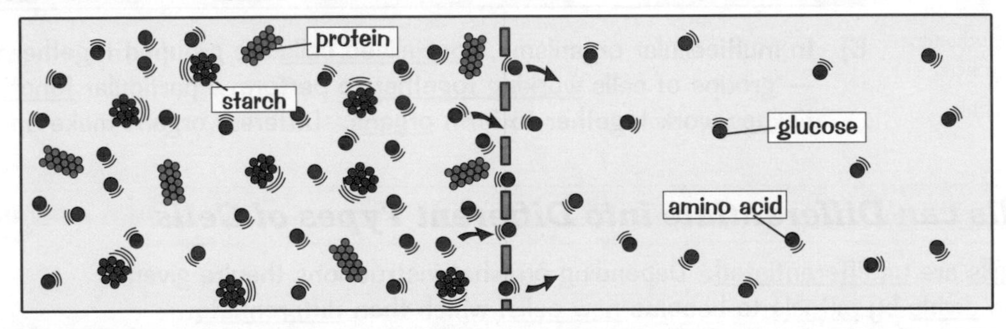

1) Particles move through the cell membrane from where there's a higher concentration (more of them) to where there's a lower concentration (not such a lot of them).
2) They're only moving about randomly of course, so they go both ways — but if there are a lot more particles on one side of the membrane, there's a net (overall) movement from that side.

Active Transport is the Opposite of Diffusion

> Active transport is the movement of particles across a membrane against a concentration gradient (i.e. from an area of lower to an area of higher concentration) using ATP released during respiration.

Here's an example of active transport at work in the digestive system:

1) When there's a higher concentration of nutrients in the gut they diffuse naturally into the blood.
2) BUT — sometimes there's a lower concentration of nutrients in the gut than in the blood.
3) Active transport allows nutrients to be taken into the blood, despite the fact that the concentration gradient is the wrong way. This is essential to stop us starving. But active transport needs ATP from respiration (see p.20) to make it work.

diffusion

active transport

Plants use active transport to obtain the minerals they need from the soil (see p.35).

Revision by diffusion — you wish...

Hopefully there'll have been a net movement of information from this page into your brain...

Q1 What is: a) diffusion b) active transport? [3 marks]

Osmosis

If you've got your head round diffusion, osmosis will be a breeze. If not, have a read of the previous page...

Osmosis is a Special Case of Diffusion, That's All

Osmosis is the net movement of water molecules across a partially permeable membrane from a region of higher water concentration to a region of lower water concentration.

1) A partially permeable membrane is just one with very small holes in it. Only tiny molecules (like water) can pass through them, and bigger molecules (e.g. sucrose) can't. A cell membrane is a partially permeable membrane.
2) The water molecules actually pass both ways through the membrane during osmosis. This happens because water molecules move about randomly all the time.
3) But because there are more water molecules on one side than on the other, there's a steady net flow of water into the region with fewer water molecules, e.g. into the sucrose solution.
4) This means the sucrose solution gets more dilute. The water acts like it's trying to even up the concentration either side of the membrane.

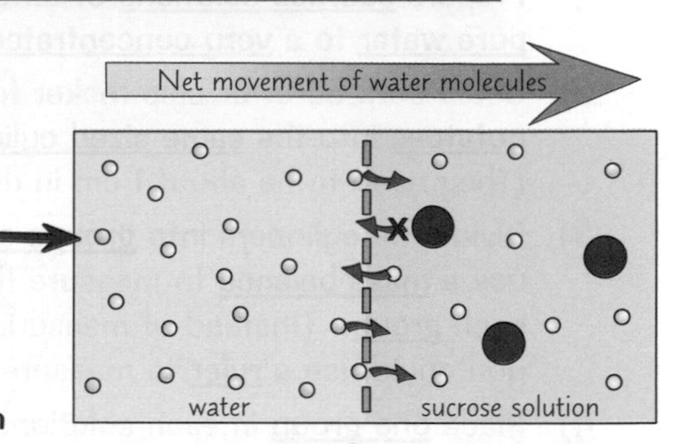

Water Potential Tells You How Concentrated a Solution is

1) You can talk about osmosis in terms of water potential — water potential is the potential (likelihood) of water molecules to diffuse out of or into a solution.
2) If a solution has a high water potential, then it has a high concentration of water molecules. If it has a low water potential, then it has a low concentration of water molecules.
3) So, you can say that osmosis is the diffusion of water molecules across a partially permeable membrane down a water potential gradient (i.e. from an area of higher water potential to an area of lower water potential).

Pure water has the highest water potential. All solutions have a lower water potential than pure water.

Plants Are Supported by Turgid Cells

1) Watering a plant increases the water potential of the soil around it. This means that all the plant cells draw water in by osmosis until they become turgid (plump and swollen). The contents of the cell push against the cell wall — this is called turgor pressure. Turgor pressure helps support the plant tissues.
2) If there's no water in the soil, a plant starts to wilt (droop). This is because the cells become flaccid — they start to lose water. The plant doesn't totally lose its shape though, because the inelastic cell wall keeps things in position. It just droops a bit.
3) Animal cells don't have cell walls so they're more bothered by their surroundings — e.g. cells can burst if they're surrounded by a solution with a higher water potential than them (see p.54).

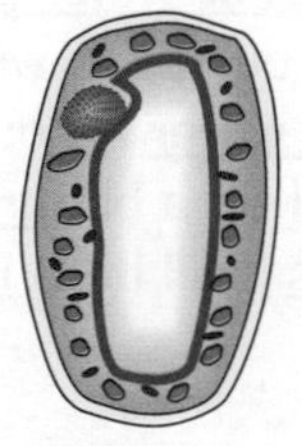
Turgid Cell

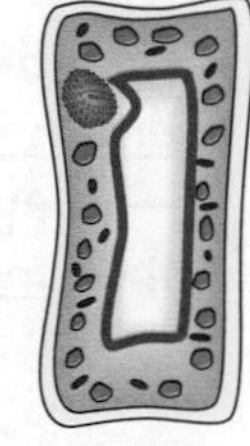
Flaccid Cell

Try saying osmosis backwards — it's not that fun, or educational...

Osmosis is why it's bad to drink sea water. The high salt content means you end up with a much lower water concentration in your blood and tissue fluid than in your cells. Lots of water moves out of your cells by osmosis, which makes them shrivel and die. So next time you're stranded at sea, remember this page...

Q1 Define osmosis. [1 mark]

Q2 A piece of carrot is placed in a solution of lower water potential than its cells. Suggest what will happen to the piece of carrot. Explain your answer. [2 marks]

PRACTICAL

Investigating Osmosis

For all you non-believers — here's an experiment you can do to see osmosis in action.

You can do an Experiment to Investigate Osmosis

This experiment involves putting potato cylinders into different concentrations of sucrose (sugar) solution to see what effect different water potentials have on them.

1) Prepare sucrose solutions of different concentrations ranging from pure water to a very concentrated sucrose solution.
2) Use a cork borer or chip maker to cut potatoes into the same sized cylinders. (They need to be about 1 cm in diameter.)
3) Divide the cylinders into groups of three and use a mass balance to measure the mass of each group. (Instead of measuring the mass you could use a ruler to measure their length.)
4) Place one group in each solution.
5) Leave the cylinders in the solution for as long as possible (making sure that they all get the same amount of time). (Try to leave them for at least 40 minutes.)
6) Remove the cylinders and pat dry gently with a paper towel.
7) Weigh each group again and record your results.
8) Calculate the % change in mass for each group.
9) Then you can plot a graph of your results.

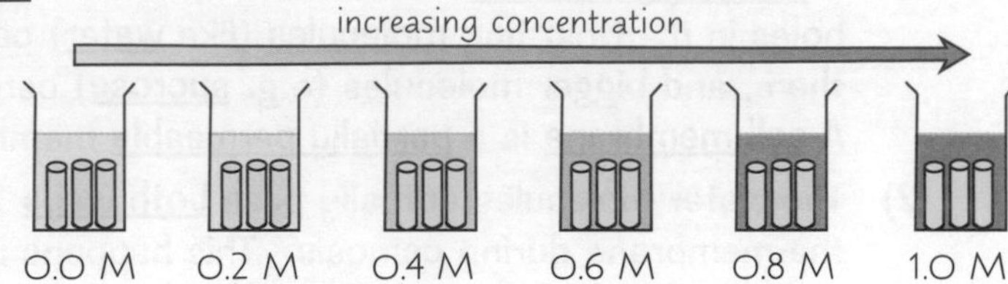

'M' is a unit of concentration. The solution with a concentration of 0.0 M is pure water.

The only thing that you should change in this experiment is the sucrose solution concentration. Everything else (e.g. the volume of solution, the size of the potato cylinders, the time the experiment runs for, etc.) must be kept the same or your results won't be valid.

A group of cylinders weighed 13.2 g at the start of the experiment. At the end they weighed 15.1 g. Calculate the percentage change in mass.

To find the percentage change in mass, use the following formula:

$$\text{percentage change} = \frac{\text{final mass} - \text{initial mass}}{\text{initial mass}} \times 100$$

$$\text{percentage change} = \frac{15.1 - 13.2}{13.2} \times 100 = 14.4\%$$

It's a positive result because the potato cylinders gained mass. If the result was negative then the potato cylinders lost mass.

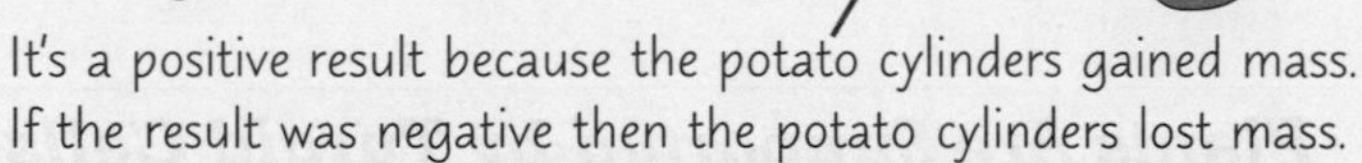

Potato cylinders in solutions with a higher water potential than the cylinders will have drawn in water by osmosis — they'll be a bit longer and their mass will have increased.

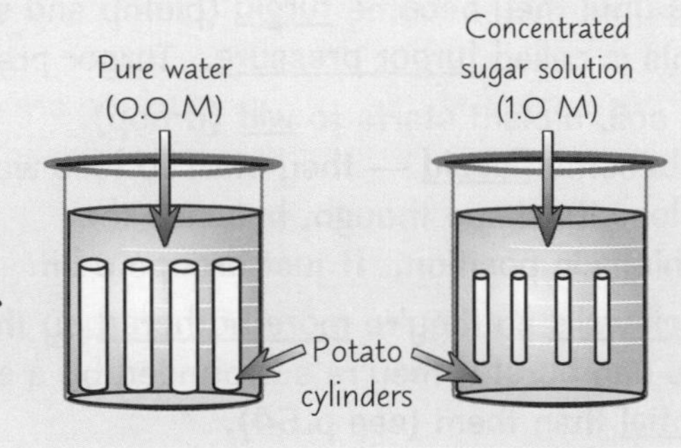

Potato cylinders in solutions with a lower water potential than the cylinders will have lost water — they'll have shrunk a bit and their mass will have decreased.

If the water potential of the sucrose solution is the same as the potato cylinders, then there will be no net water loss or gain, so they will stay the same size and mass.

So that's how they make skinny fries...

OK, it wasn't the most exciting experiment in the world — but make sure you know how to do it.

Q1 A group of equally sized potato cylinders were placed in a sucrose solution and left for one hour. The group of cylinders weighed 13.3 g at the start of the experiment and 11.4 g at the end. Calculate the percentage change in mass. [2 marks]

Exchanging Substances

Now you know about how substances move, you need to know how they get to where they're needed...

Three Main Factors Affect The Movement of Substances

The rates of diffusion, osmosis and active transport vary — they're affected by these three factors:

1) Surface Area to Volume Ratio

The rate of diffusion, osmosis and active transport is higher in cells (or cubes) with a larger surface area to volume ratio.

EXAMPLE:

Calculate the surface area to volume ratio of the cubes on the right.

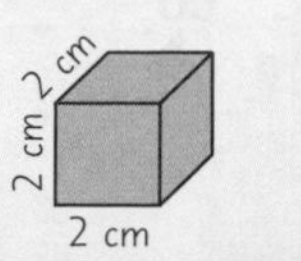

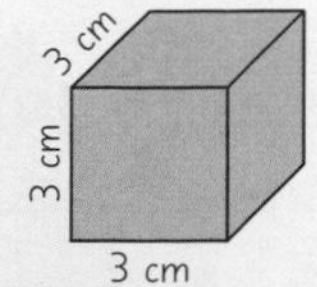

Surface area (cm^2)	2 x 2 x 6 = 24	3 x 3 x 6 = 54
Volume (cm^3)	2 x 2 x 2 = 8	3 x 3 x 3 = 27
Surface area to volume ratio	24 : 8 = 3 : 1	54 : 27 = 2 : 1

The smaller cube has a larger surface area to volume ratio. This means substances would move into and out of this cube faster.

You might also see ratios written as fractions, e.g. 2/1, or as a single number, e.g. 54 ÷ 27 = 2 cm^{-1}.

2) Temperature

As the particles in a substance get warmer they have more energy — so they move faster. This means as temperature increases, substances move in and out of cells faster.

3) Concentration Gradient

Substances move in and out of a cell faster if there's a big difference in concentration between the inside and outside of the cell. If there are lots more particles on one side, there are more there to move across.

This only increases the rate of diffusion and osmosis — concentration gradients don't affect the rate of active transport.

Exchanging Substances is Trickier in Multicellular Organisms

1) An organism needs to supply all its cells with the substances (e.g. glucose, oxygen, water, etc.) it needs to live (e.g. for processes like respiration and photosynthesis). It also needs to get rid of waste products. E.g:
   1) Proteins can't be stored by the body — so any excess amino acids are converted in the liver into fats and carbohydrates, which can be stored.
   2) Urea is produced as a waste product from the reactions.
   3) Urea is poisonous so it needs to be removed from the body.

   Urea is filtered out of the blood by the kidneys and removed from the body in the urine — see p.54.

2) Single-celled organisms exchange substances differently to multicellular organisms. As they're only one cell big, substances can diffuse straight into and out of single-celled organisms across the cell membrane. Diffusion is quite quick because:
   - Substances only have to travel a short distance.
   - Single-celled organisms have a relatively large surface area to volume ratio — this means they're able to exchange enough substances across their cell membrane to supply the volume of the cell.
3) In multicellular organisms it is more difficult to exchange substances. Diffusion across the outer membrane is too slow because:
   - Some cells are deep inside the organism — it's a long way from them to the outside environment.
   - Larger organisms have a low surface area to volume ratio — it's difficult to exchange enough substances to supply a large volume of organism through a relatively small outer surface.
4) So instead of exchanging substances through their outer membrane, multicellular organisms need specialised exchange organs, each with a specialised exchange surface — see the next two pages.
5) They also need transport systems to carry materials from the exchange organs to the body cells, and to remove waste products. In animals, the transport system is the circulatory system (see p.37). In plants, it's the xylem and phloem vessels (see p.39).

If you're bored, work out the surface area : volume of a loved one...

Time to exchange any useless facts stored in your brain with the information on this page. Then try this question...

Q1 Calculate the surface area : volume ratio of a cube with sides measuring 5 cm. [1 mark]

Exchange Surfaces

The next couple of pages are all about how exchange surfaces found in different multicellular organisms are adapted so that substances can move through them effectively. It's exciting stuff, I promise you...

Exchange Surfaces have Adaptations to Maximise Exchange

The exchange surfaces in specialised exchange organs are adapted to maximise effectiveness:

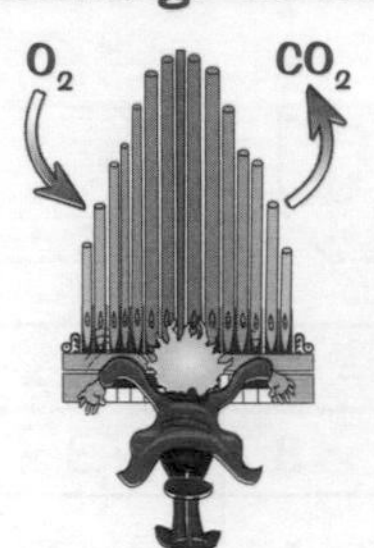

- They are thin, so substances only have a short distance to travel.
- They have a large surface area, so lots of a substance can move at once.
- Exchange surfaces in animals have lots of blood vessels, to get stuff into and out of the blood quickly.
- Gas exchange surfaces in animals (e.g. alveoli, see below) are often ventilated too — air moves in and out.

For information about why exchange surfaces are needed see previous page.

Here are a few examples of exchange surfaces found in multicellular organisms. First up, the alveoli...

Gas Exchange Happens in the Lungs

1) The job of the lungs is to transfer oxygen to the blood and to remove waste carbon dioxide from it.
2) To do this the lungs contain millions of little air sacs called alveoli where gas exchange takes place.
3) The alveoli are specialised to maximise the diffusion of oxygen (O_2) and carbon dioxide (CO_2). They have:
   - An enormous surface area (about 75 m^2 in humans).
   - Very thin walls.
   - A moist lining for dissolving gases.
   - A good blood supply.
4) The blood passing next to the alveoli has just returned to the lungs from the rest of the body via the heart (see p. 36), so it contains lots of CO_2 and very little oxygen.
5) CO_2 diffuses out of the blood (higher concentration) into the alveolus (lower concentration) to be breathed out.
6) Oxygen diffuses out of the alveolus (higher concentration) into the blood (lower concentration).

capillary network, bronchiole, air in, small artery, alveoli, small vein

Red = blood with oxygen.
Blue = blood with carbon dioxide.

air in and out, bronchiole, from heart, direction of blood flow, CO_2, high CO_2 in blood, low CO_2 in alveolus, alveolus, O_2, red blood cell, blood capillary, high O_2 in alveolus, low O_2 in blood, back to heart

The Villi Provide a Really Big Surface Area

1) The small intestine is where dissolved food molecules are absorbed out of the digestive system and into the blood.
2) The inside of the small intestine is covered in millions and millions of tiny little projections called villi.
3) They increase the surface area in a big way so that dissolved food molecules are absorbed much more quickly into the blood. They have:
   - A single layer of surface cells.
   - A very good blood supply to assist quick absorption.

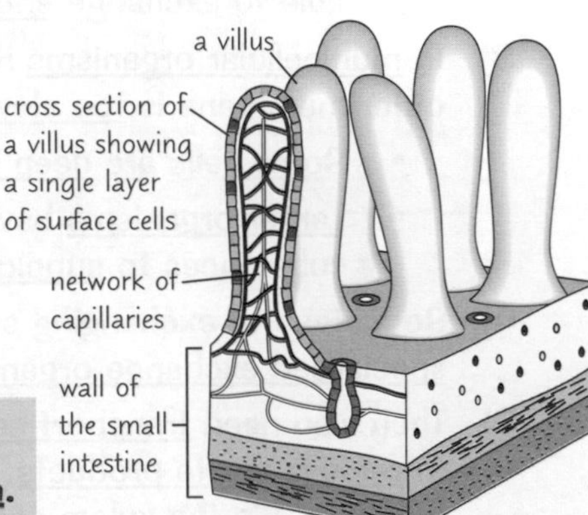

Al Veoli — the Italian gas man...

Don't turn over 'til you've learnt exactly how these specialised surfaces help to maximise exchange.

Q1 Explain why it is beneficial for an exchange surface to be just one cell thick. [1 mark]

More on Exchange Surfaces

All the stuff about maximising the exchange of substances from the previous page applies to plants too...

Leaves are Adapted for Efficient Gas Exchange

When plants photosynthesise they use up CO_2 from the atmosphere and produce oxygen as a waste product. When plants respire they use up oxygen and produce CO_2 as a waste product. So there are lots of gases moving to and fro in plants, and this movement happens by diffusion.

E.g. when the plant is photosynthesising it uses up lots of CO_2, so there's hardly any inside the leaf. This makes more CO_2 move into the leaf by diffusion (from an area of higher concentration to an area of lower concentration).

Leaves are specialised to maximise the diffusion of O_2 and CO_2:

1) Leaves are broad, so there's a large surface area for diffusion.
2) They're also thin, which means gases only have to travel a short distance.

There's more about respiration on p.20-22 and more about photosynthesis on p.25-26.

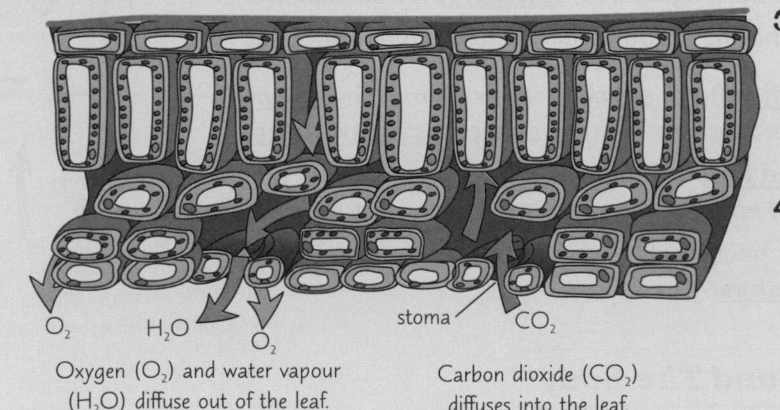

Oxygen (O_2) and water vapour (H_2O) diffuse out of the leaf.

Carbon dioxide (CO_2) diffuses into the leaf.

3) There are air spaces inside the leaf. This lets gases like CO_2 and O_2 move easily between cells. It also increases the surface area for gas exchange.
4) The lower surface is full of little holes called stomata (see p.40). They're there to let gases like CO_2 and O_2 diffuse in and out. They also allow water to escape — which is known as transpiration (see p.39).

Root Hairs Take in Water and Mineral Ions

1) The cells on plant roots grow into long 'hairs' which stick out into the soil.
2) Each branch of a root will be covered in millions of these microscopic hairs.
3) This gives the plant a big surface area for absorbing water and mineral ions from the soil:
   - There's usually a higher concentration of water in the soil than there is inside the plant, so the water is drawn into the root hair cell by osmosis.
   - Mineral ions move in by active transport, since the concentration of mineral ions in the root hair cells is usually higher than in the soil.

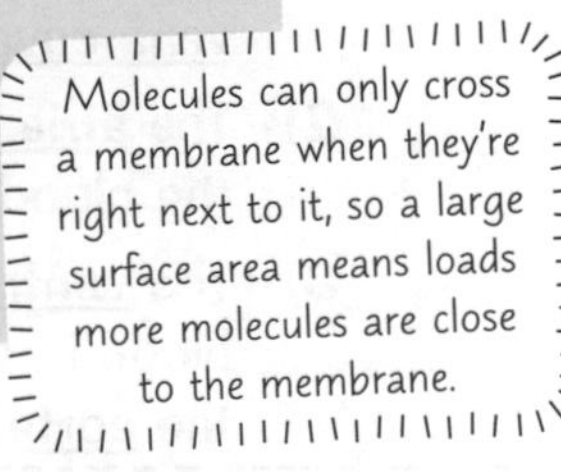

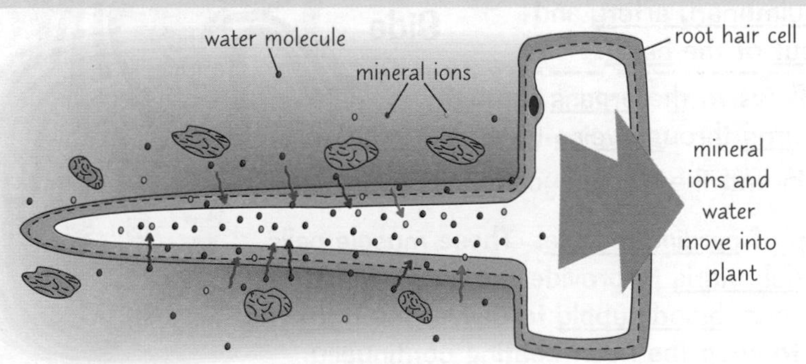

Thirsty? Go dip your hair in your drink...

Living organisms are really well adapted for getting the substances they need to their cells.
Now that you've seen loads of examples of how exchange surfaces are adapted, these questions should be a breeze...

Q1 Give three ways that leaves are specialised to maximise the diffusion of O_2 and CO_2. [3 marks]

Q2 How are plant roots adapted to be able to absorb lots of water and mineral ions from the soil? [2 marks]

The Circulatory System

As you saw on page 33, multicellular organisms need transport systems to move substances around effectively. In humans, it's the job of the circulatory system. My heart's all of a flutter just thinking about it...

The DOUBLE Circulatory System, Actually

The circulatory system is made up of the heart, blood vessels and blood.
Humans have a double circulatory system — two circuits joined together:

1) In the first one, the heart pumps deoxygenated blood (blood without oxygen) to the gas exchange surfaces in the lungs to take in oxygen. The oxygenated blood then returns to the heart.
2) In the second one, the heart pumps oxygenated blood around all the other organs of the body. The blood gives up its oxygen at the body cells (see page 38) and the deoxygenated blood returns to the heart to be pumped out to the lungs again.
3) Not all animals have a double circulatory system — fish don't, for example.
4) There are advantages to mammals having a double circulatory system though:

- Returning the blood to the heart after it's picked up oxygen at the lungs means it can be pumped out around the body at a much higher pressure.
- This increases the rate of blood flow to the tissues (i.e. blood can be pumped around the body much faster), so more oxygen can be delivered to the cells.
- This is important for mammals because they use up a lot of oxygen maintaining their body temperature.

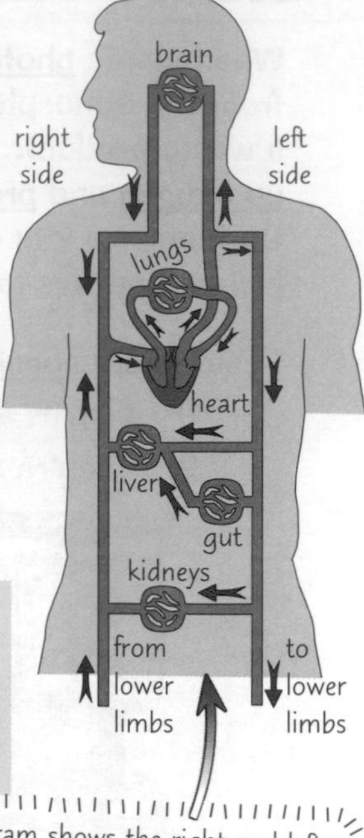

The diagram shows the right and left side of the person in the diagram, not your right and left as you look at them.

The Heart Pumps Blood Around The Body

1) The heart is a pumping organ that keeps the blood flowing around the body.
2) The heart has valves to make sure that blood flows in the right direction. When the ventricles contract, the valves to the atria close and the valves to the blood vessels open. This prevents backflow (when the blood flows backwards).
3) This is how the heart uses its four chambers (right and left atria and ventricles) to pump blood around:

Atria is plural. Atrium is when there is just one.

1) Blood flows into the two atria from the vena cava and the pulmonary vein.
2) The atria contract, pushing the blood into the ventricles.
3) The ventricles contract, forcing the blood into the pulmonary artery and the aorta, and out of the heart.
4) The blood then flows to the organs through arteries, and returns through veins (see next page).
5) The atria fill again and the whole cycle starts over.

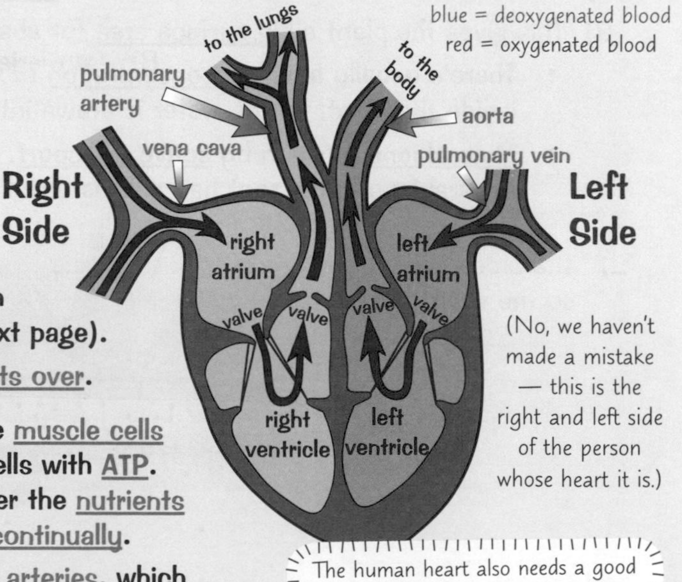

(No, we haven't made a mistake — this is the right and left side of the person whose heart it is.)

The heart is made up of cardiac muscle. These muscle cells contain loads of mitochondria to provide the cells with ATP. They also need their own blood supply to deliver the nutrients and oxygen needed to keep the heart beating continually.
Blood is supplied to the heart by two coronary arteries, which branch from the base of the aorta (the biggest artery in the body).

The human heart also needs a good blood supply to remove the carbon dioxide produced during respiration.

Okay — let's get to the heart of the matter...

Make sure you learn the names of the different parts of the heart and all the blood vessels that are attached to it.

Q1 Which chamber of the heart pumps deoxygenated blood to the lungs? [1 mark]

The Blood Vessels

If you want to know more about the circulatory system you're in luck. Because here's a whole extra page.

Blood Vessels are Designed for Their Function

There are three main types of blood vessel:

1) ARTERIES — these carry the blood away from the heart.
2) CAPILLARIES — these are involved in the exchange of materials at the tissues.
3) VEINS — these carry the blood to the heart.

Arteries and veins don't lead straight into capillaries. Arteries branch into arterioles, which are much smaller than arteries. Arterioles then branch into capillaries. The capillaries connect to venules, which join together to form veins.

Arteries Carry Blood Under Pressure

1) The heart pumps the blood out at high pressure so the artery walls are strong and elastic.
2) The walls are thick compared to the size of the lumen.
3) They contain thick layers of muscle to make them strong, and elastic fibres to allow them to stretch and spring back.
4) Arteries branch into arterioles.

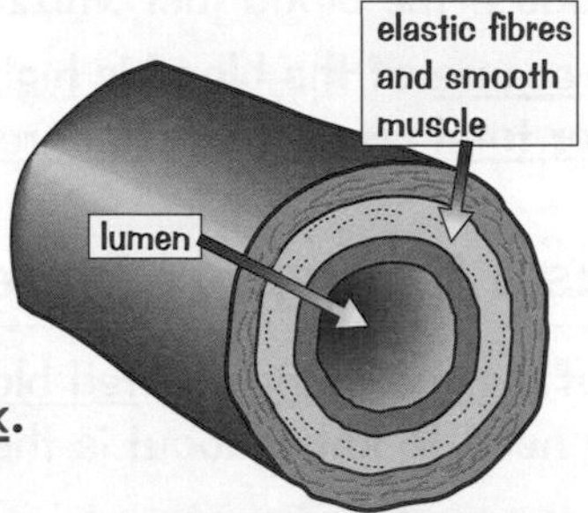

The lumen is just the hole down the middle — silly name.

Capillaries are Really Small

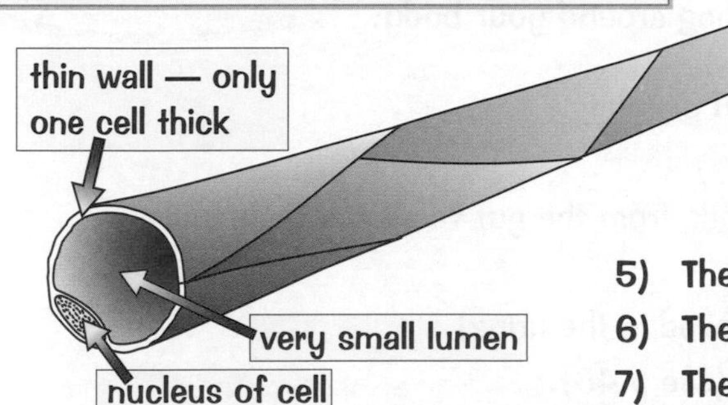

1) Arterioles branch into capillaries.
2) Capillaries are really tiny — too small to see.
3) Networks of capillaries in tissue are called capillary beds.
4) Capillaries carry the blood really close to every cell in the body to exchange substances with them.
5) They have permeable walls, so substances can diffuse in and out.
6) They supply food and oxygen, and take away waste like CO_2.
7) Their walls are usually only one cell thick. This increases the rate of diffusion by decreasing the distance over which it occurs.
8) Capillaries branch into venules.

Veins Take Blood Back to the Heart

1) Venules eventually join up to form veins.
2) The blood is at lower pressure in the veins so the walls don't need to be as thick as artery walls.
3) They have a bigger lumen than arteries to help the blood flow despite the lower pressure.
4) They also have valves to help keep the blood flowing in the right direction.

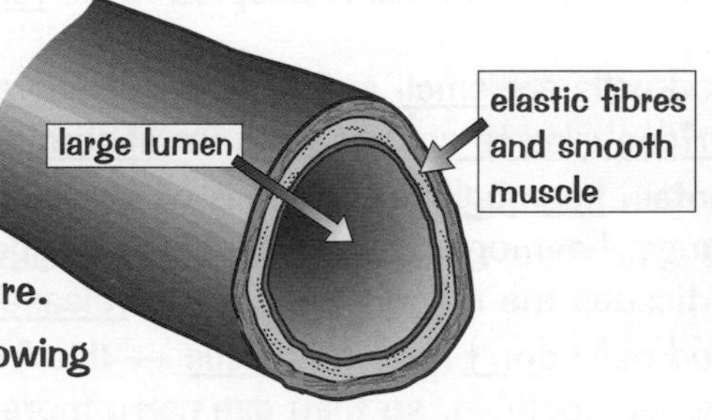

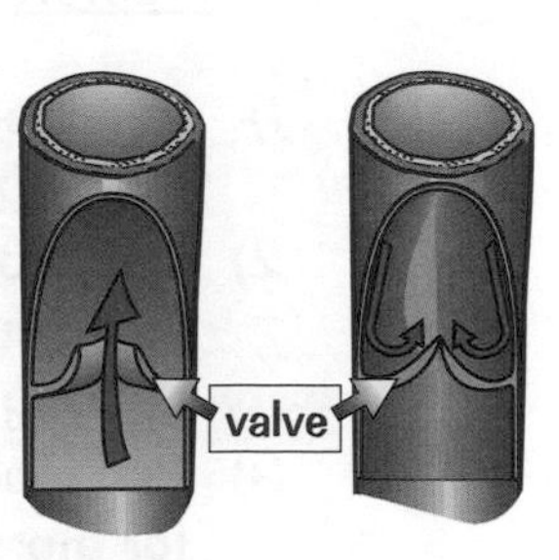

Learn this page — don't struggle in vein...

Here's an interesting fact for you — your body contains about 60 000 miles of blood vessels. That's about six times the distance from London to Sydney in Australia. Of course, capillaries are really tiny, which is how such a massive amount of them can fit in your body — they can only be seen with a microscope.

Q1 Describe how veins are adapted to carry blood back to the heart. [2 marks]

Q2 Explain how capillaries are adapted to their function. [3 marks]

The Blood

Right, a tiny bit more about the blood vessels coming up first, then onto the blood itself... (Hmmm — is it me, or is this starting to sound a tiny bit like a lecture for vampires...)

The Total Cross-Sectional Area of Vessels Affects Blood Flow

1) As the total cross-sectional area of blood vessels increases, the mean velocity of the blood flowing through the vessels decreases (i.e. blood flows more slowly through capillaries than veins or arteries).
2) Although capillaries are tiny there are so many of them that their total cross-sectional area is huge.
3) This means that blood flows slowly through capillary beds, which allows more time for the exchange of substances — it'd be no good if the blood just whizzed past the body cells.

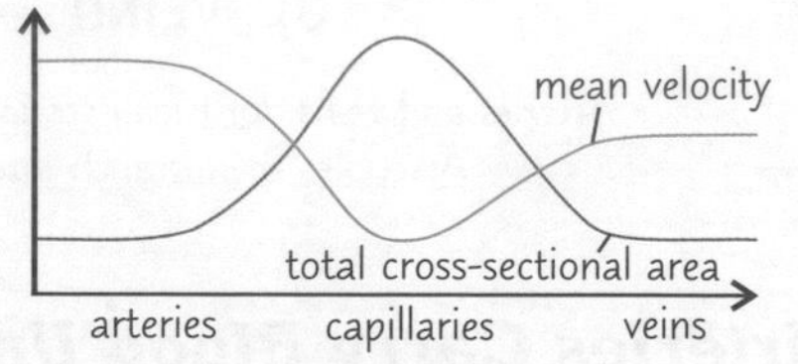

4) The mean pressure of the blood is highest in the arteries because they're closest to the heart but the larger total cross-sectional area of the capillaries causes the pressure to fall.

Blood Acts as a Transport System

Blood consists of plasma, platelets, red blood cells and white blood cells. For now, all you need to know about is the plasma and the red blood cells...

You can read about white blood cells and platelets in Topic B6 — see page 95.

Plasma is the Liquid Bit of Blood

It's basically blood minus the blood cells. Plasma is a pale yellow liquid which carries just about everything that needs transporting around your body:

1) Red blood cells (see below), white blood cells, and platelets.
2) Water.
3) Digested food products like glucose and amino acids from the gut to all the body cells.
4) Carbon dioxide from the body cells to the lungs.
5) Urea from the liver to the kidneys (where it's removed in the urine).
6) Hormones — these act like chemical messengers (see p.46).
7) Antibodies — these are proteins involved in the body's immune response (see p.95).

Red Blood Cells Have the Job of Carrying Oxygen

Red blood cells transport oxygen from the lungs to all the cells in the body. The structure of a red blood cell is adapted to its function:

Biconcave means they look like they've been pressed in (they're concave) on both sides (see diagram below).

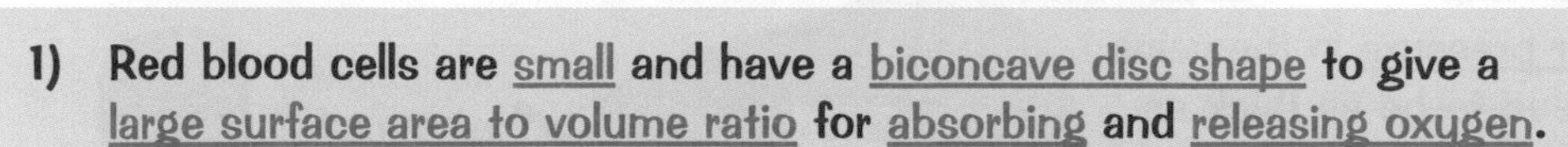

1) Red blood cells are small and have a biconcave disc shape to give a large surface area to volume ratio for absorbing and releasing oxygen.
2) They contain haemoglobin, which is what gives blood its colour — it contains a lot of iron. In the lungs, haemoglobin combines with oxygen to become oxyhaemoglobin. In body tissues the reverse happens to release oxygen to the cells.
3) Red blood cells don't have a nucleus — this frees up space for more haemoglobin, so they can carry more oxygen.
4) As they are small and very flexible they can easily pass through the tiny capillaries.

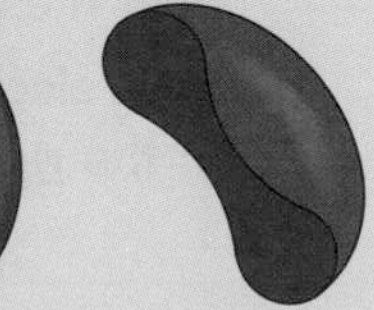

Blood's other function is to let you know you're bleeding...

Every single drop contains millions of red blood cells — all of them perfectly designed for carrying plenty of oxygen to where it's needed. Which right now is your brain, so you can get cracking with learning this page.

Q1 Describe three ways in which red blood cells are adapted to carry oxygen. [3 marks]

Plant Transport Systems and Transpiration

Plants have two separate types of transport vessel — xylem and phloem — for transporting stuff around. Both types of vessel go to every part of the plant in a continuous system, but they're totally separate.

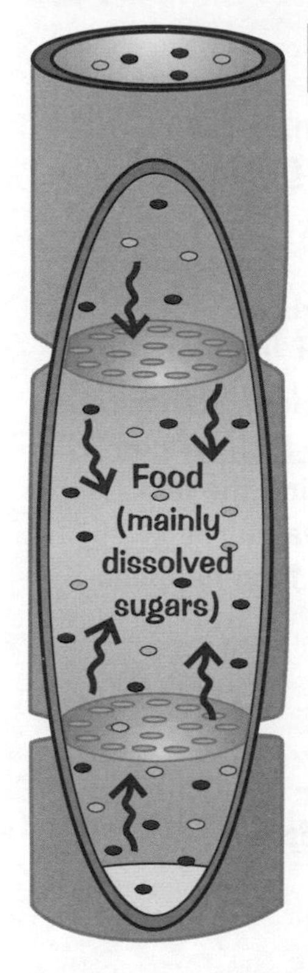

Phloem Tubes Transport Food

1) Made of columns of living cells called sieve tube elements. These have perforated end-plates to allow stuff to flow through.
2) Sieve tube elements have no nucleus. This means that they can't survive on their own, so each sieve tube element has a companion cell. These cells carry out the living functions for both themselves and their sieve cells.
3) Phloem vessels transport food substances (mainly sugars) both up and down the stem to growing and storage tissues. This movement of food substances around the plant is known as translocation.

Xylem Tubes Take Water UP

Like phloem, xylem cells don't contain any nuclei.

1) Made of dead cells joined end to end with no end walls between them and a hole (lumen) down the middle.
2) The thick side walls are made of cellulose. They're strong and stiff, which gives the plant support. The cell walls are also strengthened with a material called lignin.
3) They carry water and minerals from the roots up the shoot to the leaves in the transpiration stream (see below).

Transpiration is the Loss of Water from the Plant

1) Transpiration is caused by the evaporation and diffusion of water from a plant's surface. Most transpiration happens at the leaves.
2) This evaporation and diffusion creates a slight shortage of water in the leaf, and so more water is drawn up from the rest of the plant through the xylem vessels to replace it.
3) This in turn means more water is drawn up from the roots, and so there's a constant transpiration stream of water through the plant.

Head back to page 35 to see how root hair cells are adapted for taking up water.

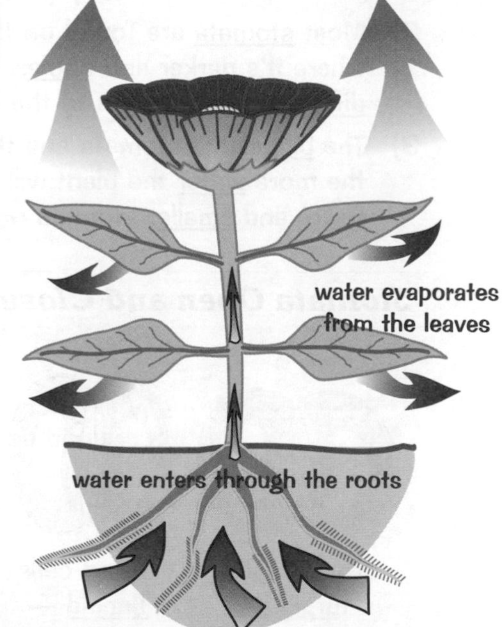

Transpiration is just a side-effect of the way leaves are adapted for photosynthesis. They have to have stomata in them so that gases can be exchanged easily (see page 35). Because there's more water inside the plant than in the air outside, the water escapes from the leaves through the stomata by diffusion.

The transpiration stream does have some benefits for the plants, however:

1) The constant stream of water from the ground helps to keep the plant cool.
2) It provides the plant with a constant supply of water for photosynthesis.
3) The water creates turgor pressure in the plant cells, which helps support the plant and stops it wilting.
4) Minerals needed by the plant can be brought in from the soil along with the water.

See page 31 for more on turgidity in plant cells.

Don't let revision stress you out — just go with the phloem...

Phloem goes up and down, whereas xylem just goes up. You could remember it as xy to the sky... it sort of rhymes.

Q1 Explain why there is a continuous upward flow of water in plants. [3 marks]

More on Transpiration

If you thought that stuff on transpiration was interesting, you're not gonna believe your luck — here's another page all about water transport in plants. I don't know about you, but I'm feeling pretty thirsty...

Transpiration Rate is Affected by Three Main Things

1) AN INCREASE IN LIGHT INTENSITY — the brighter the light, the greater the transpiration rate. Bright light increases the rate of photosynthesis, causing the stomata to open to let CO_2 in. Stomata begin to close as it gets darker because photosynthesis can't happen in the dark. When the stomata are closed, water can't escape.
2) AN INCREASE IN TEMPERATURE — the warmer it is, the faster transpiration happens. When it's warm the water particles have more energy to evaporate and diffuse out of the stomata.
3) AN INCREASE IN AIR MOVEMENT — if there's lots of air movement (wind) around a leaf, transpiration happens faster. If the air around a leaf is very still, the water vapour just surrounds the leaf and doesn't move away. This means there's a high concentration of water particles outside the leaf as well as inside it, so diffusion doesn't happen as quickly. If it's windy, the water vapour is swept away, maintaining a low concentration of water in the air outside the leaf. Diffusion then happens quickly, from an area of higher concentration to an area of lower concentration.

Plants Need to Balance Water Loss with Water Uptake

Transpiration can help plants in some ways (see previous page), but if it hasn't rained for a while and you're short of water it's not a good idea to have it rushing out of your leaves. So plants have adaptations to help reduce water loss from their leaves:

Stomata is the plural of stoma.

1) Leaves usually have a waxy cuticle covering the upper epidermis. This helps make the upper surface of the leaf waterproof.
2) Most stomata are found on the lower surface of a leaf where it's darker and cooler. This helps slow down diffusion of water out of the leaf.
3) The bigger the stomata and the more stomata a leaf has, the more water the plant will lose. Plants in hot climates really need to conserve water, so they have fewer and smaller stomata on the underside of the leaf and no stomata on the upper epidermis.

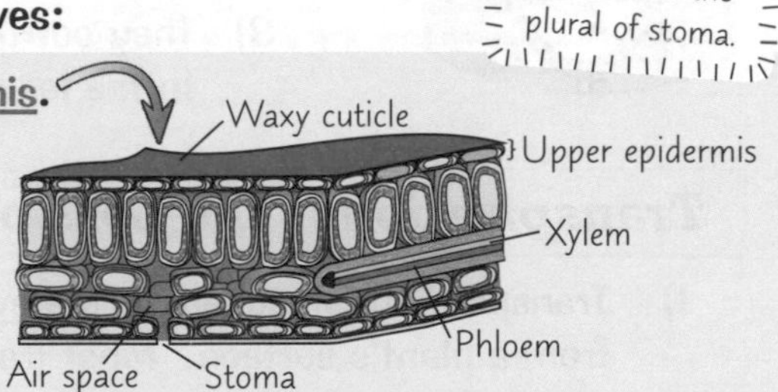

Stomata Open and Close Automatically

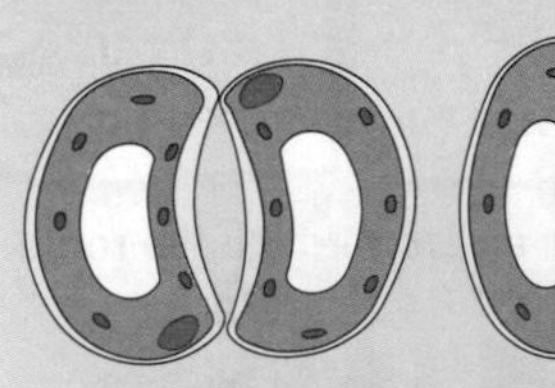
Guard cells turgid — stoma opens

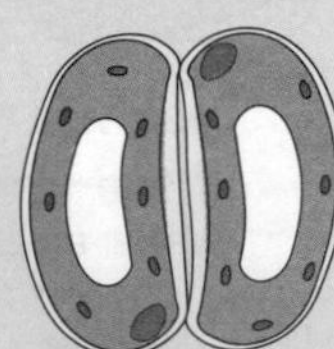
Guard cells flaccid — stoma closes

1) Stomata close automatically when supplies of water start to dry up.
2) The guard cells have a special kidney shape which opens and closes the stomata as the guard cells go turgid or flaccid (see p.31).
3) Thin outer walls and thickened inner walls make this opening and closing function work properly.
4) Open stomata allow gases in and out for photosynthesis.
5) They're sensitive to light, so they open during the day and close at night. This allows them to conserve water without losing out on photosynthesis.

I say stomaaarta, you say stomaaayta...

Here's an interesting fact — a biggish tree loses around 1000 litres of water from its leaves every day. That's about as much water as the average person drinks in a whole year, so the roots have to draw lots of water from the soil to replace it. No wonder the stomata close when the soil's dry or it's too dark.

Q1 Name the cells that control the size of stomata. [1 mark]

Q2 Explain how low light intensity affects the rate of transpiration. [2 marks]

Q3 Explain how temperature affects the rate of transpiration. [2 marks]

Investigating Transpiration

One page. That's it — that's all that's left between you and the end of this section. You can do this.

A Potometer can be Used to Estimate Transpiration Rate

PRACTICAL

A potometer is a special piece of apparatus used to estimate transpiration rate. It actually measures water uptake by a plant, but it's assumed that water uptake by the plant is directly related to water loss from the leaves (transpiration). Here's how to use a potometer:

1) Cut a shoot underwater to prevent air from entering the xylem. Cut it at a slant to increase the surface area available for water uptake.
2) Assemble the potometer in water and insert the shoot under water, so no air can enter.
3) Remove the apparatus from the water but keep the end of the capillary tube submerged in a beaker of water.
4) Check that the apparatus is watertight and airtight.
5) Dry the leaves, allow time for the shoot to acclimatise and then shut the tap.
6) Remove the end of the capillary tube from the beaker of water until one air bubble has formed, then put the end of the tube back into the water.
7) Record the starting position of the air bubble.
8) Start a stopwatch and record the distance moved by the bubble per unit time, e.g. per hour. Calculating the speed of air bubble movement gives an estimate of the transpiration rate.
9) Keep the conditions constant throughout the experiment, e.g. the temperature and air humidity.

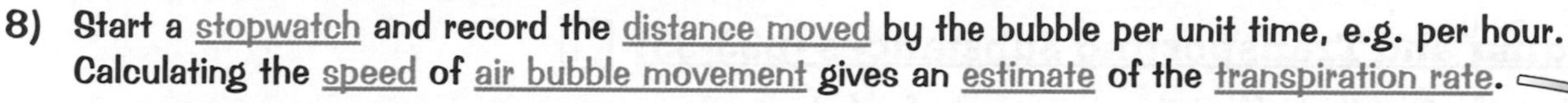

Setting up a potometer is tough — if there are air bubbles in the apparatus or the plant's xylem it will affect your results.

reservoir of water

Tap is shut off during experiment.

As the plant takes up water, the air bubble moves along the scale.

Water moves this way.

Bubble moves this way.

capillary tube with a scale

Beaker of water.

Potometers can be set up in different ways. You might see one in the exam that's a bit different to this one but they're all used to estimate transpiration rate.

A potometer was used to estimate the transpiration rate of a plant cutting. The bubble moved 25 mm in 10 minutes. Estimate the transpiration rate.

To estimate the rate of transpiration, divide the distance the bubble moved by the time taken.

$$\frac{\text{distance moved}}{\text{time taken}} = \frac{25}{10} = 2.5 \text{ mm per minute}$$

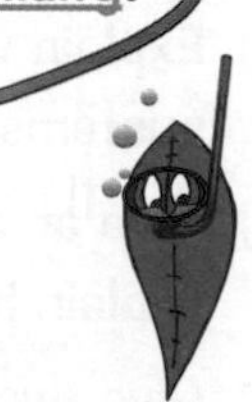

You Can See How Environmental Conditions Affect Transpiration Rates

You can use a potometer to estimate how different factors affect the transpiration rate. The set up above will be your control — you can vary an environmental condition (see below), run the experiment again and compare the results to the control to see how the change affected the transpiration rate.

1) Light intensity — You could use a lamp to increase the intensity of light that hits the plant — this should increase the transpiration rate. To decrease the light intensity, put the potometer in a cupboard (this should decrease the transpiration rate).
2) Temperature — You could increase or decrease the temperature by putting the potometer in a room that's warmer or colder than where you did the control experiment. An increase in temperature should increase the transpiration rate and a decrease in temperature should lower it.
3) Air movement — You could use a fan to increase the air movement around the plant — this should increase the transpiration rate.

Potometer — a surprisingly useless tool for measuring crockery...

You made it. Congratulations. One good way to remember the three factors that affect the rate of transpiration is to think about drying washing. A good day for drying is sunny, warm and windy. It's the same stuff. Fancy that.

Q1 Give two variables you should keep constant if investigating the effect of temperature on transpiration rate. [2 marks]

Revision Questions for Topic B2

That's Topic B2 over and done with — now, let's see if you know your stem cells from your stomata...

- Try these questions and tick off each one when you get it right.
- When you've done all the questions under a heading and are completely happy with it, tick it off.

The Cell Cycle, Cell Differentiation and Stem Cells (p28-29)

1) Briefly describe the stages involved in the cell cycle.
2) Explain why the cells produced during mitosis are genetically identical.
3) Give an example of a cell that is specialised to carry out a particular function.
4) Give two differences between embryonic stem cells and adult stem cells in animals.
5) Where are stem cells found in plants?

Diffusion, Active Transport and Osmosis (p30-32)

6) Give three substances that move across cell membranes by diffusion.
7) Explain how active transport is different from diffusion.
8) What is a partially permeable membrane?
9) Liquid A and liquid B are separated by a partially permeable membrane. There is a net movement of water from liquid B into liquid A. Which liquid has the highest water potential?
10) If potato cylinders are placed in a solution with a higher water potential than the cylinders, what will happen to the mass of the cylinders?

Exchanging and Transporting Substances (p33-35)

11) Give three factors that affect the movement of substances.
12) Explain why single-celled organisms don't require specialised exchange surfaces and transport systems to exchange substances.
13) Give an example of a specialised exchange surface found in an animal and explain how it is adapted to maximise the exchange of substances.
14) Give two substances that a plant takes in via its root hairs.

The Circulatory System, Blood Vessels and Blood (p36-38)

15) True or false? Humans have a single circulatory system.
16) How many chambers does the human heart have?
17) Is blood in the pulmonary artery oxygenated or deoxygenated?
18) Through which vessel does blood leave the left ventricle of the heart?
19) Which type of blood vessel carries blood at high pressure?
20) What is the role of plasma?
21) What is the role of red blood cells?

Plant Transport Systems and Transpiration (p39-41)

22) Explain what is meant by translocation.
23) Which type of plant transport vessel contains sieve tube elements?
24) What is carried by xylem tubes?
25) Which type of plant transport vessel is made up of dead cells?
26) Give three factors that affect the rate of transpiration.
27) Where can most stomata be found?
28) Draw a diagram showing how a potometer can be used to investigate the rate of transpiration.

The Nervous System

The nervous system is what lets you react to what goes on around you, so you'd find life tough without it.

The Central Nervous System Coordinates a Response

1) The nervous system is made up of neurones (nerve cells), which go to all parts of the body.
2) The body has lots of sensory receptors, which can detect a change in your environment (a stimulus). Different sensory receptors detect different stimuli. For example, receptors in your eyes detect light, and receptors in your skin detect touch (pressure) and temperature change.
3) When a stimulus is detected by receptors, the information is sent as nervous (electrical) impulses along sensory neurones to the central nervous system (CNS).
4) The CNS consists of the brain and spinal cord.
5) The CNS coordinates the response (in other words, it decides what to do about the stimulus and tells something to do it).
6) The CNS sends information to an effector (muscle or gland) along a motor neurone. The effector then responds accordingly — e.g. a muscle may contract or a gland may secrete a hormone.

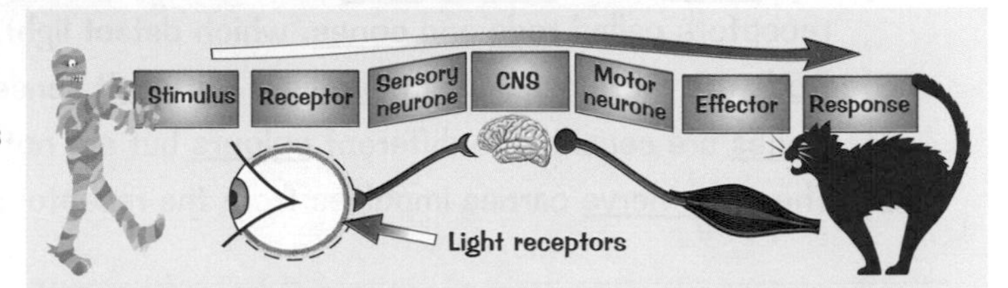

Neurones Transmit Information as Electrical Impulses

1) Electrical impulses are passed along the axon of a neurone.
2) Neurones have branched endings (dendrites) so they can connect with lots of other neurones.
3) Some axons are also surrounded by a fatty (myelin) sheath. This acts as an electrical insulator, speeding up the electrical impulse.
4) Neurones are long, which also speeds up the impulse (connecting with another neurone slows the impulse down, so one long neurone is much quicker than lots of short ones joined together).
5) The connection between two neurones is called a synapse. It's basically just a very tiny gap:

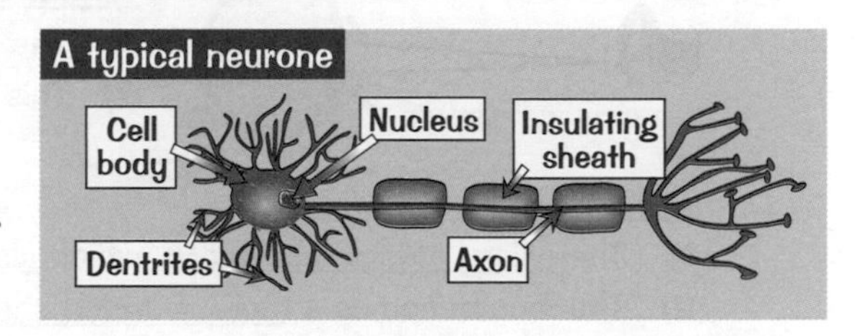

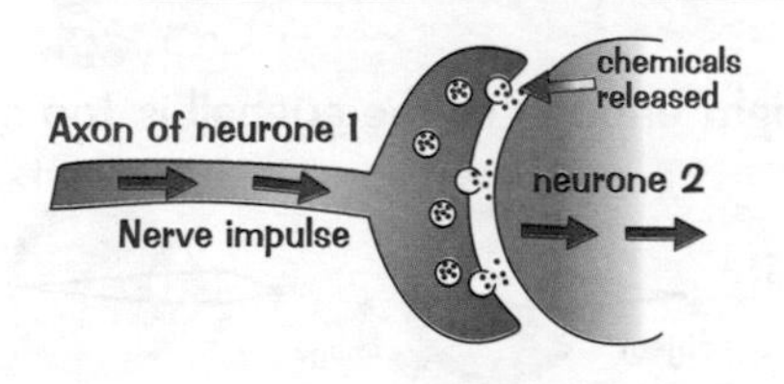

- The electrical impulse triggers the release of transmitter chemicals, which diffuse across the gap.
- These chemicals bind to receptor molecules in the membrane of the next neurone. This sets off a new electrical impulse.

Reflex Actions Stop You Injuring Yourself

1) Reflex actions are automatic (done without thinking) so they're even quicker than normal responses. The passage of information in a reflex (from receptor to effector) is called a reflex arc.
2) The conscious brain isn't involved in a reflex arc. The sensory neurone connects to a relay neurone in the spinal cord or in an unconscious part of the brain — which links directly to the right motor neurone, so no time's wasted thinking about the right response.
3) Reflex actions often have a protective role, e.g. snatching back your hand when you touch a burning hot plate happens almost before you realise you've done it.

Relay neurones just connect sensory neurones to motor neurones.

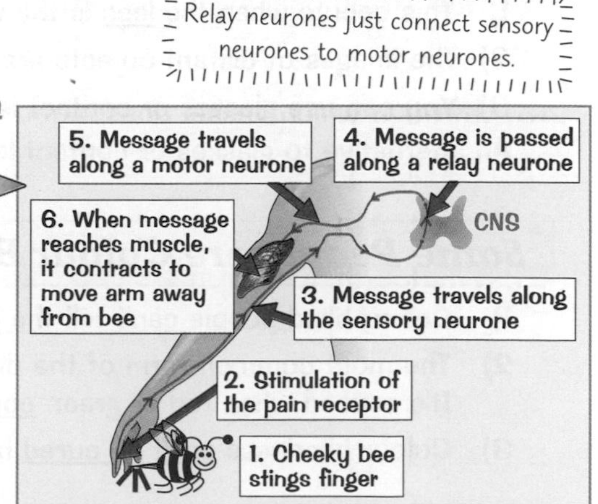

Don't let the thought of exams play on your nerves...

Make sure you understand how the different parts of the nervous system work together to coordinate a response.

Q1 Name the two main parts of the central nervous system. [2 marks]

The Eye

Receptors in the eye are sensitive to light and responsible for sight. Eye problems are pretty common though...

Learn the Eye with All Its Labels:

1) The cornea refracts (bends) light into the eye.
2) The iris controls how much light enters the pupil (the hole in the middle).
3) The lens also refracts light, focusing it onto the retina.
4) The ciliary body contains ciliary muscles, which are attached to suspensory ligaments — they work together to alter the shape of the lens (see below).
5) The retina is the light sensitive part and it's covered in receptors called rods and cones, which detect light.
6) Rods are more sensitive in dim light but can't sense colour.
7) Cones are sensitive to different colours but are not so good in dim light.
8) The optic nerve carries impulses from the receptors to the brain.

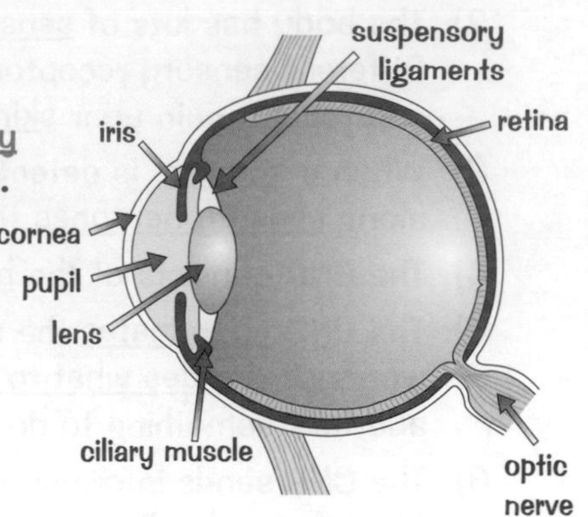

Focusing on Near and Distant Objects

The lens is elastic, so the eye can focus light by changing the shape of the lens.

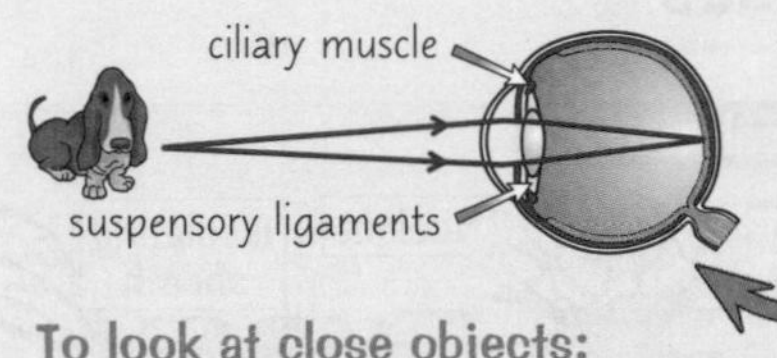

To look at distant objects:
1) The ciliary muscle relaxes, which allows the suspensory ligaments to pull tight.
2) This pulls the lens into a less rounded shape so light is refracted less.

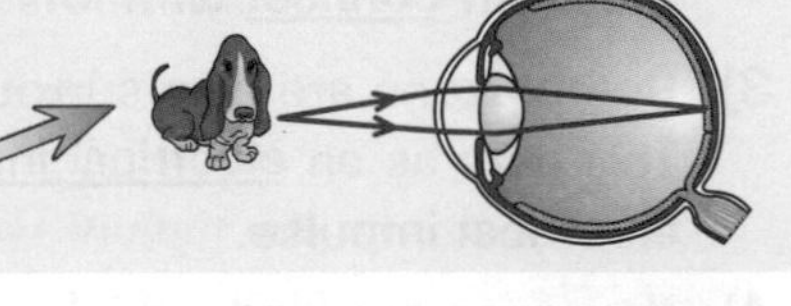

To look at close objects:
1) The ciliary muscle contracts, which slackens the suspensory ligaments.
2) The lens becomes a more rounded shape, so light is refracted more.

Some People are Long- or Short-sighted

Long-sighted people are unable to focus on near objects:
1) This occurs when the lens is the wrong shape and doesn't bend the light enough or the eyeball is too short.
2) The images of near objects are brought into focus behind the retina.
3) You can use glasses or contact lenses with a convex lens to correct it.

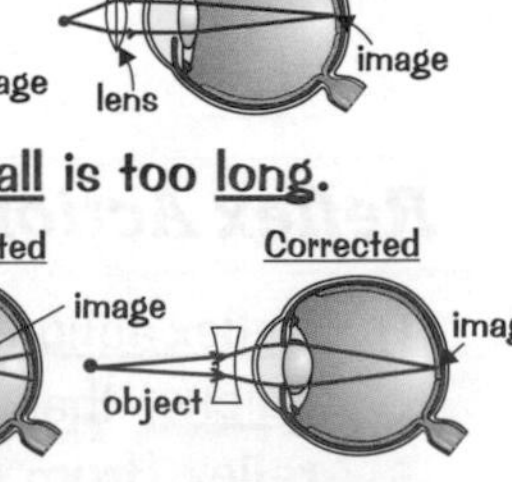

Short-sighted people are unable to focus on distant objects:
1) This occurs when the lens is the wrong shape and bends the light too much or the eyeball is too long.
2) The images of distant objects are brought into focus in front of the retina.
3) You can use glasses or contact lenses with a concave lens to correct it.

An alternative to glasses or contact lenses is to have corneal laser surgery.

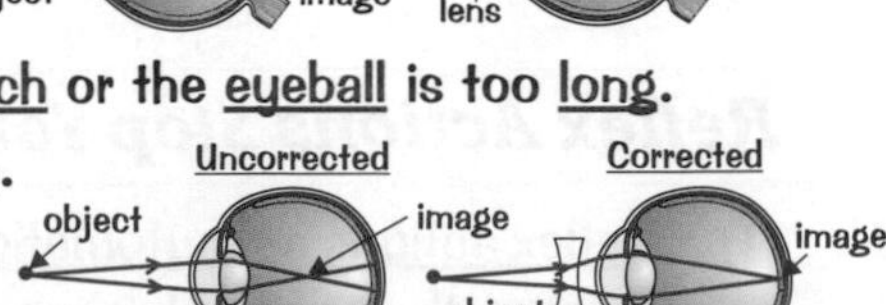

Some People are Colour Blind

1) Colour blind people can't tell the difference between certain colours.
2) The most common form of the disorder is red-green colour blindness. It's caused when red or green cones in the retina are not working properly.
3) Colour blindness can't be cured but tinted lenses can be used to help people see colours more normally.

I think I'm a little long-sighted...

If you can read this you've got better eyesight than me!

Get your eyes working hard reading and re-reading this page until you've got it well and truly sussed.

Q1 Describe the role of the cornea in the eye. [1 mark]

Q2 Describe one problem with the eye that may cause a person to be long-sighted. [1 mark]

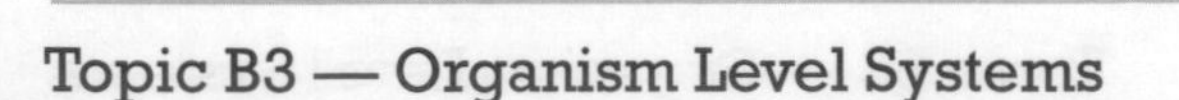

The Brain

Scientists know a bit about the brain but not as much as they'd like. Read on, it's pretty amazing stuff.

The Brain is Responsible for Complex Behaviours

The brain is made up of billions of interconnected neurones. It controls and coordinates everything you do. We know that different regions of the brain carry out different functions:

1. Cerebrum — This is the outer wrinkly bit. It's responsible for things like consciousness, intelligence, memory and language.
2. Hypothalamus — Involved in maintaining body temperature at the normal level (see p.52). Also produces hormones that control the pituitary gland.
3. Pituitary — A gland that produces many important hormones, such as some of those involved in the menstrual cycle (see page 47).
4. Medulla — Controls unconscious activities (things you don't have to think about doing) like breathing and your heart rate.
5. Cerebellum — Responsible for muscle coordination.

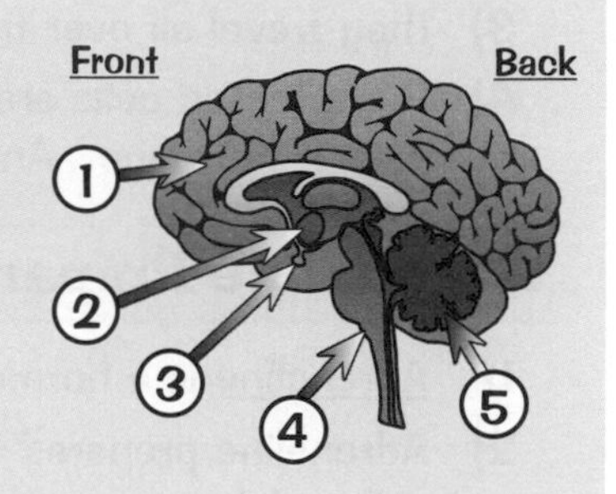

There are Problems with Studying Brain Function

Being able to study the brain is really important — it allows scientists to work out more about what each part of the brain does, which is really useful when trying to treat people with brain damage or disease.

1) Scientists sometimes use case studies to learn about the brain — they carry out detailed studies of individuals who have abnormal brain function.
2) If part of the brain has been damaged, the effect this has on the patient can tell you a lot about what the damaged part of the brain does. E.g. if an area of the brain was damaged and the patient went blind it's likely that area has something to do with vision.
3) Scientists may also use fMRI scanners (big tube-like machines) that show which parts of the brain are activated when performing certain tasks inside the scanner.
4) They can also learn a lot by examining the brains of people who have died.

However, investigating brain function can be tricky for many reasons. E.g.

1) If a person is severely brain damaged, it may be unethical to study them as they might not be able to give informed consent.
2) Studying the brains of people who have died relies on people donating their brains for research.
3) There can be problems when interpreting the results of case studies. For example, when fMRI scanners are used to study brain function, it cannot be known for sure that the same pattern of activity would occur in a normal situation (i.e. when not in a machine).

To give informed consent a person must understand what's going to happen to them and know the benefits and risks.

Treating Problems in the Brain Can be Tricky

There are many things that can go wrong with the brain or other parts of the nervous system, e.g. injuries to the brain or spinal cord, tumours, diseases, etc. These can be difficult to treat successfully:

- It's hard to repair damage to the nervous system — neurones in the CNS don't readily repair themselves and as of yet scientists haven't developed a way to repair nervous tissue in the CNS.
- If a problem occurs in a part of the nervous system that's not easy to access it can be hard to treat, e.g. it's not possible to surgically remove tumours growing in certain parts of the brain.
- Treatment for problems in the nervous system may lead to permanent damage, e.g. surgery to remove a brain tumour may leave surrounding parts of the brain permanently damaged.

A whole page dedicated to that squidgy thing in your head...

... lucky you. As technology improves, scientists are learning more and more about what goes on up there.

Q1 Give a function of: a) the hypothalamus b) the medulla c) the cerebellum. [3 marks]

Hormones and Negative Feedback Systems

The other way to send information around the body (apart from along neurones) is by using hormones.

Hormones are Chemical Messengers Sent in the Blood

1) Hormones are chemicals produced in various glands called endocrine glands. These glands make up your endocrine system.
2) Hormones are released directly into the blood. The blood then carries them to other parts of the body.
3) They travel all over the body but they only affect particular cells in particular places.
4) The affected cells are called target cells — they have the right receptors to respond to that hormone. An organ that contains target cells is called a target organ.

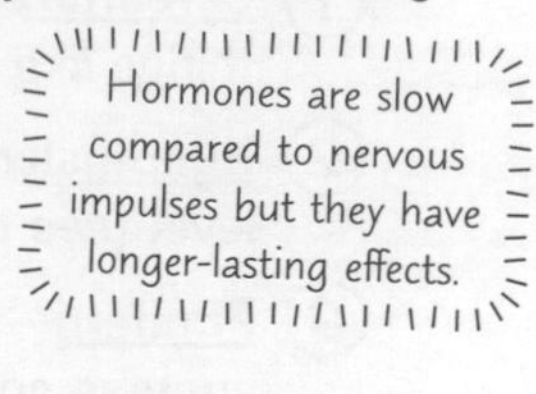

Adrenaline Prepares you for 'Fight or Flight'

1) Adrenaline is a hormone released by the adrenal glands (which are located just above the kidneys).
2) Adrenaline prepares the body for 'fight or flight' — in other words, standing your ground in the face of a threat (e.g. a predator) or bravely running away. It does this by activating processes that increase the supply of oxygen and glucose to cells. For example:

- Adrenaline binds to specific receptors in the heart. This causes the heart muscle to contract more frequently and with more force, so heart rate and blood pressure increase.
- This increases blood flow to the muscles, so the cells receive more oxygen and glucose for increased respiration.
- Adrenaline also binds to receptors in the liver. This causes the liver to break down its glycogen stores (see. p.53) to release glucose.
- This increases the blood glucose level, so there's more glucose in the blood to be transported to the cells.

3) When your brain detects a stressful situation, it sends nervous impulses to the adrenal glands, which respond by secreting adrenaline. This gets the body ready for action.

Hormone Release can be Affected by Negative Feedback

Your body can control the levels of hormones (and other substances) in the blood using negative feedback systems. When the body detects that the level of a substance has gone above or below the normal level, it triggers a response to bring the level back to normal again. Here's an example of just that:

Thyroxine Regulates Metabolism

Thyroxine is made in the thyroid gland from iodine and amino acids.

1) Thyroxine is a hormone released by the thyroid gland (found in the neck).
2) It plays an important role in regulating metabolic rate — the speed at which chemical reactions in the body occur. It's important for loads of processes in the body, such as growth and protein synthesis.
3) Thyroxine is released in response to thyroid stimulating hormone (TSH), which is released from the pituitary gland.
4) A negative feedback system keeps the amount of thyroxine in the blood at the right level — when the level of thyroxine in the blood is higher than normal, the secretion of TSH from the pituitary gland is inhibited. This reduces the amount of thyroxine released from the thyroid gland so the level in the blood falls back towards normal.

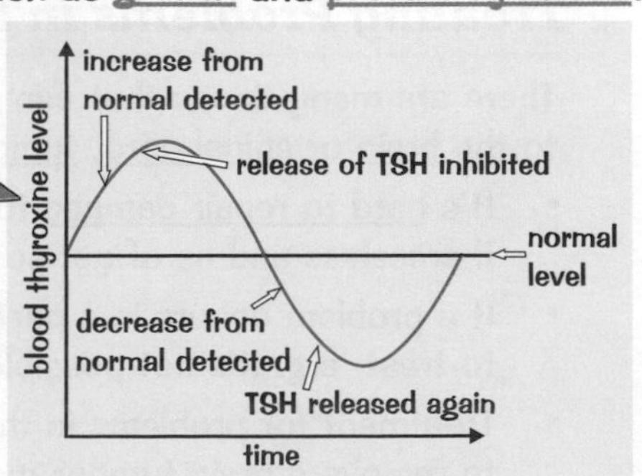

Negative feedback sucks, especially from your science teacher...

Hormones and negative feedback both crop up again in this book — best learn this page good 'n' proper.

Q1 Explain how the endocrine system allows communication within the body. [5 marks]

Hormones in Reproduction

You need to know about sex hormones and how some of them interact to control the menstrual cycle.

You Need to Know About These Sex Hormones

1) Testosterone — this is the main male sex hormone. It's produced in the testes. It stimulates sperm production and is important for the development of the male reproductive system.
2) Oestrogen — this is the main female sex hormone. It's produced in the ovaries (in the lower abdomen). It's involved in the menstrual cycle and promotes female sexual characteristics, e.g. breast development.
3) Progesterone — this is also produced by the ovaries. It helps to support pregnancy and is involved in the menstrual cycle.
4) FSH (follicle-stimulating hormone) and LH (luteinising hormone) — these hormones are released from the pituitary gland in the brain. They help to control the menstrual cycle.

The Menstrual Cycle Has Four Stages

The menstrual cycle is the monthly sequence of events in which the female body releases an egg and prepares the uterus (womb) in case it receives a fertilised egg. This is what happens at each stage:

Stage 1 Day 1 is when menstruation starts. The uterus lining breaks down and is released.

Stage 2 The lining of the uterus builds up again, from day 4 to day 14, into a thick spongy layer full of blood vessels ready to receive a fertilised egg.

Stage 3 An egg develops and is released from an ovary (ovulation) at about day 14.

Stage 4 The lining is then maintained for about 14 days, until day 28. If no fertilised egg has implanted into the uterus wall by day 28, the spongy lining starts to break down again and the whole cycle starts over.

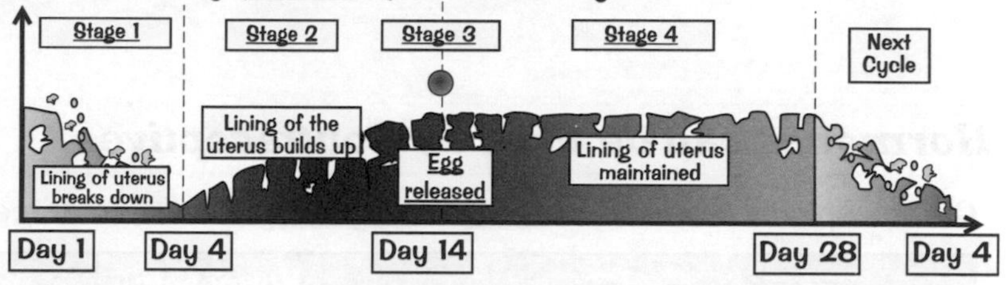

The Menstrual Cycle is Controlled by Four Hormones

1. FSH

1) Causes an egg to mature in one of the ovaries.
2) Stimulates the ovaries to produce oestrogen.

2. Oestrogen

1) Causes the lining of the uterus to thicken and grow.
2) Stimulates the production of LH.
3) Inhibits the production of FSH so that only one egg is released in each cycle.

3. LH

1) Stimulates the release of an egg at day 14 (ovulation).
2) Indirectly stimulates progesterone production.

4. Progesterone

1) Maintains the lining of the uterus. When the level of progesterone falls and there's a low oestrogen level, the lining breaks down.
2) Inhibits the production of FSH and LH.
3) A low progesterone level allows FSH to increase... and then the whole cycle starts again.

If a fertilised egg implants in the uterus (i.e. the woman becomes pregnant) then the progesterone level will stay high to maintain the uterus lining during pregnancy.

What do you call a fish with no eye — FSH...

OK, this stuff is pretty tricky. Try scribbling down everything on the page until you can get it all without peeking.

Q1 Explain the role of LH in the menstrual cycle. [2 marks]

Hormones for Fertility and Contraception

Hormones play a big role in reproduction. No surprise then that hormones are used to help infertile women have babies and to help fertile women not have babies. What a topsy-turvy world we live in.

Hormones can be Used to Treat Infertility

If a person is infertile, it means they can't reproduce naturally. Infertility can now be treated due to developments in modern reproductive technologies, many of which involve hormones.

Hormones are Used to Promote Natural Pregnancy...

1) Some women have levels of FSH (see previous page) that are too low to cause their eggs to mature. This means that no ovulation takes place (no eggs are released) and the women can't get pregnant.
2) The hormones FSH and LH can be injected by these women to stimulate ovulation.

...and They Play a Role in IVF

1) IVF ("*in vitro* fertilisation") involves collecting eggs from the woman's ovaries and fertilising them in a lab using the man's sperm. These are then grown into embryos.
2) Once the embryos are tiny balls of cells, one or two of them are transferred to the woman's uterus to improve the chance of pregnancy.
3) FSH and LH are given before egg collection to stimulate egg production (so more than one egg can be collected).

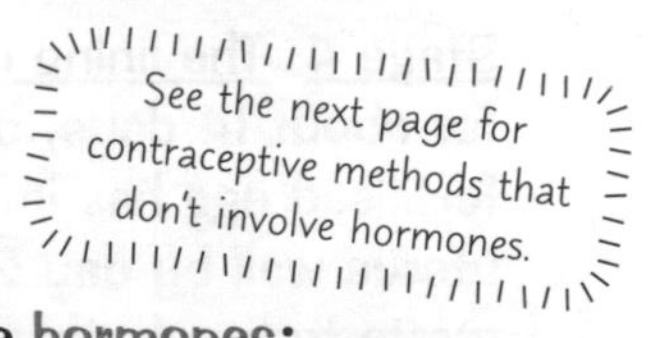

Hormones can be Used as Contraceptives

Contraceptives are used to prevent pregnancy. Some contraceptive methods involve hormones:

Contraceptive method	Hormone(s) involved	How it works
Injection — effective for up to 3 months.	Progesterone	• Stimulates the production of thick cervical mucus (at the entrance to the uterus) making it less likely that any sperm will get through and reach an egg. • Thins the lining of the uterus to reduce the chance of a fertilised egg implanting. • Prevents ovulation* by inhibiting the production of FSH and LH (see previous page). *not true for all types of mini-pill
Implant — inserted beneath the skin of the arm. Effective for 3 years.		
Intrauterine system (IUS) — a T-shaped piece of plastic inserted into the uterus. Effective for 3-5 years.		
Mini-pill (aka progesterone-only pill) — has to be taken every day.		
Combined pill — taken in a '21 day pill, 7 days no pill' cycle.	Progesterone and oestrogen	All of the effects of progesterone listed above, plus oestrogen also prevents ovulation by inhibiting FSH.
Patch — worn on the skin in a 4-week cycle (replaced once a week for 3 weeks, then no patch worn for a week).		

The mini-pill and the combined pill are 'oral contraceptives'.

If used correctly (e.g. pills taken on time) all of these contraceptive methods are more than 99% effective.

IVF... FSH... IUS... LH... — I feel like I'm at the opticians...

Hormones can be used to manipulate the menstrual cycle so that the reproductive system does what we want it to do, when we want it to do it. Great for both increasing and decreasing the chance of pregnancy.

Q1 Explain how hormones may be used to promote a natural pregnancy in an infertile woman. [3 marks]

More on Contraception

There are ways to prevent pregnancy that don't include the use of hormones. Now, as a warning, this page does include themes of a sexual nature from the outset. You might not want to read it aloud to your parents.

There are Plenty of Non-Hormonal Contraceptive Methods

1) Barrier methods — these try to stop the egg and sperm meeting. For example:
   - Condom (98% effective) — worn over the penis during intercourse to prevent sperm entering the vagina.
   - Female condom (95% effective) — worn inside the vagina during intercourse.
   - Diaphragm (92-96% effective) — fits over the cervix (opening of the uterus) to stop sperm from meeting the egg. Has to be fitted by a GP/nurse the first time it's used and has to be used with a spermicide (a chemical that kills sperm).

The figures given here for effectiveness assume that the methods are used properly.

2) Intrauterine devices (IUDs) — T-shaped devices that contain copper. They're inserted into the uterus and prevent sperm from surviving. They also alter the lining of the womb so that fertilised eggs can't implant. They're more than 99% effective and can be kept in for up to ten years.
3) 'Natural' methods — these don't use any bits and bobs like all the other methods. They refer to basically just not having sexual intercourse when the woman is most fertile (the period around ovulation) or 'withdrawal' (the man pulling the penis out before ejaculation). These methods are the least effective at preventing pregnancy as they rely on getting the timing exactly right.
4) Sterilisation — involves a surgical procedure to cut or tie tubes in the reproductive system. In women, the procedure means eggs are prevented from travelling from the ovaries to the uterus. In men, it prevents sperm from being ejaculated. The methods are over 99% effective.

There are Pros and Cons to All Forms of Contraception

In the exam you may have to evaluate hormonal (see previous page) and non-hormonal methods of contraception. Here are some things to think about:

1) Side-effects — hormonal methods can have unpleasant side-effects, e.g. heavy or irregular periods, acne, headaches, mood changes.
2) Possibility of 'doing it wrong' — barrier methods and 'natural' methods have to be done properly each time a couple have intercourse. If, for example, a condom splits or a man doesn't withdraw soon enough, then the methods won't work. The same is true with some hormonal methods, e.g. if a woman doesn't take her pills correctly or replace her patch at the right time, the methods won't work properly.
3) Medical input — many methods involve at least one trip to a nurse or doctor (e.g. to get a prescription for pills or to have a device inserted). Although these methods tend to be more effective than barrier or 'natural' methods, people may feel uncomfortable about the procedures involved.
4) Length of action — long-lasting methods (i.e. those that last several months or years) may be preferable over having to think about contraception every day or every time intercourse is on the cards.
5) Sexually transmitted infections (STIs) — these are infections that are passed from person to person during sexual intercourse. The only method of contraception that can protect against them is condoms (male or female types).

I've got this barrier thing sorted...

The winner of best contraceptive ever — just not doing it...

By now you should be pretty clued up on the different methods of contraception. Whether hormonal or non-hormonal, no method is guaranteed to be 100% effective and each method has its own pros and cons.

Q1 Give one reason why a woman may prefer to use a diaphragm rather than an oral contraceptive. [1 mark]

Q2 Give two advantages of using an intrauterine device (IUD) as a contraceptive method rather than male condoms. [2 marks]

Plant Growth Hormones

It's not just animals that have hormones, you know — plants have hormones too. They're important for controlling and coordinating a plant's growth and development. First up, plant growth hormones...

Auxins are Plant Growth Hormones

1) Auxins are plant hormones which control growth at the tips of shoots and roots. They move through the plant in solution (dissolved in water).
2) Auxin is produced in the tips and diffuses backwards to stimulate the cell elongation process which occurs in the cells just behind the tips.
3) Auxin promotes growth in the shoot, but actually inhibits growth in the root.
4) Auxins are involved in the growth responses of plants to light (phototropism) and gravity (gravitropism).

Auxins Change the Direction of Root and Shoot Growth

SHOOTS ARE POSITIVELY PHOTOTROPIC (grow towards light)

1) When a shoot tip is exposed to light, it accumulates more auxin on the side that's in the shade than the side that's in the light.
2) This makes the cells grow (elongate) faster on the shaded side, so the shoot bends towards the light.

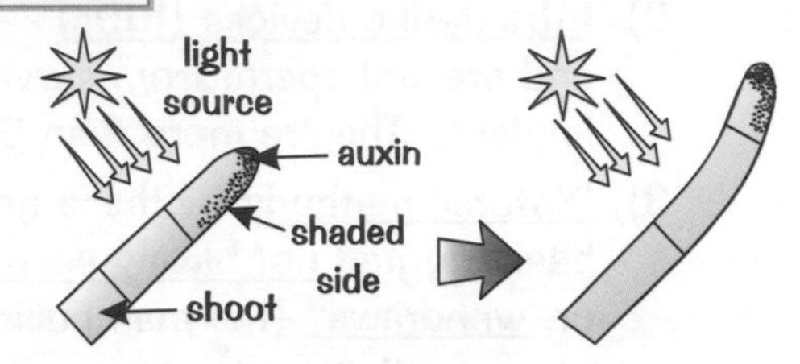

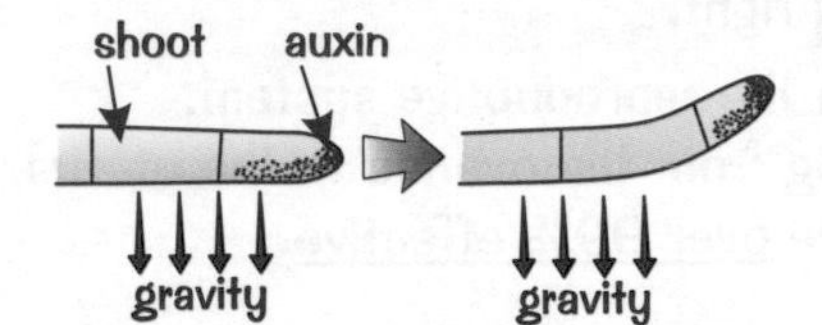

SHOOTS ARE NEGATIVELY GRAVITROPIC (grow away from gravity)

1) When a shoot is growing sideways, gravity produces an unequal distribution of auxin in the tip, with more auxin on the lower side.
2) This causes the lower side to grow faster, bending the shoot upwards.

ROOTS ARE POSITIVELY GRAVITROPIC (grow towards gravity)

1) A root growing sideways will also have more auxin on its lower side.
2) But in a root the extra auxin inhibits growth. This means the cells on top elongate faster, and the root bends downwards.

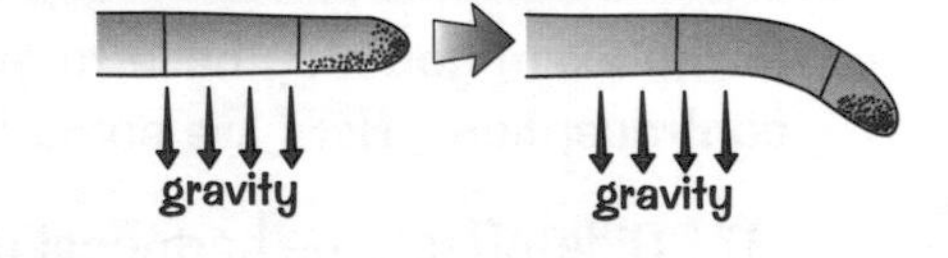

ROOTS ARE NEGATIVELY PHOTOTROPIC (grow away from light)

1) If a root starts being exposed to some light, more auxin accumulates on the more shaded side.
2) The auxin inhibits cell elongation on the shaded side, so the root bends downwards, back into the ground.

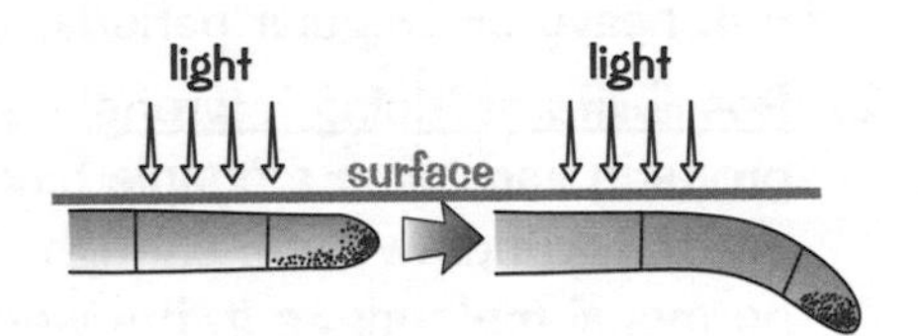

You can do a Practical to Investigate Plant Growth Responses

For example, you can investigate the effect of light on the growth of cress seeds like this...

1) Put 10 cress seeds into three different Petri dishes, each lined with moist filter paper.
2) Shine a light onto one of the dishes from above and two of the dishes from different directions.
3) Leave your poor little cress seeds alone for one week until you can observe their responses — and hey presto, you'll find the seedlings grow towards the light.
4) You know that the growth response of the cress seeds is due to light only, if you control all other variables. E.g. the temperature, distance from the lamp, type of seeds and number of seeds should be the same for each dish.

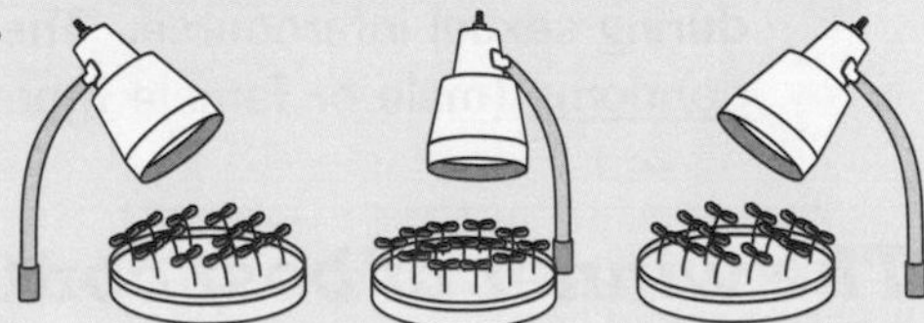

A plant auxin to a bar — 'ouch'...

Quite a bit to learn on this page — cover it up and scribble it all down till you're confident you know it all.

Q1 Name a part of a plant that is positively gravitropic. [1 mark]

Uses of Plant Hormones

Auxin isn't the only plant hormone you need to know about. There are others, which affect plants differently.

Gibberellin Stimulates Plant Stems to Grow

Seed germination is when a seed starts to grow into a plant.

1) Gibberellin (a type of plant growth hormone) stimulates seed germination, stem growth and flowering.
2) It stimulates the stems of plants to grow by stem elongation — this helps plants to grow tall.
3) Auxin and gibberellin can work together to have a really big effect on plant growth, e.g. together they help plants grow very tall.

Ethene Stimulates Shedding of Leaves and Ripening of Fruit

1) Ethene is produced by aging leaves. It stimulates cells that connect the leaf to the rest of the plant to expand — this breaks the cell walls and causes the leaf to fall off the plant.
2) Auxins inhibit the shedding of leaves. Auxins are produced by young leaves. As the leaves gets older, they produce less auxin, leading to leaf loss.
3) Ethene also stimulates enzymes that cause fruit to ripen.

Plant Hormones are Used to Control Plant Growth

Plant hormones are pretty useful — people use them to do all kinds of things...

1 As Selective Herbicides

1) Most weeds growing in fields of crops or in a lawn are broad-leaved, in contrast to grasses and cereals which have very narrow leaves.
2) Selective herbicides (weedkillers) have been developed using auxins which only affect the broad-leaved plants. They totally disrupt their normal growth patterns, which soon kills them, whilst leaving the grass and crops untouched.

2 Growing from Cuttings with Rooting Powder

1) A cutting is part of a plant that has been cut off it, like the end of a branch with a few leaves on it.
2) Normally, if you stick cuttings in the soil they won't grow, but if you add rooting powder, which contains auxins, they will produce roots rapidly and start growing as new plants.
3) This enables growers to produce lots of clones (exact copies) of a really good plant very quickly.

3 Producing Seedless Fruit

1) Fruit (with seeds in the middle) normally only grows on plants which have been pollinated by insects. If the plant doesn't get pollinated, the fruit and seeds don't grow.
2) If auxins and gibberellins are applied to the unpollinated flowers of some types of plant, the fruit will grow but the seeds won't.
3) This produces parthenocarpic fruit — fruit without any seeds.

4 Controlling Dormancy

1) Lots of seeds won't germinate until they've been through certain conditions (e.g. a period of cold or of dryness). This is called dormancy.
2) Seeds can be treated with gibberellin to alter dormancy and make them germinate at times of year that they wouldn't normally. It also helps to make sure all the seeds in a batch germinate at the same time.

You will germinate when I SAY you can — and NOT BEFORE...

Make sure you learn the effects of auxins, gibberellin and ethene and how we can use them to our advantage.

Q1 Give three ways in which gibberellin affects the natural growth and development of plants. [3 marks]

Homeostasis

Homeostasis involves balancing body functions to maintain a 'constant internal environment'. Smashing.

Homeostasis is Maintaining a Constant Internal Environment

1) Conditions in your body need to be kept steady — this is really important so that all the metabolic reactions vital for keeping you alive can continue at an appropriate rate. It can be dangerous for your health if conditions vary too much from normal levels.
2) To maintain a constant internal environment, your body needs to respond to both internal and external changes whilst balancing inputs (stuff going into your body) with outputs (stuff leaving).
3) Things that you need to keep steady include:

- Blood glucose (sugar) concentration — you need to make sure the amount of glucose in your blood doesn't get too high or too low (see next page).
- Water content — you need to keep a balance between the water you gain (in drink, food and from respiration) and the water you pee, sweat and breathe out. See pages 54-55 for more.
- Body temperature — you need to make sure it doesn't get too high or too low (see below).

Body Temperature is Controlled by the Hypothalamus

All enzymes work best at a certain temperature. The enzymes in the human body work best at about 37 °C.

1) The hypothalamus in your brain (see p.45) acts as your own personal thermostat.
2) It contains receptors that are sensitive to the blood temperature in the brain. It also receives impulses from receptors in the skin (nerve endings) that provide information about the external temperature.
3) When the hypothalamus detects a change, it causes a response in the dermis (deep layer of the skin):

When You're Too Hot...

1) Erector muscles relax, so hairs lie flat.
2) Lots of sweat (containing water and salts) is produced. When the sweat evaporates it transfers energy from your skin to the environment, cooling you down.
3) Blood vessels close to the surface of the skin dilate (widen). This is called vasodilation. It allows more blood to flow near the surface, so it can transfer more energy into the surroundings, which cools you down.

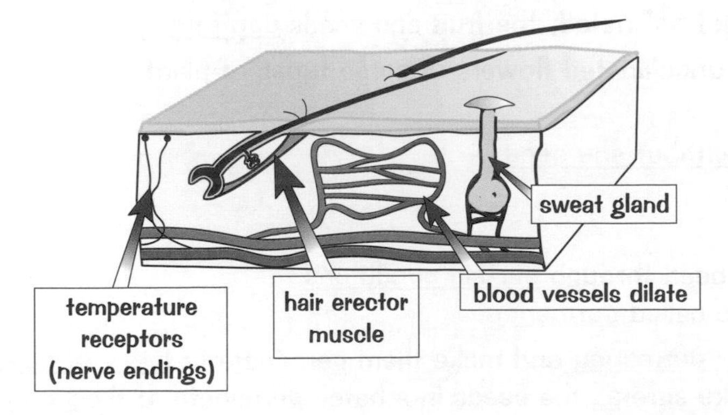

When You're Too Cold...

1) Erector muscles contract. Hairs stand on end to trap an insulating layer of air, which helps keep you warm.
2) Very little sweat is produced.
3) Blood vessels near the surface of the skin constrict (narrow). This is called vasoconstriction. It means less blood flows near the surface, so less energy is transferred to the surroundings.
4) When you're cold you shiver too (your muscles contract automatically). This needs respiration, which transfers some energy to warm the body.

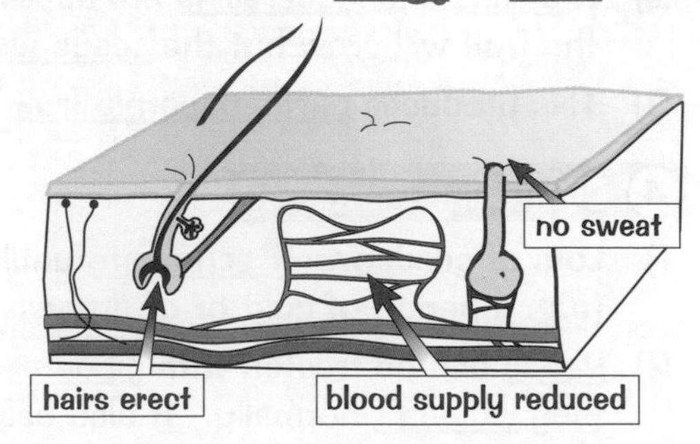

Learn about homeostasis — and keep your cool...

Homeostasis is really important for keeping processes in your body ticking over nicely. Make sure you learn the definition of homeostasis and can explain how your body responds to changes in temperature.

Q1 Explain how blood flow through the skin is affected when a person is too cold. [3 marks]

Controlling Blood Sugar Level

Blood sugar level is controlled as part of homeostasis. Insulin and glucagon are the two hormones involved.

Insulin and Glucagon Control Blood Sugar Level

1) Eating foods containing carbohydrate puts glucose into the blood from the small intestine.
2) The normal metabolism of cells removes glucose from the blood.
3) Vigorous exercise removes much more glucose from the blood.
4) Excess glucose can be stored as glycogen in the liver and in the muscles.
5) When these stores are full then the excess glucose is stored as lipid (fat) in the tissues.
6) The level of glucose in the blood must be kept steady. Changes in blood glucose are monitored and controlled by the pancreas, using the hormones insulin and glucagon, as shown:

Blood Glucose Level Too High — Insulin is Added

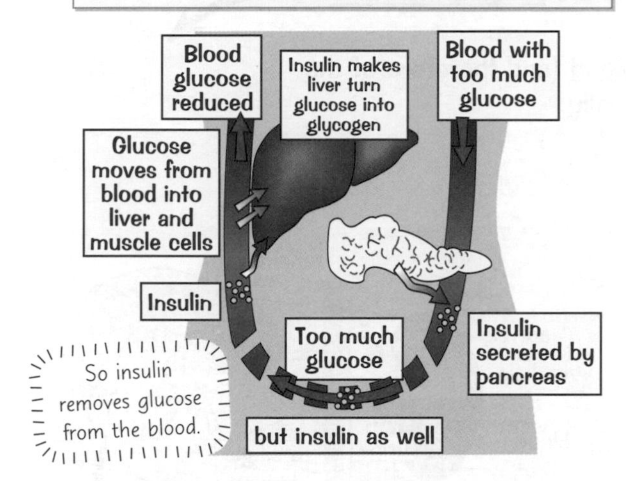

Blood Glucose Level Too Low — Glucagon is Added

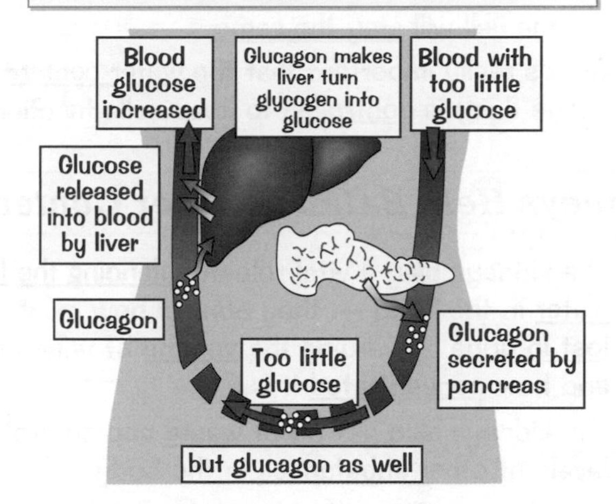

Having Diabetes Means You Can't Control Your Blood Sugar Level

Diabetes is a condition that affects your ability to control your blood sugar level. There are two types:

TYPE 1

Type 1 diabetes is where the pancreas produces little or no insulin. The result is that a person's blood glucose level can rise to a level that can kill them. People with type 1 diabetes need insulin therapy. This usually involves injecting insulin into the blood several times a day (often at mealtimes). This makes sure that glucose is removed from the blood quickly once food has been digested. This stops the level of glucose in the blood from getting too high and is a very effective treatment. The amount of insulin needed depends on the person's diet and how active they are. As well as insulin therapy, people with type 1 diabetes need to think about limiting their intake of food rich in simple carbohydrates, e.g. sugars (which cause the blood glucose to rise rapidly) and taking regular exercise (which helps to remove excess glucose from the blood).

TYPE 2

Type 2 diabetes is where a person becomes resistant to insulin (their body's cells don't respond properly to the hormone). This can also cause blood sugar level to rise to a dangerous level. Being overweight can increase your chance of developing type 2 diabetes, as obesity is a major risk factor in the development of the disease (see page 102). Type 2 diabetes can be controlled by eating a healthy diet, exercising regularly and losing weight if necessary. There are also some drugs available which improve the way that the body's cells respond to insulin.

And people used to think the pancreas was just a cushion... (true)

This stuff can seem a bit confusing at first, but if you learn those two diagrams, it'll all start to get a lot easier. Don't forget that there are two types of diabetes — and different ways of controlling them.

Q1 Describe how the production of insulin differs between type 1 and type 2 diabetes. [2 marks]

Controlling Water Content

The kidneys are really important in this whole homeostasis thing — they help regulate water content.

Balancing Water Content is Really Important

Look back at page 31 for a reminder of osmosis.

1) Body cells are surrounded by fluid called tissue fluid. It's squeezed out of the blood capillaries to supply the cells with everything they need.
2) The tissue fluid will usually have a different water potential to the fluid inside a cell. This means that water will either move into the cell from the tissue fluid, or out of the cell, by osmosis:
   - If the water potential of the tissue fluid is higher than the water potential inside the cell, there will be a net movement of water into the cell by osmosis. If too much water moves into the cell then the cell may burst — this is called lysis.
   - If the water potential inside the cell is higher, there will be a net movement of water out of the cell and into the tissue fluid. This causes the cell to shrink.
   - If the water potential of the tissue fluid and the cell are roughly the same the cell will stay the same.
3) So it's really important that the water content of the blood (and therefore of the tissue fluid) is controlled to keep cells functioning normally.

Kidneys Help Balance Water Content

1) The kidneys play a vital role in balancing the level of water in the body — they control how much water is lost in urine by varying the volume of urine produced and how concentrated it is.
2) The kidneys also get rid of waste and control the levels of other substances in the body.
3) They have millions of little structures inside them called kidney tubules (or nephrons).

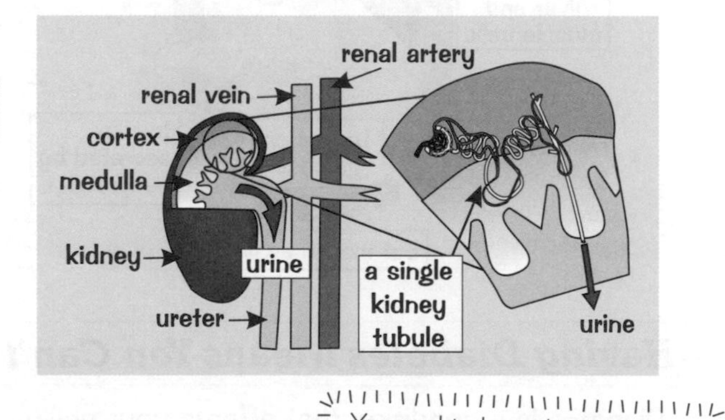

Urine is Formed in the Tubules

This is what happens at each tubule...

Blood flows through the glomerulus at high pressure and small molecules including water, sugar, salt (sodium chloride) and urea are filtered out into the capsule.

The liquid then flows along the tubule and useful substances are selectively reabsorbed:

- All the sugar is reabsorbed.
- Sufficient salt is reabsorbed. Excess salt isn't.
- Sufficient water is reabsorbed, according to the level of the hormone ADH (see next page).

Whatever isn't reabsorbed forms urine, which is excreted by the kidneys and stored in the bladder.

You need to learn the structure of the kidney and of a kidney tubule.

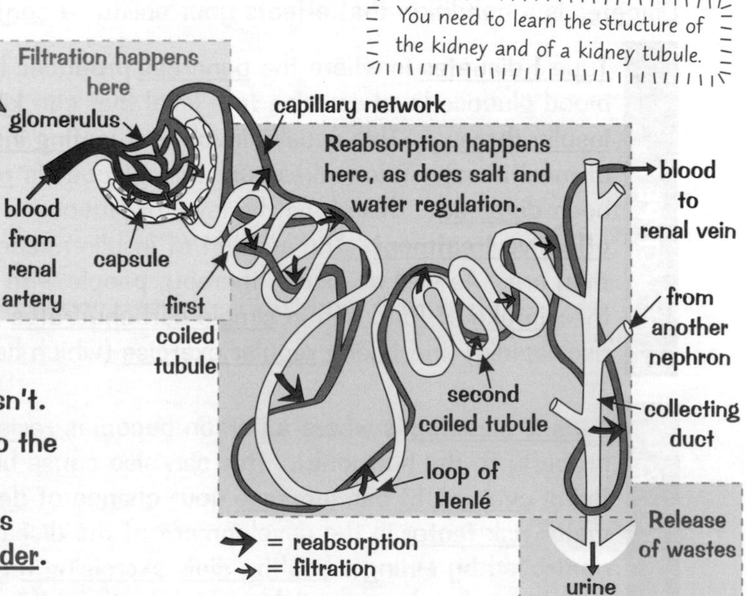

Reabsorb the facts and excrete the rest...

The kidneys are really important for making sure you have the right amount of water in your body. But they can't take all the credit — the brain is involved in the process too (as you'll find out on the next page).

Q1 Explain what might happen to a cell if the water potential of the fluid surrounding it is higher than the water potential inside it. [2 marks]

More on Controlling Water Content

Think you know all you need to know about urine production? Well you don't. Here's another page about wee.

The Concentration of Urine is Controlled by a Hormone

1) The concentration of urine is controlled by a hormone called anti-diuretic hormone (ADH). This is released into the bloodstream by the pituitary gland.
2) The brain monitors the water content of the blood and instructs the pituitary gland to release ADH into the blood according to how much is needed. ADH makes the kidney tubules more permeable so that more water is reabsorbed back into the blood.
3) The whole process of water content regulation is controlled by negative feedback (see page 46). This means that if the water content gets too high or too low a mechanism will be triggered that brings it back to normal.

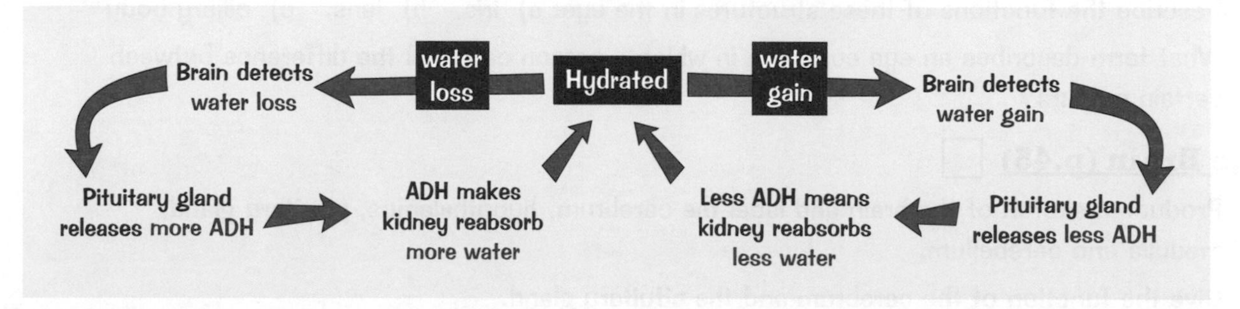

So, using negative feedback, the amount of water in your body can be closely regulated. The more water your kidneys reabsorb, the less water will pass out as urine so you'll produce a smaller volume of urine. Your kidneys will still excrete all the waste products they need to though, so your urine will be more concentrated (as it contains the same amount of waste substances but less water).

Your Urine isn't Always the Same

As you've seen, the volume and concentration of urine depends on the water content of the blood. This can vary with temperature and other changes that affect the water potential of the blood (osmotic challenges). For example:

Sweating and dehydration — when it's hot or when you exercise (which makes you hot) you sweat more (see page 52). Sweat contains water, so sweating causes water loss. Losing more water than you take in causes dehydration. This triggers more ADH to be released meaning that the kidney will reabsorb more water so only a small volume of concentrated urine will be produced. The brain also triggers feelings of thirst when you're dehydrated. This makes you want to drink more, which helps to restore water balance in the body.

Excess water intake — the kidney responds by excreting more water meaning lots of dilute urine.

High salt intake — the kidney responds by excreting more salt, which will produce concentrated urine.

Learn this lot or else urine trouble come exam time...

Make sure you understand how the brain and kidneys work together to control urine production and how this in turn helps to control water content in the body. Then you can do a little dance to celebrate the end of Topic B3.

Q1 Describe the role of ADH in the body. [3 marks]

Q2 Explain why a person may feel more thirsty than normal on a hot day. [3 marks]

Revision Questions for Topic B3

Hoorah! Another section done. Time to find out how much you really know about organism level systems...

- Try these questions and tick off each one when you get it right.
- When you've done all the questions under a heading and are completely happy with it, tick it off.

Nervous Responses and The Eye (p.43-44) ☑

1) Describe the role of sensory neurones. ☑
2) Give an example of an effector. ☑
3) Draw a diagram of a typical neurone and label all the parts. ☑
4) What is the purpose of a reflex action? ☑
5) Describe the pathway of a reflex arc from stimulus to response. ☑
6) Describe the functions of these structures in the eye: a) iris, b) lens, c) ciliary body ☑
7) What term describes an eye condition in which a person can't tell the difference between certain colours? ☑

The Brain (p.45) ☑

8) Produce a sketch of the brain and label the cerebrum, hypothalamus, pituitary gland, medulla and cerebellum. ☑
9) Give the function of the cerebrum and the pituitary gland. ☑
10) Describe two difficulties involved in investigating brain function. ☑

Hormones, The Menstrual Cycle and Controlling Fertility (p.46-49) ☑

11) What is the endocrine system? ☑
12) Give one role of thyroxine in the body. ☑
13) Explain how negative feedback helps to control the level of thyroxine in the blood. ☑
14) Describe the effect that adrenaline has on the body. ☑
15) State where each of these hormones is produced and briefly describe its role in reproduction: a) testosterone, b) oestrogen, c) progesterone, d) FSH. ☑
16) Explain how the combined pill prevents pregnancy when taken as a contraceptive. ☑
17) Describe how one non-hormonal method of contraception works and list its pros and cons. ☑

Plant Hormones (p.50-51) ☑

18) Explain how auxins make plant shoots bend towards the light. ☑
19) Describe the effects of ethene on plants. ☑
20) Describe four ways in which plant hormones are used to control plant growth. ☑

Homeostasis (p.52-55) ☑

21) What is homeostasis? Why is it important? ☑
22) Explain how body temperature is reduced when you're too hot. ☑
23) Describe the roles of insulin and glucagon in controlling a person's blood sugar level. ☑
24) Explain how type 1 and type 2 diabetes can be treated. ☑
25) Describe how the water potential of tissue fluid may cause the cells to shrink. ☑
26) Sketch a kidney tubule and label all the parts. ☑
27) Describe how the brain responds when it detects a fall in the water content of the blood. ☑
28) How does the kidney respond to an excess intake of water? ☑

The Carbon Cycle

Carbon flows through the Earth's ecosystems in the carbon cycle. The beauty of the carbon cycle is that carbon is recycled — it's used by organisms but then ends up back in the atmosphere again. Splendid.

Materials are Constantly Recycled in an Ecosystem

There's more on biotic and abiotic factors on page 60.

1) An ecosystem is all the organisms living in an area, as well as all the non-living conditions, e.g. soil quality, availability of water, temperature.
2) Materials are recycled through both the living (biotic) and non-living (abiotic) components of ecosystems:
    1) Living things are made of elements they take from the environment. For example, plants take in carbon, hydrogen, oxygen, nitrogen, etc.
    2) They turn these elements into the complex compounds (carbohydrates, proteins and fats) that make up living organisms. These are taken in by animals when they eat the plants.
    3) The elements are recycled — they return to the environment (e.g. soil or air) through waste products or when organisms die, ready to be used by new plants and put back into the food chain (see p.62).
    4) Dead organisms and waste products decay because they're broken down by decomposers (usually microorganisms) — that's how the elements get put back into the soil.

The Carbon Cycle Shows How Carbon is Recycled

Carbon is an important element in the materials that living things are made from. But there's only a fixed amount of carbon in the world. This means it's constantly recycled:

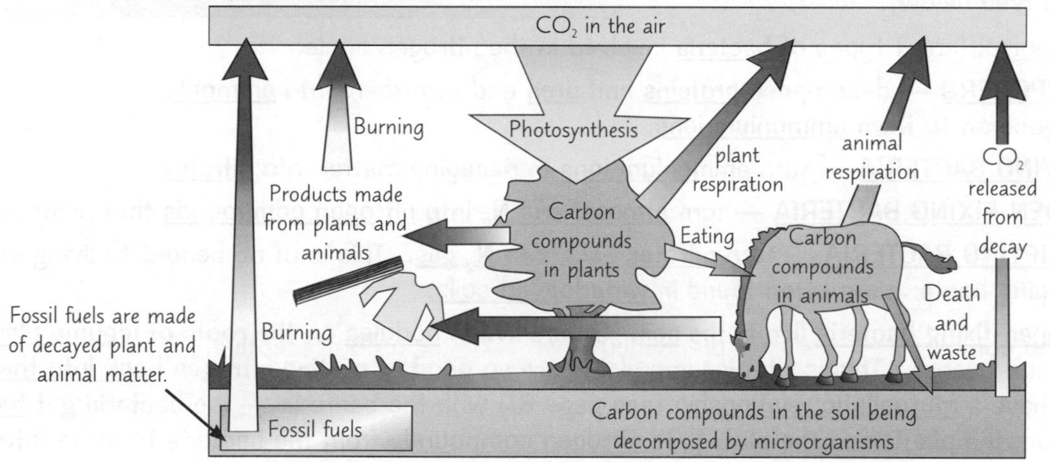

CO_2 = carbon dioxide

This diagram isn't half as bad as it looks. Learn these important points:

1) There's only one arrow going down from CO_2 in the air. The whole thing is 'powered' by photosynthesis. Green plants use the carbon from CO_2 in the air to make carbohydrates, fats and proteins.
2) Eating passes the carbon compounds in the plant along to animals in a food chain or web (see p.62).
3) Both plant and animal respiration while the organisms are alive releases CO_2 back into the air.
4) Plants and animals eventually die and decompose, or are killed and turned into useful products.
5) When plants and animals decompose they're broken down by microorganisms, such as bacteria and fungi. These decomposers release CO_2 back into the air by respiration, as they break down the material.
6) Some useful plant and animal products, e.g. wood and fossil fuels, are burned (combustion). This also releases CO_2 back into the air.
7) Decomposition of materials means that habitats can be maintained for the organisms that live there, e.g. nutrients are returned to the soil and waste material, such as dead leaves, doesn't just pile up.

Carbon cycle — isn't that what Wiggo rides...

Carbon atoms are very important — they're found in plants, animals, your petrol tank and on your burnt toast.

Q1 Suggest two reasons why chopping down trees can increase the concentration of CO_2 in the air. [2 marks]

The Nitrogen Cycle and the Water Cycle

Just like carbon, nitrogen and water are constantly being recycled. It's amazing really — the nitrogen in your proteins might once have been in the air. And before that in a plant. Or even in some horse wee. Nice.

Nitrogen is Recycled in the Nitrogen Cycle...

1) The atmosphere contains 78% nitrogen gas, N_2. This is very unreactive and so it can't be used directly by plants or animals. Nitrogen is needed for making proteins for growth, so living organisms have to get it somehow.
2) Plants get their nitrogen from the soil, so nitrogen in the air has to be turned into nitrates before plants can use it. Nitrogen compounds are then passed along food chains as animals eat plants (and each other).
3) Decomposers (bacteria and fungi in the soil) break down proteins in rotting plants and animals, and urea in animal waste, into ammonia, which goes on to form ammonium ions. This returns the nitrogen compounds to the soil — so the nitrogen in these organisms is recycled.
4) Nitrogen fixation is the process of turning N_2 from the air into nitrogen compounds in the soil which plants can use. There are two main ways that this happens:
   a) Lightning — there's so much energy in a bolt of lightning that it's enough to make nitrogen react with oxygen in the air to give nitrates.
   b) Nitrogen-fixing bacteria in roots and soil (see below).

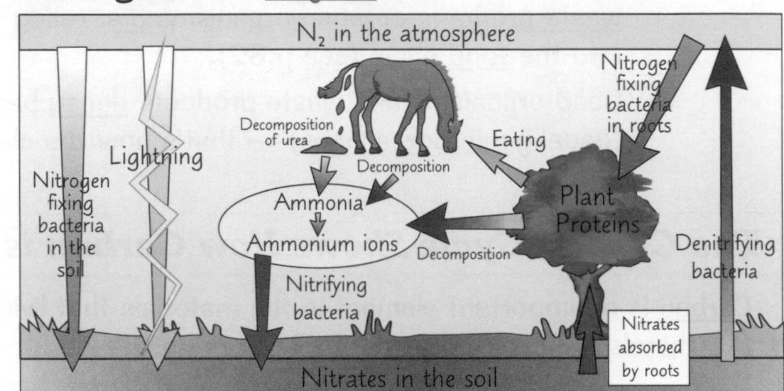

5) There are four different types of bacteria involved in the nitrogen cycle:
   a) DECOMPOSERS — decompose proteins and urea and turn them into ammonia, which goes on to form ammonium ions.
   b) NITRIFYING BACTERIA — turn ammonium ions in decaying matter into nitrates.
   c) NITROGEN-FIXING BACTERIA — turn atmospheric N_2 into nitrogen compounds that plants can use.
   d) DENITRIFYING BACTERIA — turn nitrates back into N_2 gas. This is of no benefit to living organisms. Denitrifying bacteria are often found in waterlogged soils.
6) Some nitrogen-fixing bacteria live in the soil. Others live in nodules on the roots of legume plants (e.g. peas and beans). This is why legume plants are so good at putting nitrogen back into the soil. The plants have a mutualistic relationship (see page 61) with the bacteria — the bacteria get food (sugars) from the plant, and the plant gets nitrogen compounds from the bacteria to make into proteins. So the relationship benefits both of them.

...and Water is Recycled in the Water Cycle

1) The Sun makes water evaporate from the land and sea, turning it into water vapour. Water also evaporates from plants via transpiration (see p.39).
2) The warm water vapour is carried upwards (as warm air rises). When it gets higher up it cools and condenses to form clouds.
3) Water falls from the clouds as precipitation (usually rain, but sometimes snow or hail) and is returned to the land and sea.
4) The flow of fresh water through the water cycle allows nutrients to be transported to different ecosystems.

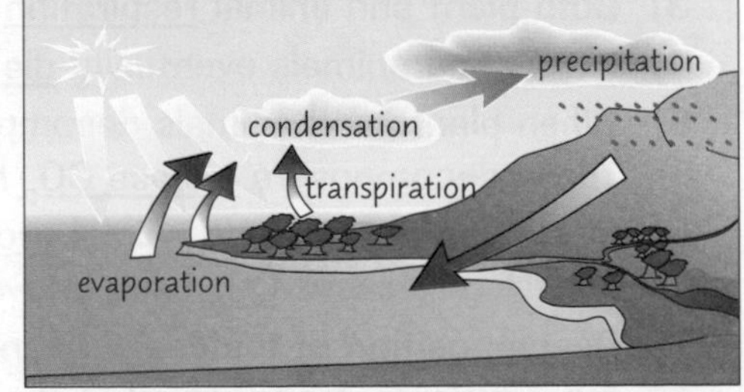

It's the cyyyycle, the cyycle of liiiiife...

Bacteria do all the hard work in the nitrogen cycle. Aided by a bolt or two of lightning. Naturally. And who knew rain could be so useful. Getting soaked on the way to school is a small price to pay for all that lovely fresh water...

Q1 Describe how the nitrogen compounds in dead leaves are turned into nitrates in the soil. [2 marks]

Decomposition

Decomposition is really important — without it there'd be dead stuff and waste material piling up everywhere. So hurrah for the little microoganisms who aren't afraid of a bit of roadkill for breakfast. Yum.

Microorganisms Help Recycle Materials Through Decomposition

Hooray!

1) As you may remember from page 57, organisms contain elements that need to be returned to the soil or air so that they can be used by new plants. These elements are returned to the environment in waste products produced by the organisms, or when the organisms die.
2) Waste products and dead organisms are broken down by decomposers.
3) The main type of decomposers are microorganisms, such as bacteria and fungi.

Learn These Factors that Affect the Rate of Decomposition...

The rate of decomposition is affected by the following environmental factors:

1) Oxygen Availability

- Many decomposers need oxygen for aerobic respiration (see page 20) so the rate of decomposition increases where there is plenty of oxygen available.
- When there are low oxygen levels, the rate of decomposition is slower. Some decomposers can respire anaerobically (without oxygen — see p.21) but this transfers less energy, so these decomposers work more slowly.

See p.17-19 for more on enzymes.

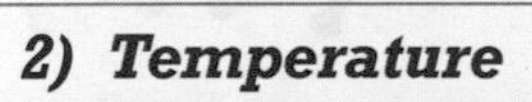

2) Temperature

Most decomposers work best in warm conditions — the rate of decomposition is highest at around 50 °C. This is because decomposers contain enzymes, which digest the dead/waste material. The rate of enzyme-controlled reactions varies with temperature — at lower temperatures the rate of reaction is slower and above certain temperatures the enzymes become denatured and the reaction stops.

3) Water Content

Decomposers need water to survive, so the rate of decomposition increases in moist conditions. However, waterlogged soils don't contain much oxygen (which many decomposers need to respire — see above) so the rate decreases if there is too much water.

You can Calculate the Rate of Decomposition

You need to be able to calculate the rate at which biological material decomposes. Here's an example:

EXAMPLE:

A block of cheese was left out of the fridge. The graph below shows the amount of mould that formed on the cheese. Mould is a fungus that decomposes the cheese.

Calculate the average rate at which the cheese decomposed during the first week, giving your answer as units of mould/day.

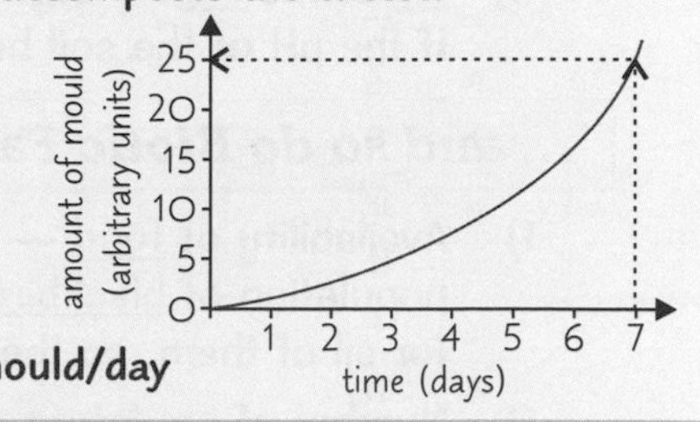

1) Draw a line on your graph at 7 days and read off the amount of mould that had formed.
2) Divide the amount of mould by the number of days. $\frac{25}{7}$
3) Calculate the answer and don't forget to give the units. = 3.6 units of mould/day

G, G, G, E♭, F, F, F, D — sorry, just decomposing Beethoven's 5th...

So if you want your strawberries to last a bit longer — pop them in the fridge, preferably without washing them first. Personally, I'd just eat them all in one go with lots and lots of cream. But I guess that's not really the point.

Q1 Michael would like to make compost to put on his vegetable patch using his food waste. Compost is decayed remains of animal and plant matter that can be used as fertiliser. Give two things he could do to make sure that the waste decomposed quickly. [2 marks]

Ecosystems and Interactions Between Organisms

It's tough in the wild — there's always competition for food and other resources. So if the environment changes, e.g. there's not enough food or it's too hot, it can be the last straw for some organisms...

Ecosystems are Organised into Different Levels

Ecosystems have different levels of organisation:

1) Individual — A single organism.
2) Population — All the organisms of one species in a habitat.
3) Community — All the organisms (different species) living in a habitat.
4) Ecosystem — A community of organisms along with all the non-living (abiotic) conditions (see below).

A habitat is the place where an organism lives, e.g. a rocky shore or a field.

A species is a group of similar organisms that can reproduce to give fertile offspring.

Organisms Compete for Resources to Survive

Organisms need things from their environment and from other organisms in order to survive and reproduce:

1) Plants need light, space, water and minerals (nutrients) from the soil.
2) Animals need space (territory), food, water and mates.

Organisms compete with other species (and members of their own species) for the same resources. E.g. red and grey squirrels live in the same habitat and eat the same food. Competition with the grey squirrels for these resources means there's not enough food for the reds — so the population of red squirrels is decreasing.

Environmental Changes Affect Communities in Different Ways

The environment in which plants and animals live changes all the time. These changes are caused by abiotic (non-living) and biotic (living) factors and affect communities in different ways — for some species population size may increase, for others it may decrease, or the distribution of populations (where they live) may change. Here are some examples of the effects of abiotic and biotic factors:

Abiotic Factors Affect Communities...

1) Temperature — e.g. the distribution of bird species in Germany is changing because of a rise in average temperature. For instance, the European Bee-Eater bird is a Mediterranean species but it's now present in parts of Germany.
2) Moisture level — e.g. daisies grow best in soils that are slightly damp. If the soil becomes waterlogged or too dry, the population of daisies will decrease.
3) Light intensity — e.g. as trees grow and provide more shade, grasses may be replaced by e.g. fungi, mosses etc., which are better able to cope with the low light intensity.
4) pH of the soil — e.g. most species of heather grow best in acidic soils. If the pH of the soil becomes too alkaline, the heather population will decrease.

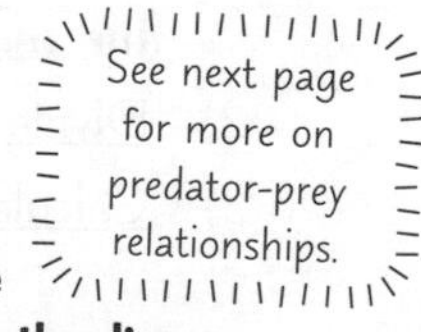

... and so do Biotic Factors

1) Availability of food — e.g. if there's a bumper year for berries, then the population of blackbirds might increase because there will be enough food for all of them, so they are more likely to survive and reproduce.
2) Number of predators — e.g. if the number of lions (predator) decreases then the number of gazelles (prey) might increase because fewer of them will be eaten by the lions.

See next page for more on predator-prey relationships.

Revision — an abiotic factor causing stress in my community...

Organisms like everything to be just right — temperature, light, food... I'd never get away with being that fussy.

Q1 What is meant by the term 'community' in the organisation of an ecosystem? [1 mark]

Q2 Give two abiotic factors that could affect the community in an ecosystem. [2 marks]

More on Interactions Between Organisms

The organisms in an ecosystem are always interacting — well, if you can call eating one another interacting... However, some organisms take interaction to a whole new level and become totally dependent on one another.

Populations of Prey and Predators Go in Cycles

In a community containing prey and predators (as most of them do of course):

1) The population of any species is usually limited by the amount of food available.
2) If the population of the prey increases, then so will the population of the predators.
3) However as the population of predators increases, the number of prey will decrease.

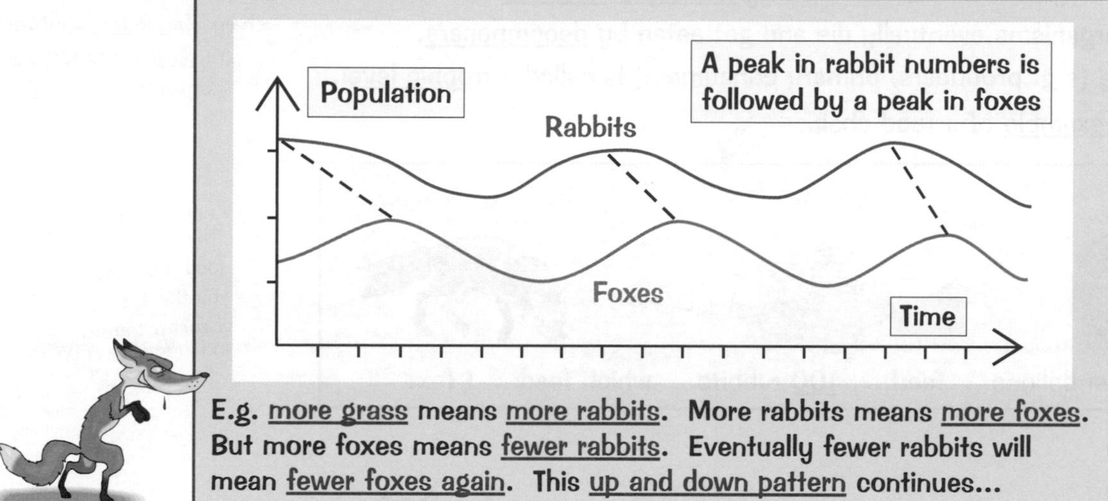

E.g. more grass means more rabbits. More rabbits means more foxes. But more foxes means fewer rabbits. Eventually fewer rabbits will mean fewer foxes again. This up and down pattern continues...

4) Predator-prey cycles are always out of phase with each other. This is because it takes a while for one population to respond to changes in the other population. E.g. when the number of rabbits goes up, the number of foxes doesn't increase immediately because it takes time for them to reproduce.
5) Predator-prey cycles show how interdependent (affected by one another) populations are.

Parasitic and Mutualistic Relationships are Other Types of Interdependence

Some organisms depend entirely on other species to survive. So where an organism lives and its abundance (population size) is often influenced by the distribution and abundance of these species.

1) PARASITES live off a host. They take what they need to survive, without giving anything back. This often harms the host — which makes it a win-lose situation.
    - Tapeworms absorb lots of nutrients from the host, causing them to suffer from malnutrition.
    - Fleas are parasites. Dogs gain nothing from having fleas (unless you count hundreds of bites).
2) MUTUALISM is a relationship where both organisms benefit — so it's a win-win relationship.
    - Clownfish live among the poisonous tentacles of sea anemones. They are the only fish that can survive the toxins, so they are protected from their predators. In return, the clownfish help protect the anemones by eating the parasites that could cause them harm.
    - Lots of plants are pollinated by insects, allowing them to reproduce. In return, the insects get a sip of sweet, sugary nectar.

My sister's a parasite — she takes my shoes, my dresses...

In summary, everything affects everything else. But, it's probably best if you learn the proper terms for the exams.

Q1 A cow's stomach is an ideal environment for some types of microorganisms. Without these microorganisms, cows are unable to digest grass fully. What type of interdependence is this an example of? Explain your answer. [2 marks]

Food Chains and Food Webs

OK, I'll level with you. This isn't the most interesting page in the world, but hey — life's like that. At least you're not being eaten by a load of rabbits...

Food Chains Show What's Eaten by What in an Ecosystem

1) **Food chains always start with a producer, e.g. a plant. Producers make (produce) their own food using energy from the Sun.**
2) **Producers are eaten by primary consumers. Primary consumers are then eaten by secondary consumers and secondary consumers are eaten by tertiary consumers.**
3) **All these organisms eventually die and get eaten by decomposers.**
4) **Each stage (e.g. producers, primary consumers) is called a trophic level.**

   Here's an example of a food chain:

Consumers are organisms that eat other organisms. 'Primary' means 'first', so primary consumers are the first consumers in a food chain. Secondary consumers are second and tertiary consumers are third.

The arrows in a food chain show you the direction of energy transfer.

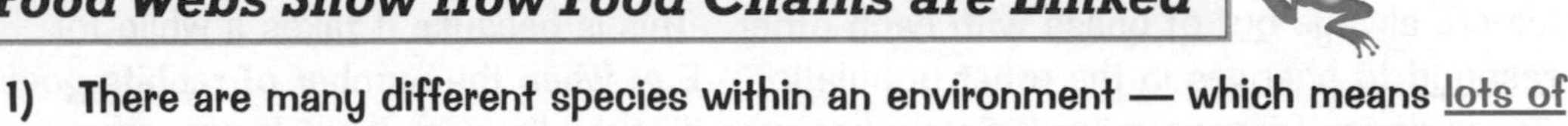

Food Webs Show How Food Chains are Linked

1) **There are many different species within an environment — which means lots of different possible food chains. You can draw a food web to show them.**
2) **All the species in a food web are interdependent, which means if one species changes, it affects all the others.**

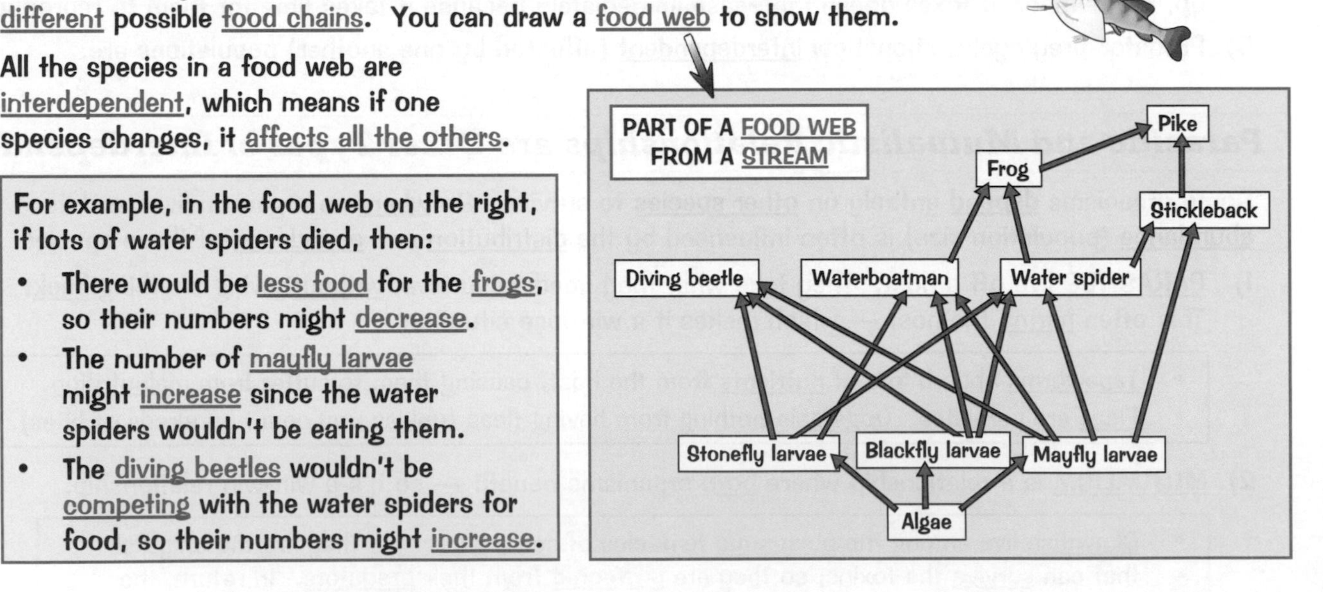

For example, in the food web on the right, if lots of water spiders died, then:
- **There would be less food for the frogs, so their numbers might decrease.**
- **The number of mayfly larvae might increase since the water spiders wouldn't be eating them.**
- **The diving beetles wouldn't be competing with the water spiders for food, so their numbers might increase.**

Food webs — nothing to do with ordering pizza online, I'm afraid...

Food webs are handy for looking at relationships between individual species. Unfortunately you hardly ever see simple food webs in the real world — they're normally as tangled together and interlinked as a bowl of spaghetti.

Q1 The diagram on the right shows part of a food web.
Using the diagram:

weed → aphid → ladybird
wheat → mouse → hawk
wheat → aphid
wheat → human

a) name a secondary consumer. [1 mark]
b) name the trophic level that wheat belongs to. [1 mark]
c) suggest what might happen to the other species if the population of mice increased. [4 marks]

Pyramids of Biomass and Number

The amount of biomass (the mass of living material) decreases as you move up a trophic level. Pyramids of biomass are used to show how the biomass changes. Basically it's just a pretty picture.

You Need to be able to Understand and Draw Pyramids of Biomass

Luckily it's pretty easy — they'll give you all the information you need to do it in the exam. Here's an example of a food chain you might be given:

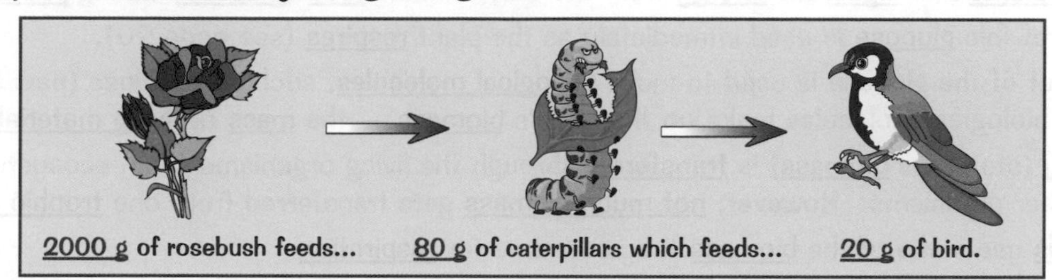

1) Each bar on a pyramid of biomass shows the mass of living material at that stage of the food chain — basically how much all the organisms at each level would 'weigh' if you put them all together.
2) So the 'rosebush' bar on this pyramid would need to be longer than the 'caterpillars' bar, which in turn should be longer than the 'bird' bar... and so on.
3) The rosebush goes at the bottom because it's at the bottom of the food chain — it's the producer.
4) Then the primary consumers (caterpillars) go on top of the producer, the secondary consumers (birds) go on top of the primary consumers, and so on.
5) Biomass pyramids are almost always pyramid-shaped because biomass is lost at each stage in the food chain (see next page).
6) It can sometimes be difficult to construct an accurate pyramid of biomass because some organisms feed at more than one trophic level. For example, in the food chain shown on the next page, birds might feed on both ladybirds and greenflies.

20 g bird
80 g caterpillars
2000 g rosebush

Pyramids of Numbers can be Different Shapes

1) Pyramids of numbers are similar to pyramids of biomass, but each bar on a pyramid of numbers shows the number of organisms at that stage of the food chain — not their mass.
2) Pyramids of numbers are sometimes other shapes (not just pyramids):

Pyramid of Numbers

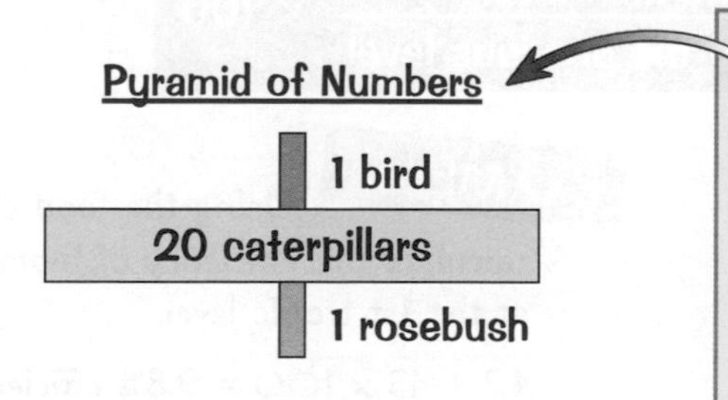

The 'caterpillars' bar on this pyramid is longer than the 'rosebush' bar, because one rosebush can feed a number of caterpillars. (But the biomass of the rosebush is much bigger than the biomass of the caterpillars — which is why the biomass pyramid (see above) is the right shape.)

Constructing pyramids is a breeze — just ask the Egyptians...

Pyramids of numbers could also have a big bar across the top if, for example, there were loads of fleas feeding on one fox. But the tiny fleas would still have less biomass than the fox, so the biomass pyramid would look normal.

Q1 What does each bar on a pyramid of biomass represent? [1 mark]

Q2 Look at the two diagrams on the right. One is a pyramid of biomass and one is a pyramid of numbers. Which one is the pyramid of numbers? Explain your answer. [2 marks]

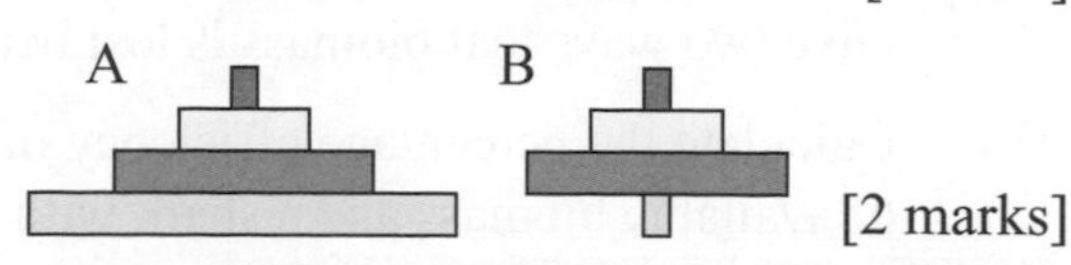

Biomass Transfer

Great, steak for dinner — some biomass from a cow to help you grow. But you'll need some of that biomass for respiration, so you can move about and revise. And some will be indigestible. This is how biomass is lost...

Biomass is Lost Between each Trophic Level

1) Energy from the Sun is the source of energy for nearly all life on Earth.
2) Green plants and algae use energy from the Sun to make food (glucose) during photosynthesis.
3) Some of this glucose is used immediately as the plant respires (see page 20).
4) The rest of the glucose is used to make biological molecules, such as cellulose (part of plant cell walls). These biological molecules make up the plant's biomass — the mass of living material.
5) Energy (stored as biomass) is transferred through the living organisms of an ecosystem when organisms eat other organisms. However, not much biomass gets transferred from one trophic level to the next.
6) Animals use some of the biomass they consume for respiration to provide energy for movement, keeping warm, etc.

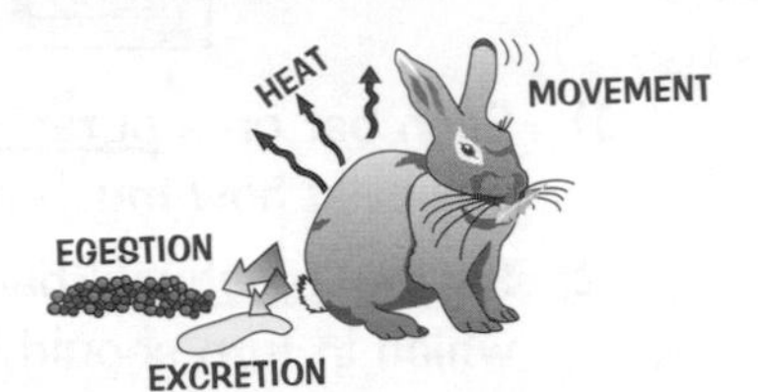

7) Biomass is also lost from the food chain through egestion and excretion.
   - Egestion is getting rid of undigested food — i.e. animal's faeces.
   - Excretion is getting rid of the waste products from chemical reactions in the body, e.g. through sweating, urinating and breathing out.
8) This explains why you get biomass pyramids — most biomass is lost, so doesn't get to the next level up.
9) It also explains why you hardly ever get food chains with more than about five trophic levels. So much biomass is lost at each stage that there's not enough left to support organisms after that many stages.

You Need to be Able to Interpret Data on Biomass Transfer

1) The numbers show the amount of biomass available to the next level. So 43 kg is the amount of biomass available to the greenflies, and 4.2 kg is the amount available to the ladybirds.

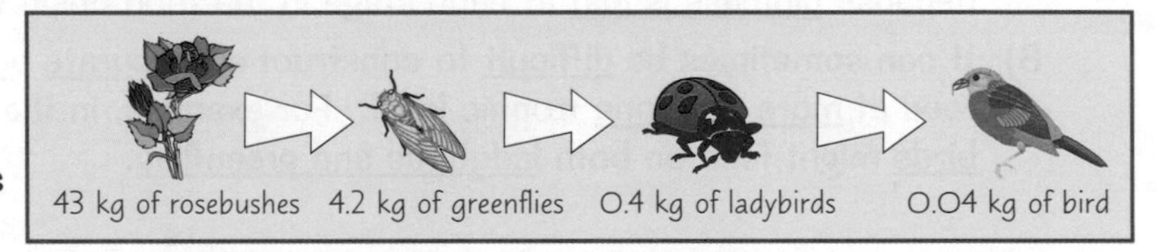

2) You can work out how much biomass has been lost at each level by taking away the biomass that is available to the next level from the biomass that was available from the previous level.
3) You can also calculate the efficiency of biomass transfer — this just means how good it is at passing on biomass from one level to the next.

$$\text{efficiency} = \frac{\text{biomass available to the next level}}{\text{biomass that was available to the previous level}} \times 100$$

The 'efficiency of biomass transfer' is sometimes referred to as the 'percentage biomass transferred'.

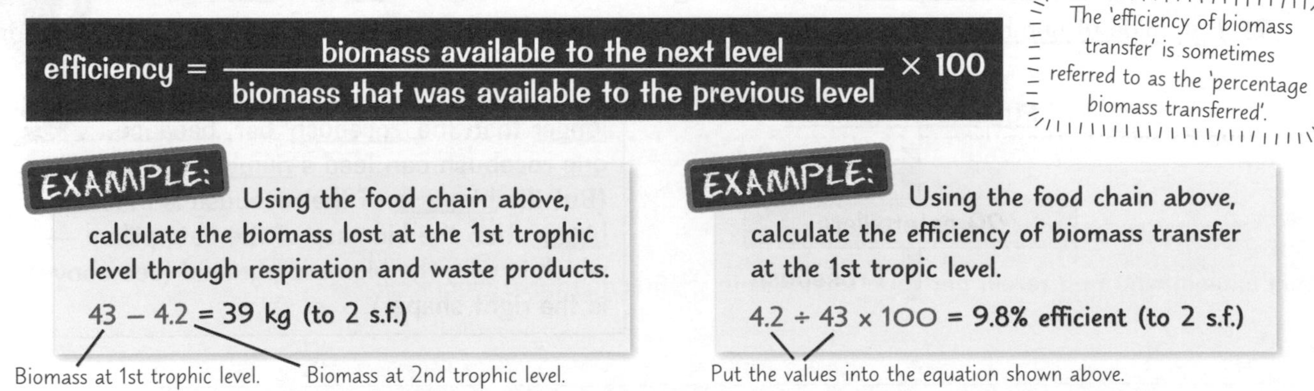

Ah ah ah ah stayin' alive, stayin' alive...

Staying alive is important, but it sure does require a lot of biomass. Organisms really aren't very efficient at transferring biomass to the next trophic level — they lose loads through respiration and so on. Chew on that...

Q1 Give two ways that biomass is lost between trophic levels. [2 marks]

Q2 Calculate the percentage efficiency of biomass transfer between some large fish with 995 kg of available biomass and a shark with 110 kg of available biomass. [1 mark]

Revision Questions for Topic B4

Well, that's Topic B4 all done and dusted — time to see if you've got community level systems sussed...

- Try these questions and tick off each one when you get it right.
- When you've done all the questions under a heading and are completely happy with it, tick it off.

Recycling and Decomposition in Ecosystems (p.57-59)

1) How does carbon in the atmosphere enter food chains?
2) What is the role of microorganisms in the carbon cycle?
3) What is the role of nitrogen-fixing bacteria in the nitrogen cycle?
4) Which microorganisms turn nitrates into N_2 gas?
5) List the four main processes in the water cycle.
6) What happens to waste products and dead organisms in ecosystems?
7) Explain how temperature affects the rate of decomposition.
8) Why does the rate of decomposition decrease when soils become waterlogged?

Ecosystems and Interactions Between Organisms (p.60-61)

9) What is meant by the term 'population' in the organisation of ecosystems?
10) Give two resources that plants compete for in ecosystems.
11) Suggest how light intensity might affect a community.
12) Give two biotic factors that affect communities in ecosystems.
13) Explain why the populations of predators and prey often change in cycles.
14) What is a parasitic relationship?

Food Chains and Food Webs (p.62)

15) Name the trophic levels represented in the food chain below:

    Grass ⟶ Grasshopper ⟶ Frog ⟶ Snake

16) In the food chain shown above, suggest what effect a decline in the population of frogs would have on the population of grasshoppers.
17) What is a food web?

Pyramids of Biomass and Biomass Transfer (p.63-64)

18) Draw a pyramid of biomass for the food chain below:

    Oak tree ⟶ Deer ⟶ Bear

19) True or false? The pyramid of numbers for the food chain above would be a normal pyramid shape.
20) Give two ways that glucose, made during photosynthesis, is used by plants.
21) What is egestion?
22) Explain why you rarely get food chains with greater than five trophic levels.
23) Give the formula for calculating the efficiency of biomass transfer.

Genes and Variation

You may remember the structure of DNA from page 15. Well, now you get to learn why DNA is so important...

Chromosomes Are Really Long Molecules of DNA

1) The genome is the entire genetic material of an organism.
2) The genetic material is stored in the nucleus and is arranged into chromosomes.
3) Each chromosome is one very long molecule of DNA that's coiled up.
4) A gene is a short length of a chromosome.
5) Genes determine the production of proteins (see p.16).

   This controls the development of different characteristics, e.g. dimples, and how an organism functions.
6) Genes can exist in different versions. Each version gives a different form of a characteristic, like blue or brown eyes. The different versions of the same gene are called alleles or variants (see next page).

Organisms of the Same Species Have Differences

1) Different species look... well... different — my dog definitely doesn't look like a daisy.
2) But even organisms of the same species will usually look at least slightly different — e.g. in a room full of people you'll see different colour hair, individually shaped noses, a variety of heights, etc.
3) These differences are called the variation within a species.
4) Variation can be genetic — this means it's caused by differences in genotype. Genotype is all of the genes and alleles that an organism has. An organism's genotype affects its phenotype — the characteristics that it displays.
5) An organism's genes are inherited (passed down) from its parents (see page 68).
6) It's not only genotype that can affect an organism's phenotype though — interactions with its environment (conditions in which it lives) can also influence phenotype. For example, a plant grown on a nice sunny windowsill could grow luscious and green. The same plant grown in darkness would grow tall and spindly and its leaves would turn yellow — these are environmental variations.
7) Most variation in phenotype is determined by a mixture of genetic and environmental factors. For example, the maximum height that an animal or plant could grow to is determined by its genes. But whether it actually grows that tall depends on its environment (e.g. how much food it gets).

Variation can be Continuous or Discontinuous

Continuous variation is when the individuals in a population vary within a range — there are no distinct categories, e.g. humans can be any height within a range, not just tall or short. Other examples include an organism's mass, and the number of leaves on a tree. Characteristics that are influenced by more than one gene or that are influenced by both genetic and environmental factors usually show continuous variation.

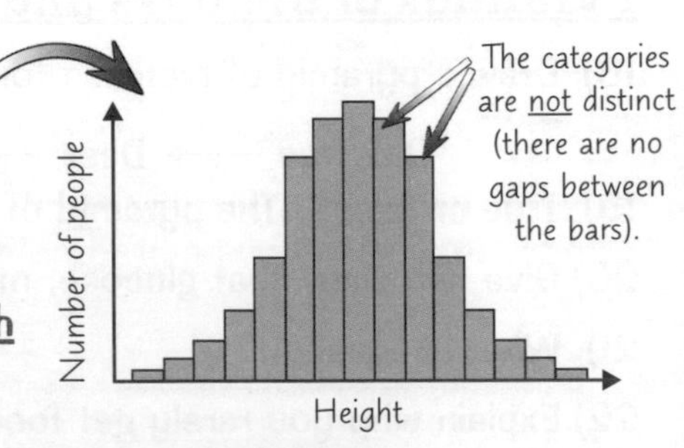

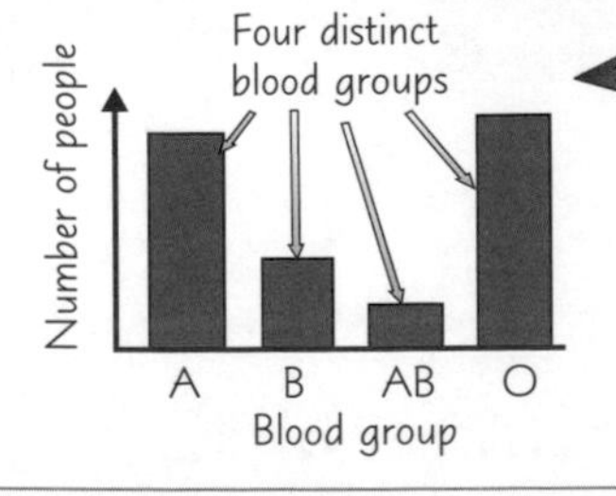

Discontinuous variation is when there are two or more distinct categories — each individual falls into only one of these categories, there are no intermediates. For example, humans can only be blood group A, B, AB or O. Characteristics that are only influenced by one gene and that aren't influenced by the environment are likely to show discontinuous variation.

Environmental variation — pretty much sums up British weather...

It's dead important that you understand this page — it'll help everything else in this topic make much more sense.

Q1 Explain how your height is influenced by both your genome and the environment. [2 marks]

Genetic Variants

You saw on the previous page that organisms show variation, largely due to differences in their DNA. These genetic differences come about partly due to sexual reproduction (see next page) and partly due to mutations.

Mutations are Changes to the Genome

1) Occasionally, a gene may mutate. A mutation is a rare, random change in an organism's DNA that can be inherited.

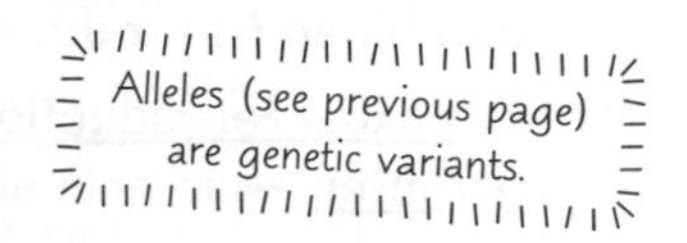

2) Mutations mean that the sequence of DNA bases in the gene is changed, which produces a genetic variant (a different form of the gene).
3) As the sequence of DNA bases in a gene codes for the sequence of amino acids that make up a protein, gene mutations sometimes lead to changes in the protein that it codes for.
4) Most genetic variants have very little or no effect on the protein the gene codes for. Some will change it to such a small extent that its function is unaffected. This means that most mutations have no effect on an organism's phenotype.
5) Some variants have a small influence on the organism's phenotype — they alter the individual's characteristics but only slightly. For example:

> Some characteristics, e.g. eye colour, are controlled by more than one gene. A mutation in one of the genes may change the eye colour a bit, but the difference might not be huge.

6) Very occasionally, variants can have such a dramatic effect that they determine phenotype. For example:

> The genetic disorder, cystic fibrosis, can be caused by the deletion of just three bases but it has a huge effect on phenotype. The gene codes for a protein that controls the movement of salt and water into and out of cells. However, the protein produced by the mutated gene doesn't work properly. This leads to excess mucus production in the lungs and digestive system, which can make it difficult to breathe and to digest food.

Variants Can Affect Coding and Non-Coding DNA

As you know, DNA contains lots of genes (sequences of DNA bases) that code for particular proteins. However, a DNA molecule also contains lots of sequences of bases that don't code for proteins — these portions are known as non-coding DNA. Mutations aren't fussy — they can occur in either coding or non-coding DNA.

1) As you saw above, mutations in coding DNA affect the proteins coded for by the gene. This can affect the protein's structure and the way that it functions, e.g. the active site of an enzyme may be altered so that it no longer fits its substrate, meaning it can no longer function (see page 18).
2) Mutations in non-coding DNA can affect how genes are expressed — i.e. whether or not genes are 'switched on'. They can stop the transcription of mRNA (see page 16) so the protein coded for by that gene is not produced at all.

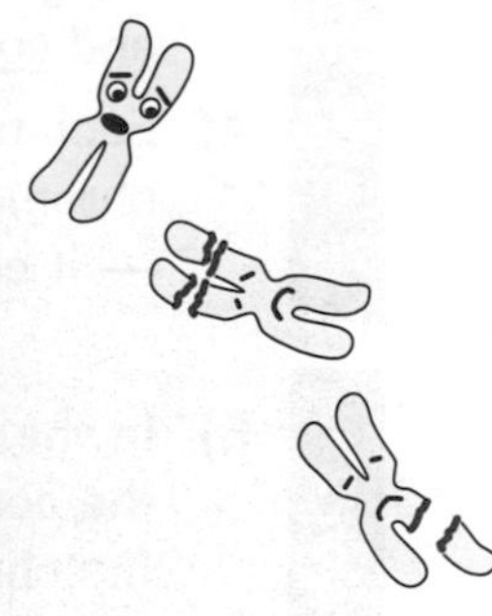

Remember, when mutations affect the proteins produced in an organism, it can influence the organism's phenotype.

I was hoping for the 'grow wings' mutation — I'm still waiting...

Mutations might sound alarming but remember, most are tiny changes that you don't even notice. And mutations introduce variation, and variation can be good (see p.73) so chin up and learn this page.

Q1 Explain why a gene mutation may affect the phenotype of an organism. [3 marks]

Sexual Reproduction and Meiosis

If you've ever wondered why you look a bit like your mum and a bit like your dad but not exactly like your brothers and sisters (unless you're an identical twin), then today's your lucky day...

Sexual Reproduction Produces Genetically Different Cells

1) Sexual reproduction is where genetic information from two organisms (a father and a mother) is combined to produce offspring which are genetically different to either parent.
2) In sexual reproduction, the mother and father produce gametes — in animals these are sperm and egg cells.
3) Gametes only contain half the number of chromosomes of normal cells — they are haploid. Normal cells (with the full number of chromosomes) are called diploid.
4) At fertilisation, a male gamete fuses with a female gamete to produce a fertilised egg. The fertilised egg ends up with the full set of chromosomes (so it is diploid).
5) The fertilised egg then undergoes cell division (by mitosis — see p.28) and develops into an embryo.
6) The embryo inherits characteristics from both parents as it's received a mixture of chromosomes (and therefore genes) from its mum and its dad.

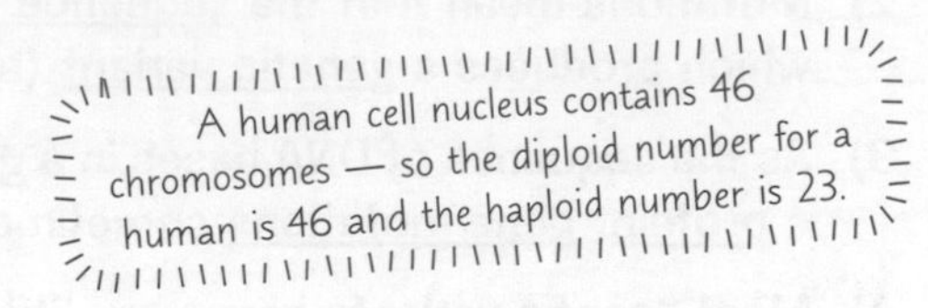

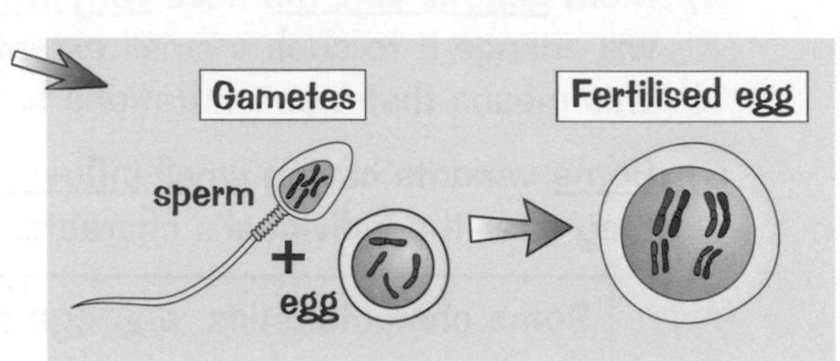

Gametes are Produced by Meiosis

Meiosis is a type of cell division. It's different to mitosis because it doesn't produce identical cells. In humans, meiosis only happens in the reproductive organs (ovaries and testes).

Division 1

1) Before the cell starts to divide, it duplicates its DNA (so there's enough for each new cell). One arm of each X-shaped chromosome is an exact copy of the other arm.
2) In the first division in meiosis (there are two divisions) the chromosomes line up in pairs in the centre of the cell. One chromosome in each pair came from the organism's mother and one came from its father.
3) The pairs are then pulled apart, so each new cell only has one copy of each chromosome. Some of the father's chromosomes and some of the mother's chromosomes go into each new cell.
4) Each new cell will have a mixture of the mother's and father's chromosomes. Mixing up the genes like this is really important — it creates genetic variation in the offspring.

Division 2

5) In the second division the chromosomes line up again in the centre of the cell. It's a lot like mitosis. The arms of the chromosomes are pulled apart.
6) You get four haploid gametes — each only has a single set of chromosomes. The gametes are all genetically different.

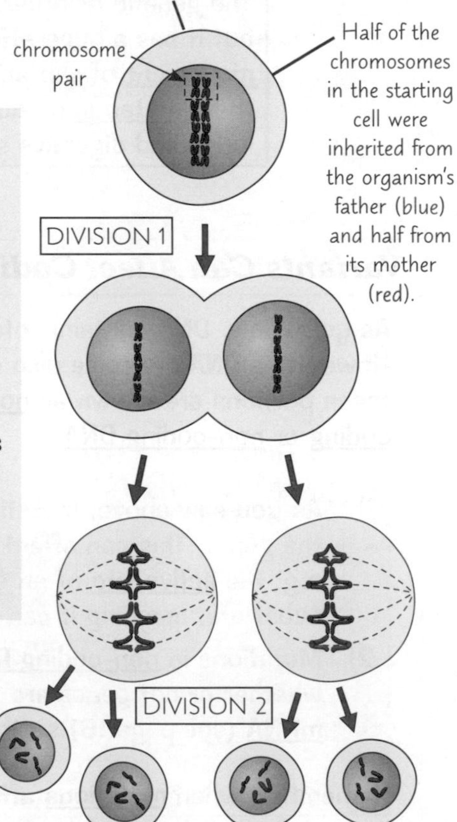

Now that I have your undivided attention...

Remember — in humans, meiosis only occurs in the reproductive organs, when gametes are made.

Q1 Explain why gametes need to be haploid. [2 marks]

Q2 How does meiosis introduce genetic variation? [2 marks]

Comparing Asexual and Sexual Reproduction

Another page, another form of reproduction... And a lovely comparison between the two. Oh so much joy...

Asexual Reproduction Involves Mitosis

1) In asexual reproduction there's only one parent so the offspring are genetically identical to that parent.
2) Asexual reproduction happens by mitosis — an ordinary cell makes a new cell by dividing in two (see p.28).
3) The new cell has exactly the same genetic information (i.e. genes) as the parent cell — it's called a clone.
4) Bacteria, some plants and some animals reproduce asexually.

Both Types of Reproduction Have Advantages and Disadvantages

Reproducing is very important to all organisms — it's how they pass on their genes.
Some organisms reproduce sexually, some reproduce asexually and some can do both.
The different methods of reproduction have advantages and disadvantages:

	ASEXUAL REPRODUCTION	SEXUAL REPRODUCTION
ADVANTAGES	• Asexual reproduction can produce lots of offspring very quickly. • For example, bacteria, such as *E. coli*, can divide every half an hour.	• Creates genetic variation within the population. • This means that if the environmental conditions change, its more likely that some individuals will have characteristics that enable them to survive. • Over time this leads to evolution (see page 73) as species become better adapted to their environment.
	• Only one parent is needed — this means organisms can reproduce whenever conditions are favourable without having to wait for a mate. • For example, aphids produce asexually during summer when there is plenty of food.	
DISADVANTAGES	• There's no genetic variation between offspring. • So, if the environment changes and conditions become unfavourable, the whole population can be affected. • For example, Black Sigatoka is a disease that affects banana plants, which reproduce asexually. So, if there's an outbreak of the disease, it's likely that all banana plants in the population will be affected as there are none that are resistant to it.	• Sexual reproduction takes more time and energy than asexual reproduction, so organisms produce fewer offspring in their lifetime. • For example, organisms need to find and attract mates, which takes time and energy. E.g. male bowerbirds build their females an attractive structure and then dance for them.
		• Two parents are needed for sexual reproduction. This can be a problem if individuals are isolated. • For example, polar bears often live alone, so male polar bears may have to walk up to 100 miles to find a mate.

Asexual reproduction — bacteria's answer to life in the fast lane...

So, both sexual and asexual reproduction have their pros and cons. If you want to find out a little more, try discussing with any organisms you meet how their reproductive strategies are working out for them.

Q1 Strawberry plants can reproduce asexually.
Discuss the advantages and disadvantages of this form of reproduction. [4 marks]

Genetic Diagrams

This page is about how characteristics are inherited — it involves drawing little diagrams too, which is (a bit) fun.

Alleles are Different Versions of the Same Gene

1) Most of the time you have two copies of each gene (i.e. two alleles, see p.67) — one from each parent.
2) If the alleles are different, you have instructions for two different versions of a characteristic (e.g. freckles or no freckles) but you only show one version of the two (e.g. freckles). The version of the characteristic that appears is caused by the dominant allele. The other allele is said to be recessive. The characteristic caused by the recessive allele only appears if both alleles are recessive.
3) In genetic diagrams, letters are used to represent genes. Dominant alleles are always shown with a capital letter (e.g. 'C') and recessive alleles with a small letter (e.g. 'c').
4) If you're homozygous for a trait you have two alleles the same for that particular gene, e.g. CC or cc. If you're heterozygous for a trait you have two different alleles for that particular gene, e.g. Cc.
5) Remember, an organism's genotype is the genes and alleles it has and its phenotype is the characteristics that it displays.

Characteristics can also be called 'phenotypic features'.

Genetic Diagrams show the Possible Alleles in the Offspring

Some characteristics are controlled by a single gene, e.g. blood group — this is called single gene inheritance. Genetic diagrams help to predict the phenotype of the offspring when you know the genotype of the parents.

Imagine you're cross-breeding hamsters, and that some have a boring disposition while others have superpowers. And suppose you know that the behaviour is due to one gene...

Let's say that the allele which causes the superpowers is recessive — so use a 'b'.
And boring behaviour is due to a dominant allele — call it 'B'.

1) A superpowered hamster must have the genotype bb (i.e. it must be homozygous for this trait).
2) However, a boring hamster could have two possible genotypes — BB (homozygous) or Bb (heterozygous), because the dominant allele (B) overrules the recessive one (b).
3) Here's what happens if you breed from two heterozygous hamsters:

Parents' phenotypes: boring, boring
Parents' genotypes: Bb, Bb
Gametes' genotypes: B, b, B, b
Offsprings' genotypes: BB, Bb, Bb, bb
Offsprings' phenotypes: boring, boring, boring, superpowered!

There's a 75% chance of having a boring hamster, and a 25% chance of a superpowered one. To put that another way... you'd expect a 3:1 ratio of boring:superpowered hamsters. Or another way... out of 100 hamsters, the proportion of them you'd expect to be superpowered would be 25.

4) If you breed two homozygous hamsters there's only one possible offspring you can end up with. E.g. breeding BB and bb hamsters can only give offspring with a Bb genotype — and they'd all have a boring phenotype.

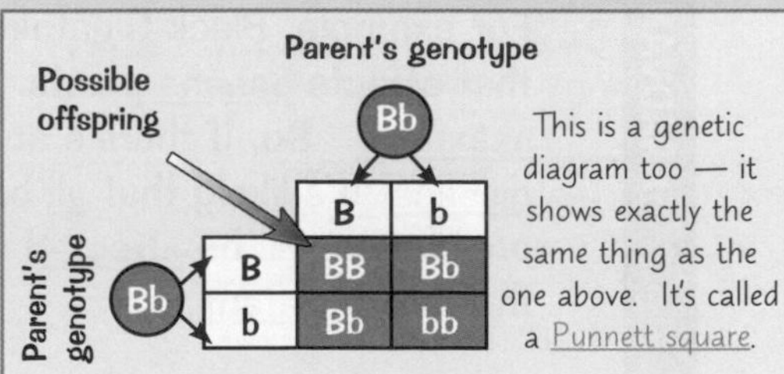

This is a genetic diagram too — it shows exactly the same thing as the one above. It's called a Punnett square.

However, it's not always quite this simple — most characteristics are actually controlled by multiple genes, e.g. height. (You don't need to be able to draw the genetic diagrams for these though.)

Your meanotype determines how nice you are to your sibling...

At first glance this stuff can look quite confusing, but the more you go over it, the more it makes sense.

Q1 People with albinism lack pigment in their skin and eyes, and can appear pale-skinned and white-haired. The gene for albinism (a) is recessive. A heterozygous man has a baby with a woman with albinism.
a) Draw a genetic diagram for the cross. b) What is the chance that the baby will have albinism? [3 marks]

Sex Chromosomes and The Work of Mendel

Now you get to find out exactly why you are a boy or a girl. And why Mendel is the Granddaddy of Genetics.

Your Chromosomes Control Whether You're Male or Female

1) There are 23 pairs of chromosomes in every human body cell. The 23rd pair are labelled XY. These are sex chromosomes — they decide whether you turn out male or female.

- Males have an X and a Y chromosome: XY
  The Y chromosome causes male characteristics.
- Females have two X chromosomes: XX
  The lack of a Y chromosome causes female characteristics.

2) Like other characteristics, sex is determined by a gene.
3) The Y chromosome carries a gene which makes an embryo develop into a male as it grows. Females, who always have two X chromosomes, don't have this gene and so they develop in a different way.
4) The genetic diagram for sex inheritance is fairly similar to a bog-standard one. It just shows the sex chromosomes rather than different alleles.

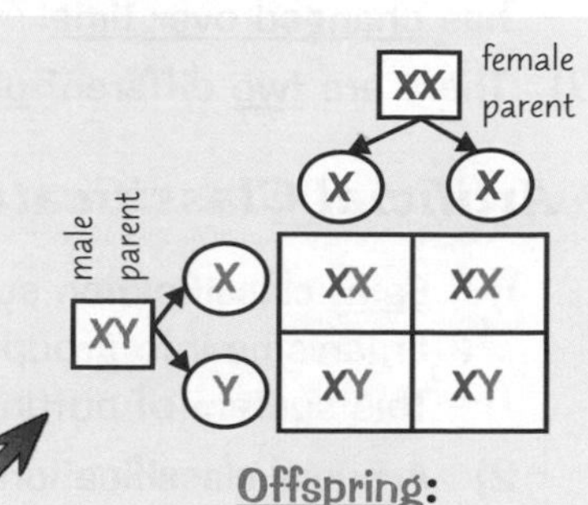

Offspring:
Two XX genotypes and two XY genotypes, so there's a 50% chance of having either a boy or a girl. This means there is a 50:50 ratio of boys to girls.

Mendel Helped Us Understand Genetics

Gregor Mendel was a monk who was alive in the 1800s. On his garden plot, he noted how characteristics in plants were passed on from one generation to the next. The results of his research were published in 1866 and eventually became the foundation of modern genetics. He carried out crosses for height in pea plants:

1) Mendel crossed a tall pea plant with a dwarf pea plant. All the offspring were tall.
2) So, Mendel took two of the tall plants from the first set of offspring and crossed them. This time, 75% of the offspring were tall but 25% were dwarf plants.
3) This is explained nicely by a genetic diagram:

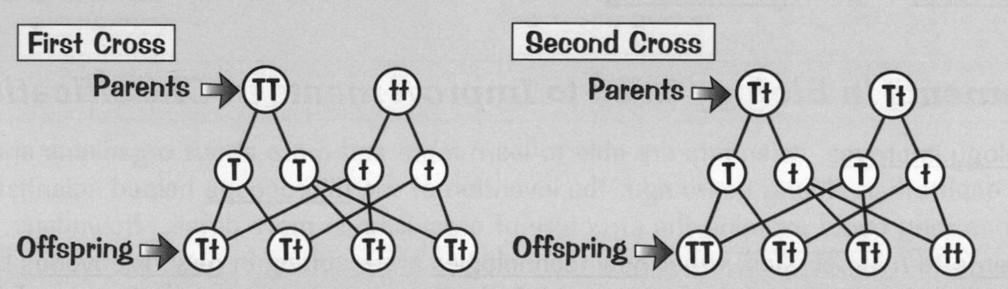

4) Mendel had shown that the height characteristic in pea plants was determined by separate "inherited factors" passed on from each parent. The ratios of tall and dwarf plants in the offspring showed that the factor for tall plants, T, was dominant over the factor for dwarf plants, t.

We now know that the "inherited factors" are of course genes. But back then nobody knew anything about DNA. It wasn't until a long time after Mendel's death that other scientists linked his inherited factors with genes and chromosomes — and realised the significance of his work.

Have you got the Y-factor...

Who'd have thought that swapping an X chromosome for a Y could make such a massive difference — I thought my brother was a new species. Learn the diagram for sex determination, then it's biscuit time.

Q1 Draw a genetic diagram showing that there's an equal chance of a baby being a boy or a girl. [2 marks]

Classification

It seems to be a basic human urge to want to classify things — that's the case in biology anyway...

Classification is Organising Living Organisms into Groups

1) Looking at the similarities and differences between organisms allows us to classify them into groups.
2) Scientists have been doing this for thousands of years but the way in which organisms are classified has changed over time.
3) There are two different classification systems you need to know about, artificial and natural.

Artificial Classification Systems Use Observable Features

1) Early classification systems only used observable features (things you can see) to place organisms into groups, e.g. whether they lay eggs, can fly or can cook a mean chilli... This system of putting organisms into groups is known as an artificial classification system.
2) Artificial classification systems are still used to make keys so that scientists can easily identify and group organisms (see page 79) but they're no longer seen as the best way to classify organisms.

Natural Classification Systems use Evolutionary Relationships

1) As people began to understand more about evolution, evolutionary relationships became much more important when classifying organisms.
2) Natural classification systems use information about organisms' common ancestors and about their common structural features to sort organisms. For example, even though bats and humans have many differences, the bone structure of a bat wing is similar to that of a human hand, so in a natural classification system, bats and humans are grouped together.
3) In natural classification systems, living things are divided into five kingdoms (e.g. the plant kingdom, the animal kingdom).
4) The kingdoms are then subdivided into smaller and smaller groups — phylum, class, order, family, genus, species.
5) The hierarchy ends with species — the groups that contain only one type of organism (e.g. humans, dogs, *E. coli*). A species is defined as a group of similar organisms that are able to reproduce to give fertile offspring.

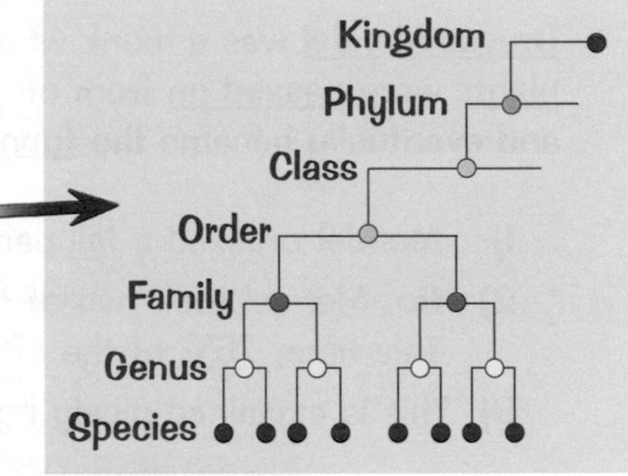

Developments in Biology Lead to Improvements in Classification

As technology improves, scientists are able to learn more and more about organisms and how they're related to each other. Many years ago, the invention of the microscope helped scientists to classify organisms as they could examine the structure of organisms in more detail. Nowadays, as well as improvements to microscopes, other new technologies are resulting in new discoveries being made and the relationships between organisms being clarified. For example, new evolutionary relationships are continually being discovered through molecular phylogenetics.

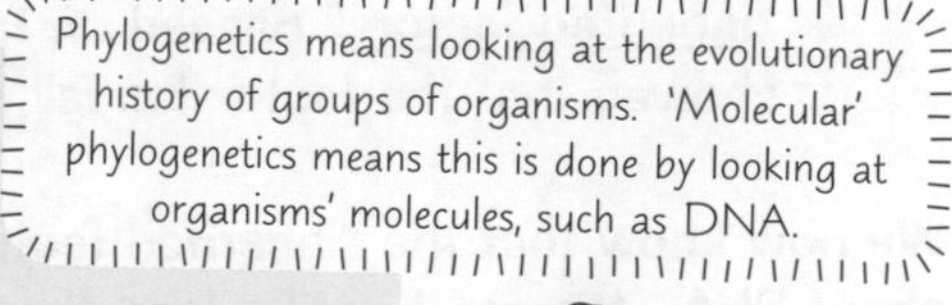

Phylogenetics means looking at the evolutionary history of groups of organisms. 'Molecular' phylogenetics means this is done by looking at organisms' molecules, such as DNA.

- DNA sequencing is used in molecular phylogenetics to see how closely related organisms are.
- DNA sequencing is a technique that compares the sequence of DNA bases for different species (see page 15). The more similar the DNA sequence between species, the more closely related they are. E.g. the base sequence for human and chimpanzee DNA is about 94% the same.

My brother's been reclassified — he's back with the apes...

As new techniques enable us to study organisms at the level of their genes, our classification systems get better.

Q1 Describe the main difference between an artificial and a natural classification system. [2 marks]

Evolution and Natural Selection

The theory of evolution states that one of your (probably very distant) ancestors was a blob in a swamp somewhere. Something like that, anyway. It's probably best to read on for more details...

Natural Selection Increases Advantageous Phenotypes

1) Populations of species usually show a lot of genetic variation — this means that there's a big mix of gene variants (alleles) present in the population.
2) Variants arise when DNA randomly mutates (see page 67).
3) The resources living things need to survive are limited. Individuals must compete for these resources to survive — only some of the individuals will survive.
4) Some genetic variants give rise to characteristics that are better suited to a particular environment (e.g. being able to run away from predators faster). This means that these organisms have an advantageous phenotype. These individuals will have a better chance of survival and so have an increased chance of breeding and passing on their genes.
5) This means that a greater proportion of individuals in the next generation will inherit the advantageous variants and so they'll have the phenotypes that help survival.
6) Over many generations, the characteristic that increases survival becomes more common in the population. The 'best' characteristics are naturally selected and the species becomes more and more adapted to its environment. Here's an example:

As well as mutations, sexual reproduction also creates genetic variation (see page 68).

Once upon a time maybe all rabbits had short ears and managed OK. Then one day a mutated gene meant that one rabbit popped out with big ears. This rabbit could hear better and was always the first to dive for cover at the sound of a predator. Pretty soon he's fathered a whole family of rabbits with big ears, all diving for cover before the other rabbits, and before you know it, there are only big-eared rabbits left — because the rest just didn't hear trouble coming quick enough.

FOX!

Evolution is a Change in Inherited Characteristics

1) Natural selection leads to the evolution of species. Here's how evolution is defined:

Evolution is the change in inherited characteristics of a population over time, through the process of natural selection.

2) The speed at which a species evolves depends partly on how quickly it reproduces — some species reproduce very quickly (e.g. bacteria can be ready to start dividing in just 20 minutes), whereas others reproduce much more slowly (e.g. usually humans only start reproducing after around 20-30 years).
3) Being quick to reproduce means that inherited characteristics are passed on to future generations much more quickly, so the time taken for the population to adapt to its environment is reduced.
4) Evolution can mean that a species' phenotype changes so much that a completely new species is formed (i.e. the old and new version of the species wouldn't be able to breed together to produce fertile offspring).

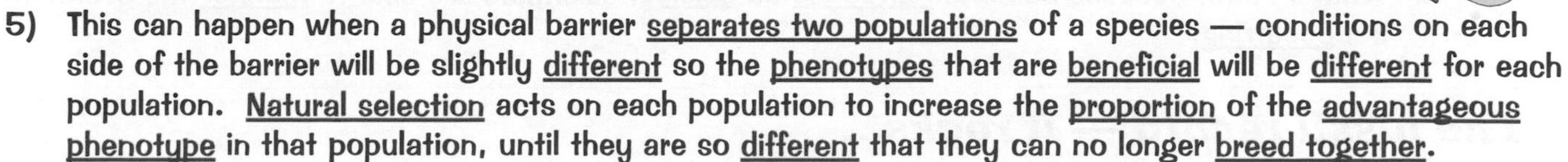

5) This can happen when a physical barrier separates two populations of a species — conditions on each side of the barrier will be slightly different so the phenotypes that are beneficial will be different for each population. Natural selection acts on each population to increase the proportion of the advantageous phenotype in that population, until they are so different that they can no longer breed together.

'Natural selection' — sounds like vegan chocolates...

It's no good being really great at surviving if for some reason you don't breed and pass on your genes. And you'll only be good at surviving by having great parents or by awesome mutations in your DNA.

Q1 Musk oxen have thick fur, which is an adaptation to the cold climate in which they live. Explain how the musk oxen may have developed this adaptation over many years. [4 marks]

Evidence for Evolution

If you're sitting there thinking evolution is a load of old codswallop, here's a bit of evidence to help sway you...

There is Good Evidence for Evolution

Scientists believe that all complex organisms on Earth have evolved from simple organisms that existed about 3500 million years ago. Of course, they wouldn't think this without good evidence to back it up. Fossil records and antibiotic resistance in bacteria both provide evidence for evolution:

Fossils are the Remains of Plants and Animals

1) A fossil is any trace of an animal or plant that lived long ago. They are most commonly found in rocks.
2) They can tell us a lot about what the organisms looked like and how long ago they existed. Generally, the deeper the rock, the older the fossil.
3) By arranging fossils in chronological (date) order, gradual changes in organisms can be observed. This provides evidence for evolution, because it shows how species have changed and developed over many years. For example, if you look at the fossilised bones of a horse, you can put together a family tree to suggest how the modern horse might have evolved.

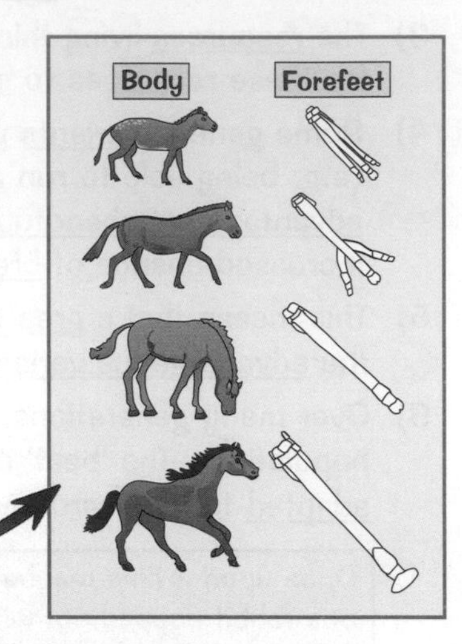

Bacteria Can Evolve and Become Antibiotic-Resistant

1) Like all organisms, bacteria sometimes develop random mutations in their DNA, which introduces new variants into the population. These can lead to changes in the bacteria's phenotype — for example, a bacterium could become less affected by a particular antibiotic (a substance designed to kill bacteria or prevent them from reproducing).
2) For the bacterium, this ability to resist antibiotics is a big advantage. The bacterium is better able to survive, even in a host who's being treated with antibiotics, and so it lives for longer and reproduces many more times.
3) This leads to the resistant variant being passed on to offspring and becoming more and more common over time — it's just natural selection.

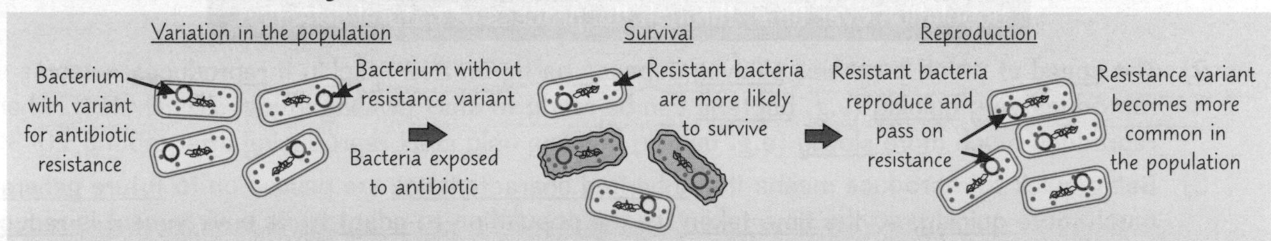

4) The emergence of antibiotic-resistant bacteria provides evidence for evolution (as there is a change in the inherited characteristics of a population over time, through the process of natural selection). What's more, because bacteria reproduce so quickly, scientists are able to monitor the evolution as it's occurring.

The fossil record — it rocks...

Life on Earth is still evolving — the evidence is right under our feet and under our microscopes.

Q1 Which of the following statements best describes how antibiotic resistance provides evidence of evolution?

A The proportion of bacteria in a population killed by antibiotics increases over several generations.

B Over time, antibiotics are able to kill bacteria with the antibiotic-resistant variant.

C In the presence of antibiotics, bacterial cells develop antibiotic-resistant mutations before they die.

D Over time, the antibiotic-resistant variant becomes more common in the population. [1 mark]

Q2 Describe how fossils provide evidence for evolution. [2 marks]

Darwin and Wallace

It was two clever chaps — Darwin and Wallace — who came up with the theory of evolution by natural selection. Little did they know we'd still be harping on about them 150 years later...

Darwin Came up With The Theory of Evolution by Natural Selection...

1) Charles Darwin was the guy that came up with the theory of evolution by natural selection.
2) Darwin spent 5 years on a voyage around the world studying plants and animals.
3) He noticed that there was variation in members of the same species and that those with characteristics most suited to the environment were more likely to survive. He also noticed that characteristics could be passed on to offspring.
4) He wrote his theory of evolution by natural selection to explain his observations.

Charles Darwin

... and Wallace Contributed Too

1) Alfred Russel Wallace was a scientist working at the same time as Darwin.
2) He also came up with the idea of natural selection and worked with Darwin on it.
3) Wallace's observations provided evidence to help support the theory of evolution by natural selection. E.g. he realised that warning colours are used by some species (e.g. butterflies) to deter predators from eating them — an example of an advantageous adaptation that had evolved by natural selection.
4) But, it was Darwin's famous book 'On the Origin of Species' that made other scientists pay attention to the theory so Darwin is usually better remembered than Wallace.

Ideas About Evolution have Influenced Modern Biology

The theory of evolution by natural selection is still relevant today — we now understand that all life changes through the process of evolution and we have all descended from a common ancestor. This has affected lots of different areas of biology including:

- classification — this is now much more based on evolutionary relationships (see p.72).
- antibiotic resistance — we now understand the importance of finishing a course of antibiotics to prevent resistant bacteria spreading and we know we need to constantly develop new antibiotics to fight newly-evolved resistant bacteria (see previous page).
- conservation — we now understand the importance of genetic variation and how it helps populations adapt to changing environments. This has led to conservation projects to protect species (see below).

Seedbanks Are Used to Store Biodiversity

Biodiversity is the variety of living organisms in an area — it's really important that we maintain biodiversity on Earth (see page 83). Changes in the environment can mean that species need to evolve in order to survive in the new conditions. Some species become extinct if they can't evolve quickly enough, which reduces biodiversity. Seedbanks are one way that people are trying to protect biodiversity.

1) A seedbank is a store of lots of seeds (and therefore genetic material) from lots of different species of plant. They help to conserve biodiversity by storing the seeds of a wide variety of plants.
2) If the plants become extinct in the wild the stored seeds can be used to grow new plants.
3) Seedbanks also help to conserve genetic variation. For some species, they store a range of seeds from plants with different characteristics (and so different alleles). E.g. in modern agriculture, there's often little genetic variation in crop species grown, so they could easily be wiped out by a particular pest. However, traditional versions of the crop species may have alleles for pest resistance. If they're stored in a seedbank, their seeds can produce crops that can cope with the pests, if needed.

If my bank accepted seeds, I wouldn't have to write these gags...

Biology wouldn't be what it is today without Darwin and Wallace, but at the time their ideas were revolutionary.

Q1 Describe Wallace's role in developing the theory of evolution by natural selection. [1 mark]

Revision Questions for Topic B5

Right, that wraps up Topic B5 — time to find out how much of it you've got stored away in your noggin.

- Try these questions and tick off each one when you get it right.
- When you've done all the questions under a heading and are completely happy with it, tick it off.

Genes and Variants (p.66-67)

1) What is an organism's genome?
2) Describe what is meant by the term 'phenotype'.
3) What affects an organism's phenotype apart from its genotype?
4) Give one example of continuous variation.
5) Explain how a mutation leads to the formation of a genetic variant.
6) How likely is it that a variant will have a really big effect on an organism's phenotype?

Reproduction (p.68-69)

7) What are gametes?
8) What does it mean if a cell is 'haploid'?
9) Why does asexual reproduction produce offspring that are genetically identical?
10) Give one advantage of sexual reproduction compared to asexual reproduction.

Genetic Diagrams and Inheritance (p.70-71)

11) In a genetic diagram, is a capital letter used to represent a dominant or recessive allele?
12) What does it mean to be homozygous for a characteristic?
13) If two flowers with the genotypes RR and rr are bred together, what will the possible genotypes of their offspring be?
14) What are the 23rd pair of chromosomes labelled as in a female?
15) Describe how the work of Mendel contributed to our understanding of genetics.

Classification (p.72)

16) How are organisms divided into groups in a natural classification system?
17) What is the smallest group that organisms are divided into in the natural classification hierarchy?
18) Describe how DNA sequencing is used in classification.

Evolution (p.73-75)

19) How is evolution defined?
20) Why might the speed of evolution vary from species to species?
21) How might evolution lead to the development of new species on Earth?
22) Explain how antibiotic-resistant bacteria provide evidence for evolution.
23) Describe how Darwin came up with the theory of evolution by natural selection.
24) Name the scientist that worked with Darwin on his theory.
25) Give three ways in which the theory of evolution by natural selection has influenced modern biology.
26) What is a seedbank?

Investigating Distribution and Abundance

This is where the fun starts. Studying ecology gives you the chance to rummage around in bushes. Hurrah.

Organisms Live in Different Places

1) The abundance of an organism is how many individuals you find in an area (i.e. population size).
2) The distribution of an organism is where an organism is found in a habitat, e.g. in a part of a field.
3) You need to know how to investigate the distribution and abundance of organisms in a habitat.
4) Most of the time it would be too time consuming to measure the number of individuals and distribution of every species in the area you're investigating. So instead you take samples.
5) Abundance can be estimated by counting the number of individuals (or working out percentage cover — see p.80) in samples taken. These results then need scaling up for the total area (see next page).
6) There are a couple of ways to study the distribution of an organism. You can:
   - measure how common an organism is in two sample areas (e.g. using quadrats) and compare them.
   - study how the distribution changes across an area, e.g. by placing quadrats along a transect (p.80).
7) You need to know about the sampling methods coming up below and on the next few pages.

Pooters Are For Collecting Ground Insects*

1) Pooters are jars that have rubber bungs sealing the top, and two tubes stuck through the bung.

rubber bung
breathe in through flexible tube
fine mesh stops the insect from being breathed in
long, flexible tube to point at insect

2) If you suck on the shorter tube, and put the end of the longer tube over an insect, it'll be sucked into the jar.

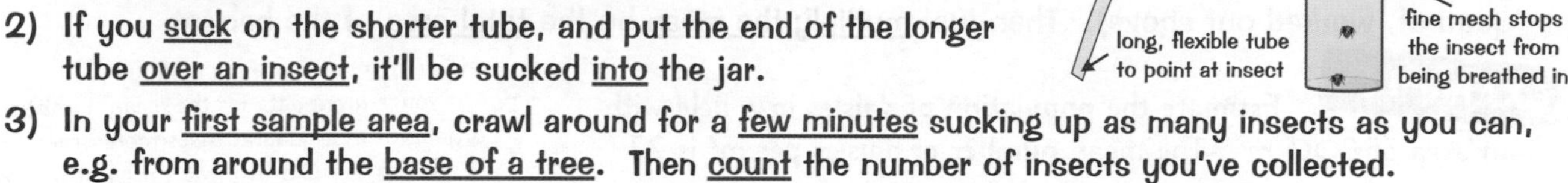

3) In your first sample area, crawl around for a few minutes sucking up as many insects as you can, e.g. from around the base of a tree. Then count the number of insects you've collected.
4) Do this in your second sample area and compare what you find. Spend the same amount of time sampling in each area, and choose sample areas of a similar size.

Pitfall Traps Are Another Way to Investigate Ground Insects

1) Pitfall traps are steep-sided containers that are sunk in a hole in the ground. The top is partly open.
2) Leave the trap overnight in your first sample area. Insects that come along fall into the container and can't get out again, so you can count them.
3) Then set up a pitfall trap in your second sample area and compare what you find.

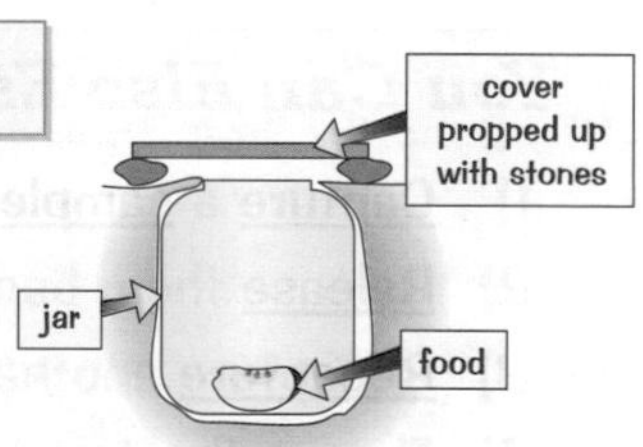

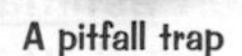
A pitfall trap

Nets Are Used For Collecting Animals From Long Grass and Water

1) A SWEEP NET is a net lined with strong cloth for collecting insects, spiders, etc. from long grass.
2) To use one, stand still in your first sample area and sweep the net once from left to right through the grass. Then quickly sweep the net up and turn the insects out into a container to count them.
3) Repeat the sweep in your second sample area and compare the numbers of organisms you find.

1) A POND NET is a net used for collecting insects, water snails, etc. from ponds and rivers.
2) To use one, stand in your first sample area and sweep the net along the bottom of the pond or river. Turn the net out into a white tray with a bit of water in to count the organisms you've caught.
3) Then sweep your pond net in your second sample area and compare what you find.

Health and safety advises placing tiny cones around pitfall traps...

For these experiments, you should repeat the measurements several times and then take the average result.

Q1 A student wants to find out which ground insects are present in two different areas of a woodland over a 24-hour period. Suggest a method the student could use to sample the areas. [3 marks]

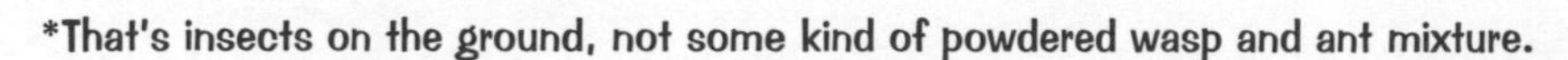
*That's insects on the ground, not some kind of powdered wasp and ant mixture.

More on Investigating Distribution and Abundance

A bit more on studying the <u>distribution</u> and <u>abundance</u> of organisms. First up, using <u>quadrats</u>...

Use a Quadrat to Study The Distribution of Small Organisms

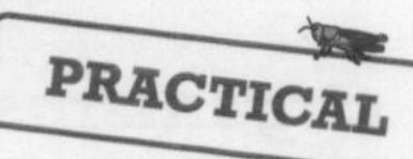

A <u>quadrat</u> is a <u>square</u> frame enclosing a <u>known area</u>, e.g. 1 m². To compare <u>how common</u> an organism is in <u>two sample areas</u>, just follow these simple steps:

1) Place a <u>1 m² quadrat</u> on the ground at a <u>random point</u> within the <u>first</u> sample area. E.g. divide the area into a grid and use a random number generator to pick coordinates. Otherwise, if all your samples are in <u>one spot</u> and everywhere else is <u>different</u>, the results you get won't be <u>valid</u>. For more about <u>random sampling</u> take a look at page 108.
2) <u>Count</u> all the organisms you're interested in <u>within</u> the quadrat.
3) <u>Repeat</u> steps 1 and 2 lots of times. (The <u>larger</u> the <u>sample size</u> the better, see p.5.)
4) <u>Work out</u> the <u>mean</u> number of organisms per quadrat within the first sample area.
5) <u>Repeat</u> steps 1 to 4 in the <u>second</u> sample area.
6) Finally <u>compare</u> the two means. E.g. you might find 2 daisies per m² in the shade, and 22 daisies per m² (lots more) in an open field.

A quadrat

1 m

1 m

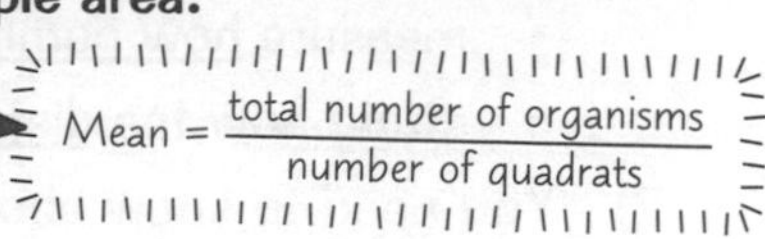

Estimate Population Sizes by Scaling Up from a Small Sample Area

To work out the <u>population size</u> of an organism in one sample area you need to work out the <u>mean number of organisms per m²</u> (if your quadrat has an area of 1 m², this is the same as the mean number of organisms per quadrat, worked out above). Then just <u>multiply the mean</u> by the <u>total area</u> of the habitat.

EXAMPLE: Estimate the population of daisies in a field with an area of 800 m². The mean number of daisies per m² is 22.

Multiply the mean number of daisies per m² by the area.

Population size = 22 × 800 = 17 600 daisies

If you're given data for the mean number of organisms in a quadrat that's more or less than 1 m² (e.g. per 0.5 m²), you can't just multiply this number by the total area to get your estimate. Calculate organisms per m² first.

You Can Also Estimate Population Sizes Using Capture-Recapture

1) <u>Capture</u> a <u>sample</u> of the population and <u>mark</u> the animals in a <u>harmless</u> way.
2) <u>Release</u> them back into the environment.
3) <u>Recapture</u> another sample of the population. <u>Count</u> how many of this sample are marked.
4) Then <u>estimate</u> population size with this equation:

$$\text{Population Size} = \frac{\text{number in first sample} \times \text{number in second sample}}{\text{number in second sample previously marked}}$$

EXAMPLE: A pitfall trap was set up in an area of woodland. 30 woodlice were caught in an hour and marked on their shell, before being released back into the environment. The next day, 35 woodlice were caught in an hour, only 5 of which were marked. Estimate the population size.

All you need to do is put the numbers into the population size equation (shown above).

Population size = (30 × 35) ÷ 5 = 210 woodlice

(30 = number in the first sample; 35 = number in the second sample; 5 = number in the second sample previously marked)

When using the capture-recapture method you have to make a number of <u>assumptions</u>. These include: there has been <u>no change</u> in the <u>population size</u> between the samples (e.g. births and deaths) and the <u>marking</u> hasn't affected individuals' <u>chance of survival</u> (e.g. making them more visible to predators).

Drat, drat and double drat — my favourite use of quadrats...

Choosing which sampling method to use often depends on the type of organism. E.g. quadrats are great for organisms that don't move such as plants, but nets and traps are better for organisms that move around, like insects.

Q1 Capture-recapture was used to estimate the population of crabs on a beach. In the first sample 22 were caught. A second sample had 26 crabs, 4 of which were marked. Estimate the population size. [2 marks]

Using Keys and Factors Affecting Distribution

Yep, there's still some more to learn about this stuff. On this page we cover some practical bits and bobs along with how abiotic and biotic factors affect the distribution of organisms. You're in for a treat, so get excited.

Keys are Used to Identify Creatures

1) A key is a series of questions that you can use to figure out what an unknown organism is.
2) Keys are very useful when you're carrying out sampling as they help you to correctly identify the organisms that you find.
3) To use a key you start at question 1, and the answer to that question (which you know by looking at your mystery organism) is used to narrow down your options of what it could be.
4) Sometimes keys will just have statements, rather than questions, that are followed by a number of options — e.g. 'number of legs' followed by some different options (see below).
5) As you answer more and more questions you narrow down your options further until eventually you're just left with one possible species your organism could be.

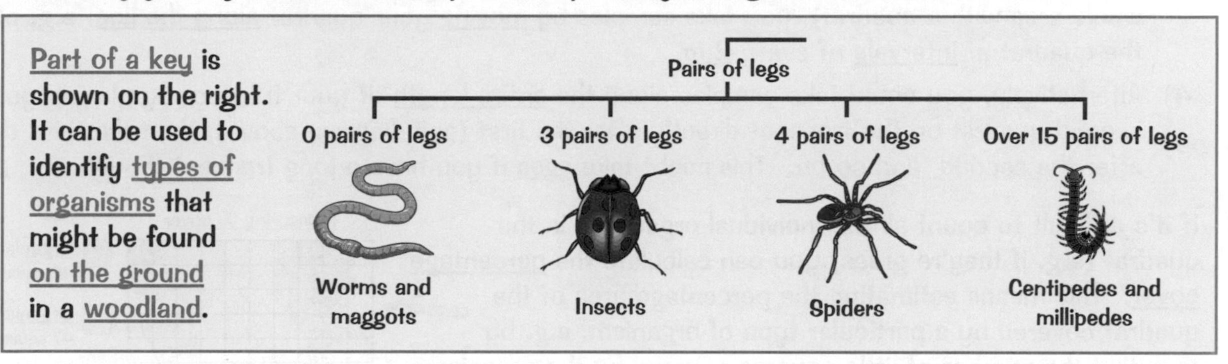

The Distribution of Organisms is Affected by Abiotic and Biotic Factors

1) The distribution of organisms is affected by abiotic factors such as temperature, moisture level, light intensity and soil pH (see page 60). For example, in a playing field, you might find that daisies are more common in the open than under trees, because there's more light available in the open.
2) Biotic factors can also affect the distribution of organisms (see p.60). E.g. competition between species might result in a different distribution of these species than if this competition didn't exist.

You Need to Know How to Measure Abiotic Factors

If you find there's a difference in the distribution of organisms, you can investigate the factors that might be causing it. For example, when looking into the distribution of daisies in the playing field mentioned above, you could measure light intensity both under the trees and in the open — finding a difference in light intensity could provide evidence for the idea that this is affecting the distribution of daisies.

Here's how you can measure the following abiotic factors:

1) Use a thermometer to measure the temperature in different places.
2) Use an electronic device called a light sensor to measure light intensity.
3) Use a soil moisture meter to measure the level of moisture in some soil.
4) Measure soil pH using indicator liquid — water is added to a soil sample and then an indicator liquid (e.g. universal indicator) is added that changes colour depending on the pH. The colour is compared to a chart to find out the pH of the soil. Electronic pH monitors can also be used which produce a pH value for the sample being tested — water is added to the soil sample and an electronic probe is placed into the sample to generate a numerical value for pH.

There's more on measuring temperature and pH on p.109-110.

Identification keys — not much use in the world of home security...

Keys help you identify organisms you've found when sampling. This is pretty important when you want to talk about the different organisms that you've seen — it's not much use saying you found six slimy things in a pond...

Q1 Give two abiotic factors that might be measured on a sandy shore. [2 marks]

Using Transects

Quadrats back out — transects are another way of investigating the distribution and abundance of organisms...

Transects are Used to Investigate Distribution

PRACTICAL

1) You can investigate how the distribution of an organism gradually changes across an area (e.g. from a hedge towards the middle of a field) using lines called transects.
2) When you sample along the length of a transect using a quadrat (see page 78) this is called a belt transect.
3) To do a belt transect follow the steps below:

transect

quadrat

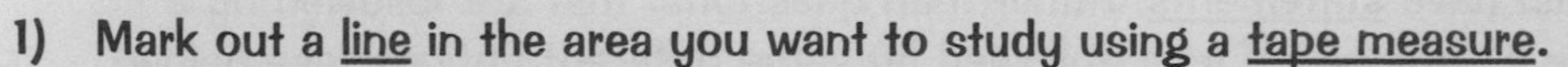

1) Mark out a line in the area you want to study using a tape measure.

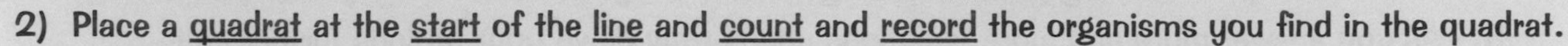

2) Place a quadrat at the start of the line and count and record the organisms you find in the quadrat.
3) Then, instead of picking a second sampling site at random (which you'd do if you were sampling a whole area with a quadrat), you take samples by moving your quadrat along the line, e.g. placing the quadrat at intervals of every 2 m.
4) Alternatively, you could take samples along the entire length of your transect by placing your second quadrat on the transect directly after the first (see diagram above), then the third directly after the second, and so on. This might take ages if you have a long transect though.

4) If it's difficult to count all the individual organisms in the quadrat (e.g. if they're grass) you can calculate the percentage cover. This means estimating the percentage area of the quadrat covered by a particular type of organism, e.g. by counting the number of little squares covered by the organisms.
5) You can plot the results of a transect in a kite diagram (see below). This allows you to map the distribution of organisms in an area.

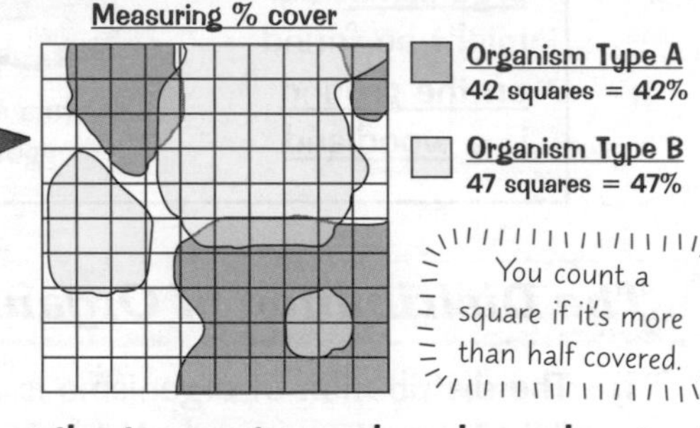

You count a square if it's more than half covered.

6) Taking measurements of abiotic factors (see p.60) at points along the transect can show how changes in these affect the distribution and abundance of organisms in the habitat. For example, in a coastal habitat, changes in salinity and soil depth result in zones where different types of plants grow (see below).

Kite Diagrams Show the Abundance and Distribution of Organisms

Kite diagrams can be used to show the data collected in a belt transect — e.g. the kite diagram below shows the distribution and abundance of organisms along a transect in coastal sand dunes:

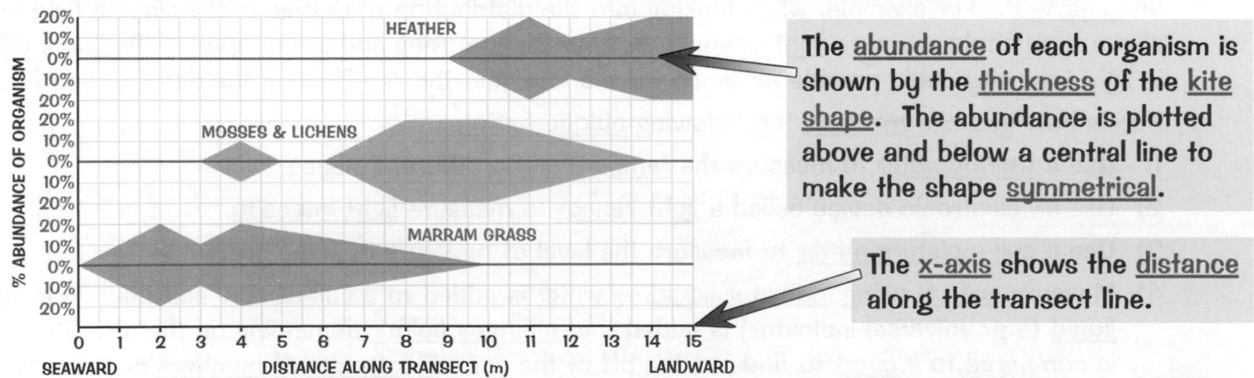

The abundance of each organism is shown by the thickness of the kite shape. The abundance is plotted above and below a central line to make the shape symmetrical.

The x-axis shows the distance along the transect line.

From the kite diagram you can see that marram grass was distributed between 0 and 10 m along the transect. At 2 m along the transect the abundance of marram grass was 20% (i.e. it covered 20% of the quadrat). At 7 m the abundance of marram grass was 10%.

Disclaimer: no kites were harmed in the making of this page...

Transects involve using quadrats in a very organised way. It's exciting, I know, so here's a question to tackle...

Q1 Explain how you would set up a belt transect to record the abundance of species across a field. [5 marks]

Human Impacts on Ecosystems

Time for something less joyous. We humans can have some really damaging negative impacts on ecosystems...

Human Interactions have an Impact on Ecosystems

1) Like all organisms, we humans have an impact on the ecosystems around us.
2) The human population on Earth has grown hugely in the last couple of centuries and is continuing to rise.
3) When the Earth's population was much smaller, the impacts of human activity were usually small and local. Nowadays though, our actions can have a far more widespread effect.
4) Our increasing population puts pressure on the environment, as we take land and resources to survive.
5) But people around the world are also demanding a higher standard of living (and so demand luxuries to make life more comfortable — cars, smartphones, etc.). So we use more raw materials (e.g. oil to make plastics), but we also use more energy for the manufacturing processes. This all means we're taking more and more resources from the environment more and more quickly.
6) Unfortunately, many raw materials are being used up quicker than they're being replaced. So if we carry on like we are, one day we're going to run out.
7) As we produce and consume things we create waste (e.g. waste chemicals), and if we don't handle it properly it can cause harmful pollution like sewage and toxic gases.
8) These human actions are negatively impacting both local biodiversity (the number of species in the local area) and global biodiversity (the number of species on the entire planet) in many ways...

Land Use by Humans is a Negative Interaction with Ecosystems

1) Humans reduce the amount of land and resources available to other animals and plants.
2) The four main human activities that do this are: building, farming, dumping waste and quarrying for metal ores.
3) When land is used by humans, the ecosystem is often changed in a way which has a negative impact on biodiversity. For example:

Habitat destruction

- Woodland clearance — this is often done to increase the area of farmland and can result in a reduction in the number of tree species, so reducing biodiversity. It also destroys the habitats of other organisms — species will die or be forced to migrate elsewhere, further reducing biodiversity.
- Monoculture — this is when areas of land are used to grow a single crop, e.g. in Africa, large areas of land are being used for palm oil plantations. This is an efficient way to grow crops for farmers but can lead to a reduction in biodiversity — this is because habitats are cleared to make way for the large fields that are normally used for monoculture.

Impact of waste on land

Pollution that results from waste produced by human activities kills plants and animals, which reduces biodiversity — for example:

- We use toxic chemicals for farming (e.g. pesticides and herbicides). We also bury nuclear waste underground, and we dump a lot of household waste in landfill sites.
- Sewage and toxic chemicals from industry can pollute lakes, rivers and oceans, affecting the plants and animals that rely on them for survival (including humans). And the chemicals used on land (e.g. fertilisers, pesticides and herbicides) can be washed into water.
- Smoke and gases released into the atmosphere can pollute the air, e.g. sulfur dioxide can cause acid rain.

I'm sorry but I'd prefer it if biodiversity was low inside my house...

I don't know about you but I feel a bit guilty. Our desire for a better standard of living is bad news for the planet.

Q1 Describe how the construction of houses on a meadow could reduce local biodiversity. [2 marks]

More Human Impacts on Ecosystems

Some more human impacts on ecosystems are on the menu for this page. First up, another negative interaction (crikey), but don't despair, things will start looking up after that...

Hunting is Another Negative Human Interaction with Ecosystems

1) Some animal species are hunted, which (shockingly) reduces their numbers.
   For example: Species of rhino are hunted for their horns and this has contributed to them becoming endangered.
2) If too many individuals are killed, it might result in the extinction of the species.
   For example: Fishing on a big scale can reduce fish stocks to such a low level that it might cause a species to die out completely.

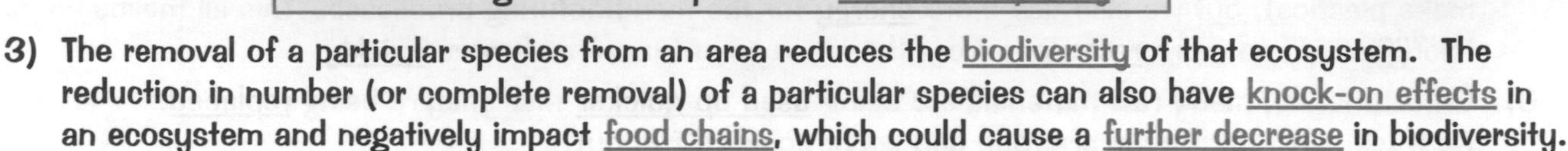

3) The removal of a particular species from an area reduces the biodiversity of that ecosystem. The reduction in number (or complete removal) of a particular species can also have knock-on effects in an ecosystem and negatively impact food chains, which could cause a further decrease in biodiversity.

Conservation of Species is a Positive Interaction with Ecosystems

Conservation schemes can help to protect biodiversity by conserving species or their habitats. Examples of conservation methods include:

Protecting habitats

This includes things such as controlling water levels to conserve wetlands and coppicing (trimming trees) to conserve woodlands. This allows organisms to continue living in their natural habitat.

Controlling or preventing the introduction of harmful species

Some schemes aim to prevent the introduction of harmful species that would threaten local biodiversity — e.g. those that could reduce the numbers of a species by competing with it or eating it. An example of this in the UK is the control of grey squirrels in some areas. Grey squirrels are not native to Britain and they compete with the native red squirrel and have caused their populations to decline.

Creating protected areas for organisms

Protected areas include places like national parks and nature reserves. Both organisms and habitats are protected in these areas by restricting the development of the land — this includes building houses and using the land for farming. Protected areas can also be found in the sea where human activities like fishing are controlled to protect marine ecosystems.

Protecting organisms in safe areas away from their natural habitat

For animals, safe areas include zoos and for plants they include botanical gardens and seed banks (see p.75). In these areas, organisms can be protected from harmful activities such as hunting and habitat destruction. Safe areas can also be used to increase numbers of particular organisms before they are released into the wild — for animals this is known as captive breeding. This method is useful for reintroducing organisms if they become extinct in the wild.

My room is a protected area from the species Brother Horriblis...

Make sure you get your head around how humans can interact with ecosystems in both positive and negative ways. Negative interactions result in a reduction in the level of biodiversity, whereas positive interactions can maintain or even increase levels of biodiversity. Imagine that, we can have a beneficial effect rather than causing destruction...

Q1 A plant species is nearly extinct in the wild as a result of its habitat being damaged. Explain how botanical gardens and habitat protection could be used to increase the number of individuals of the plant species growing in the wild. [2 marks]

Maintaining Biodiversity

Trying to preserve biodiversity can be tricky but there are benefits for doing it, so it's pretty worthwhile...

Maintaining Biodiversity Benefits Wildlife and Humans

Conservation schemes help maintain biodiversity by protecting species (see previous page). As well as benefitting endangered species they often help humans too:

1) Protecting the human food supply — over-fishing has greatly reduced fish stocks in the world's oceans. Conservation programmes can ensure that future generations will have fish to eat.
2) Ensuring minimal damage to food chains — if one species becomes extinct it will affect all the organisms that feed on and are eaten by that species, so the whole food chain is affected. This means conserving one species may help others to survive.
3) Providing future medicines — many of the medicines we use today come from plants. Undiscovered plant species may contain new medicinal chemicals. If these plants are allowed to become extinct, perhaps through rainforest destruction, we could miss out on valuable medicines.
4) Providing industrial materials and fuels — plant and animal species are involved in the production of industrial materials (e.g. wood, paper, adhesives and oils) and some fuels. If these species become extinct these important resources may become more difficult to produce.

Ecotourism is Another Benefit of Maintaining Biodiversity

1) Ecotourism is tourism that focuses on the appreciation of nature and its conservation whilst having a minimal negative impact on the local ecosystem. Maintaining areas with high biodiversity provides an opportunity for ecotourism to take place in these areas — people are drawn to visit beautiful, unspoilt landscapes.

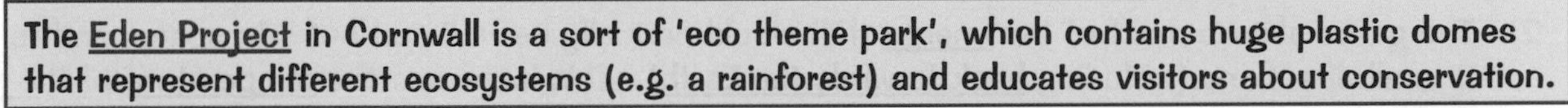
The Eden Project in Cornwall is a sort of 'eco theme park', which contains huge plastic domes that represent different ecosystems (e.g. a rainforest) and educates visitors about conservation.

2) Ecotourism helps bring money into areas where conservation work is taking place — e.g. when tourists buy stuff in local shops and cafes it supports the local economy. Tourists spending money at ecotourism attractions (like the Eden project's gift shop) also helps to fund conservation work.

Maintaining Biodiversity can be Challenging

Ways of maintaining biodiversity are great in theory but they can be difficult to do in the real world. Here are a few examples of why:

Agreements about conservation schemes can be difficult to arrange

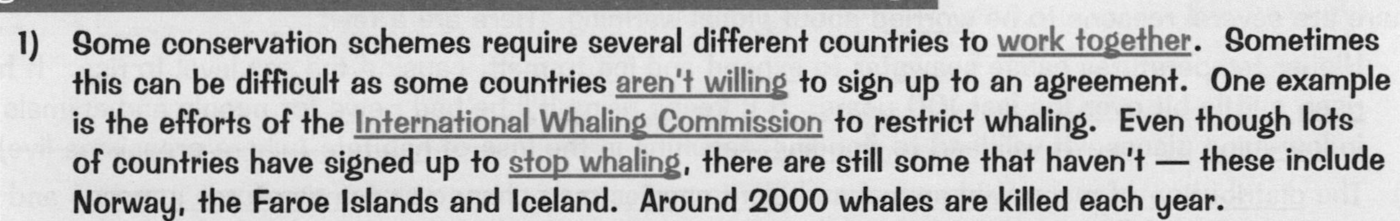
1) Some conservation schemes require several different countries to work together. Sometimes this can be difficult as some countries aren't willing to sign up to an agreement. One example is the efforts of the International Whaling Commission to restrict whaling. Even though lots of countries have signed up to stop whaling, there are still some that haven't — these include Norway, the Faroe Islands and Iceland. Around 2000 whales are killed each year.
2) On a smaller scale, conservation schemes can be objected to by local residents. E.g. people might not be keen if a scheme reduces their income (e.g. a ban on logging or fishing restrictions).

Conservation schemes can be difficult to monitor

E.g. keeping track of fishing quotas (restrictions on the amount of fish that can be caught at sea) can be tricky. This can be a pain if you're trying to work out how successful a scheme is and also if you want to see if people are sticking to it.

It's a shame exams aren't an endangered species...

Hmmm, I guess the maintenance of biodiversity can be a bit tricky but if it keeps food on the table I'm keen...

Q1 Explain why maintaining biodiversity could be important for providing medicines in the future. [2 marks]

Impacts of Environmental Change

Now you know how to measure the distribution of organisms (see pages 77-80), it's time to learn about how their distribution might be changed as a result of environmental factors.

Environmental Changes Affect The Distribution of Organisms

Environmental changes can cause the distribution of organisms to change. A change in distribution means a change in where an organism lives. Environmental changes that can affect organisms in this way include:

1) A change in the AVAILABILITY of WATER. For example:

   The distribution of some animal and plant species in the tropics changes between the wet and the dry seasons — i.e. the times of year where there is more or less rainfall, and so more or less water available. E.g. each year in Africa, large numbers of giant wildebeest migrate, moving north and then back south as the rainfall patterns change.

2) A change in ATMOSPHERIC GASES. For example:

   The distribution of some species changes in areas where there is more air pollution. E.g. some species of lichen can't grow in areas where sulfur dioxide is given out by certain industrial processes.

3) A change in the TEMPERATURE — see below.

These changes can be caused by seasonal factors, geographic factors or human interaction. E.g. a rise in average temperatures is due to global warming, which has been caused by human activity (see below).

Global Warming is Linked to Changes in Atmospheric Gases

1) The temperature of the Earth is a balance between the energy it gets from the Sun and the energy it radiates back out into space. Gases in the atmosphere naturally act like an insulating layer.
2) The gases absorb most of the energy that would normally be radiated out into space, and re-radiate it in all directions (including back towards the Earth). This increases the temperature of the planet. Recently we've started to worry that this effect is getting a bit out of hand.
3) There are several different gases in the atmosphere which help keep the energy in. They're called "greenhouse gases", and the main ones whose levels we worry about are carbon dioxide (CO_2) and methane — because the levels of these two gases are rising quite sharply.
4) The Earth's average temperature is gradually increasing because of rising levels of these gases — this is global warming. Global warming is a type of climate change and causes other types of climate change, e.g. changing rainfall patterns.

The Consequences of Global Warming Could be Pretty Serious

There are several reasons to be worried about global warming. Here are a few:

1) Higher temperatures cause seawater to expand and ice to melt, causing the sea level to rise. It has risen a little bit over the last 100 years. If it keeps rising it'll be bad news for people and animals living in low-lying places. It will lead to flooding, resulting in the loss of habitats (where organisms live).
2) The distribution of many wild animal and plant species may change as temperatures increase and the amount of rainfall changes in different areas. Some species may become more widely distributed, e.g. species that need warmer temperatures may spread further as the conditions they thrive in exist over a wider area. Other species may become less widely distributed, e.g. species that need cooler temperatures may have smaller ranges as the conditions they thrive in exist over a smaller area.
3) There could be changes in migration patterns, e.g. some birds may migrate further north, as more northern areas are getting warmer.
4) Biodiversity (see p.81) could be reduced if some species are unable to survive a change in the climate, so become extinct.

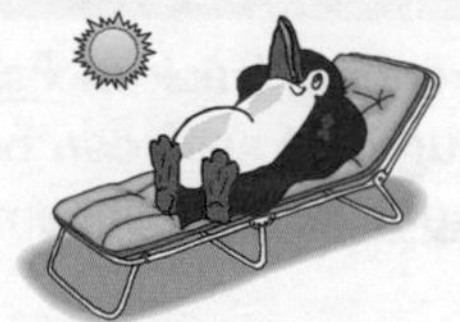

A release of gas often affects the distribution of people in a room...

So environmental changes can have some big impacts on the distribution of organisms. Here's a question for you.

Q1 Explain how a warmer climate might result in the distribution of a species changing. [2 marks]

Food Security

Food security doesn't mean putting a lock on your biscuit tin. Food security is about everyone in the world having access to enough food. It might help to think of it being about 'securing' enough food to feed everyone.

Not Everyone Has 'Food Security'

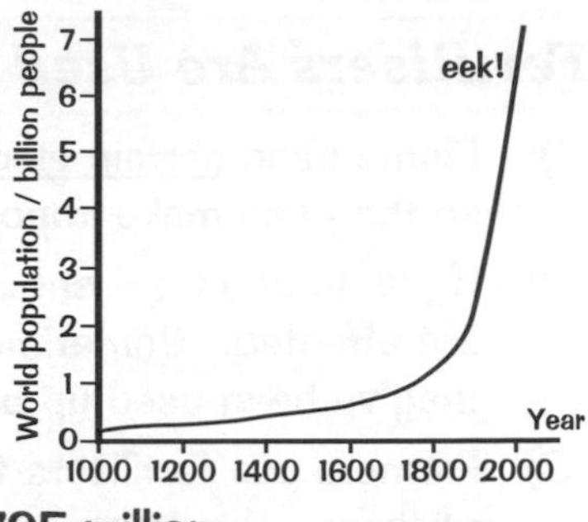

1) As you saw on p.81 the world's population is rising very quickly, and it's not slowing down — look at the graph...
2) This means that global food production must increase too, so that we all have access to enough food that is safe for us to eat and has the right balance of nutrition — this is known as 'food security'.
3) The United Nations World Food Programme estimates that the number of undernourished people worldwide between 2014 and 2016 is 795 million.
4) As the world's population continues to grow, we need to produce more food so that each person still has the same amount of food to eat. By 2050 it's predicted that the world will need to produce around 60% more food than we do at the moment to keep everyone fed.

Several Different Factors Affect the Level of Food Security

One factor affecting the level of food security is the rising human population (see above) but there are others that you need to know about too:

Changing diets in wealthier populations

1) As people become wealthier their diets are likely to change to include a wider variety of foods. An example of this is people eating more meat, which is expensive to buy.
2) This increased demand for meat can be bad news for food security. There's less energy and less biomass every time you move up a stage in a food chain, so for a given area of land, you can produce a lot more food for humans by growing crops rather than by having grazing animals. Plus, animals being reared to be eaten are often fed crops that would otherwise be eaten by humans (e.g. corn)

New pests and pathogens

Pests (e.g. certain insects) and pathogens (e.g. bacteria, fungi and viruses — see p.92) can result in the loss of crops or livestock and could lead to widespread famine.

Sustainability

Sustainability means meeting the needs of today's population without harming the environment so that future generations can still meet their own needs. If we use unsustainable methods to produce food (e.g. farming practices that permanently damage the environment or rely on non-renewable resources) this is likely to negatively impact the level of food security.

Environmental change

1) Environmental changes may impact our ability to produce food. For example, changes to the global climate such as increased temperature could affect the growth patterns of crops which could result in a reduction in yield, and rising sea levels could reduce the land available for food production.
2) Other changes such as pollution could also reduce our ability to grow crops.

Cost of agricultural inputs

1) Agriculture relies on several inputs such as fuel (e.g. for transporting food to where it can be sold), chemicals (e.g. fertilisers and pesticides — see next page), animal feed, etc.
2) The high input costs of farming (e.g. the price of seeds, machinery and livestock) can make it too expensive for people in some countries to start or maintain food production, meaning that there sometimes aren't enough people producing food to feed everyone. These high input costs can also be passed onto consumers in the form of high food prices which some might not be able to afford.

Food insecurity — potatoes with a lack of self-confidence...

Increasing global food security is a pretty big deal — the next few pages cover some ways of doing this.

Q1 Describe how the outbreak of a new crop pathogen could impact the level of food security. [2 marks]

Ways of Increasing Agricultural Yields

Yield is the amount of food produced by a certain area of land in a given time. There are different ways of increasing yield, which all help increase the level of food security (see previous page).

Fertilisers Are Used to Ensure Crops Have Enough Nutrients

1) Plants need certain elements, e.g. nitrogen, potassium and phosphorus, so they can make important compounds like proteins.
2) If plants don't get enough of these elements, their growth and life processes are affected. Sometimes these elements are missing from the soil because they've been used up by a previous crop planted in the same soil.
3) Farmers use fertilisers to replace these missing elements or provide more of them. This helps to increase the crop yield by boosting plant growth.
4) However, fertilisers can cause environmental problems. Excess fertiliser can run off fields and end up in ponds, rivers and lakes, which can result in the death of organisms living in the water.

Pest Control Stops Pests Eating Crops

Pests include microorganisms, insects and mammals (e.g. rats). Pests that feed on crops are killed using various methods of pest control. This means fewer plants are damaged or destroyed, increasing crop yield. You need to know about two forms of pest control — pesticides and biological control:

Pesticides

1) Pesticides are a form of chemical pest control which are sprayed onto crops to kill the pests that damage them. They're often poisonous to humans, so they must be used carefully to keep the amount of pesticide in food below a safe level.
2) There are several different types of pesticide which target different types of pest. Insecticides kill insects, herbicides kill unwanted plants (e.g. weeds) and fungicides destroy fungi.
3) Some pesticides also harm other wildlife that aren't pests, like bees and ladybirds. This can cause a shortage of food for animals higher up the food chain.
4) Also, some pesticides stick around and can be passed along food chains — this can kill organisms further up. E.g. they can end up consuming a lot of pesticide that has accumulated in organisms lower down the chain.

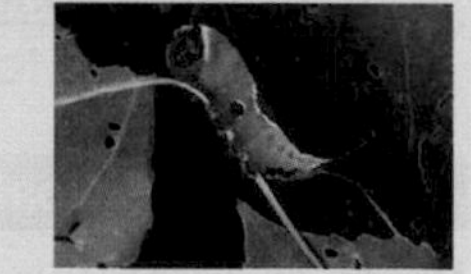

Biological control

1) Biological control is an alternative to using pesticides. It involves using other organisms to reduce the numbers of pests. This is done by encouraging wild organisms or adding new ones.
2) The helpful organisms could be predators (e.g. ladybirds eat aphids), parasites (e.g. some flies lay their eggs on slugs, eventually killing them), or disease-causing (e.g. bacteria that affect caterpillars).
3) Biological control can have a longer-lasting effect than spraying pesticides, and be less harmful to wildlife. But introducing new organisms can cause problems — e.g. cane toads were introduced to Australia to eat beetles, but they're now a major pest themselves because they poison the native species that eat them.
4) Biological control can be considered a safer alternative to pesticides. This is because no chemicals are used, so there's less pollution, risk to people eating the food and no passing of chemicals along food chains.

"Oi aphids — you'd better stay outta my field or you'll regret it..."

Fertilisers and methods of pest control are useful for making sure yields are kept as high as possible and land is used as effectively as it can be.

The table shows the yield of potatoes that a farmer has produced during the last four years.

Year	1	2	3	4
Yield of potatoes (tonnes per hectare)	30	28	32	35

a) Calculate the mean yield, to the nearest tonne per hectare, across all the years shown. [2 marks]

b) In year 5, the farmer used a new fungicide and saw a 6% increase in yield compared to the previous year. Calculate the yield that was achieved in year 5 to the nearest tonne per hectare. [2 marks]

More Ways of Increasing Agricultural Yields

Fertilisers and pest control aren't the only options for increasing yields. Oh no, there are a few more that you need to know about. I know you can't wait to read about them so I won't waffle on any longer...

Hydroponics is Where Plants are Grown Without Soil

1) Hydroponics is where plants are grown in nutrient solutions (water and fertilisers) rather than soil.
2) Plants can be supported and have their roots dangling into nutrient solution or they can be planted in a growth medium such as gravel, coir (brown fibres from coconuts) or perlite (a naturally occurring mineral that looks like white gravel).
3) Hydroponics is often used to grow glasshouse tomatoes and other salad crops on a commercial scale, or in areas where it's difficult or impossible to grow plants in soil (such as places with harsh climates (e.g. little rainfall) or barren soil).

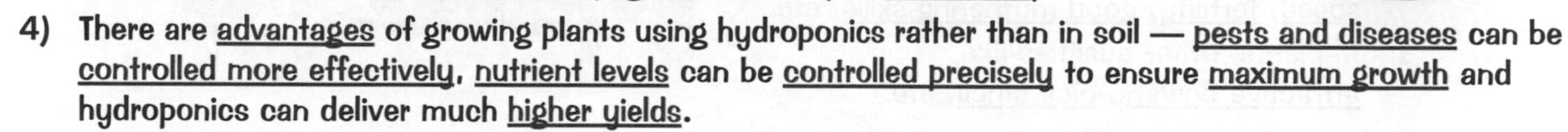

4) There are advantages of growing plants using hydroponics rather than in soil — pests and diseases can be controlled more effectively, nutrient levels can be controlled precisely to ensure maximum growth and hydroponics can deliver much higher yields.

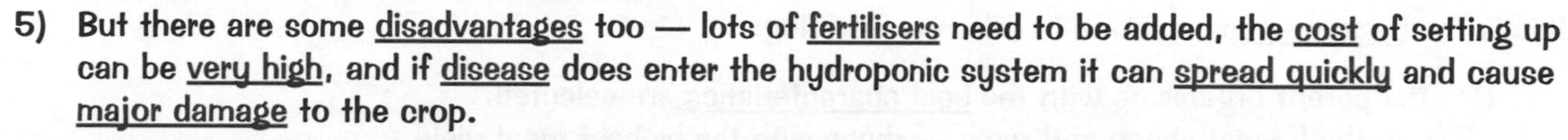

5) But there are some disadvantages too — lots of fertilisers need to be added, the cost of setting up can be very high, and if disease does enter the hydroponic system it can spread quickly and cause major damage to the crop.

Crop Plants can be Genetically Modified to Increase Yield

1) Genetic modification can be used to transfer useful genes into plants and animals. This means they'll develop the useful characteristics of the inserted gene.
2) Genetically modified (GM) crops are crop plants that have had their genes modified. They are currently being grown in various parts of the world but some people are strongly opposed to GM food (for more about this see p.90).
3) Crops can be genetically modified to increase food production in many different ways. For example:

GM animals are yet to be used as a food source. Research is ongoing but there's some opposition to it.

> Crops can be made to be:
> - Insect-resistant — This prevents the crop being damaged by insects which increases crop yield. It also means that farmers don't have to spray as many pesticides so other wildlife isn't harmed (see previous page).
> - Virus-resistant — This means that they won't be damaged by disease caused by a virus. E.g. scientists have developed plum trees that have been genetically modified to be resistant to the plum pox virus.
> - Herbicide-resistant — This means farmers can spray their crops to kill weeds without affecting the crop itself.

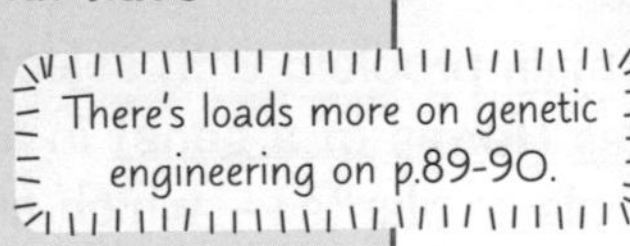

There are Other Genetic Methods for Increasing Crop Yields

One method is using information gathered from looking at the genomes (see p.66) of plants to help create new breeds of crops that produce higher yields.

> Scientists are researching genes that make crops more resistant to certain abiotic and biotic factors, e.g. genes that play a role in how efficiently crops use water or that give resistance to disease. By identifying plants with these beneficial genes, scientists can attempt to get these genes into new crop breeds using selective breeding techniques (see next page).

Coming soon, plants that'll whine if they've not got enough water...

So tomatoes that you see in the shop might never have been planted in soil. Crazy. Hydroponics is pretty complicated to carry out but can produce high yields. Altering the genetics of crops can also boost yields.

Q1 a) Describe what it means when crops are grown using hydroponics. [2 marks]
b) Give an example of where hydroponics might be a good alternative to growing crops in soil. [1 mark]

Selective Breeding

'Selective breeding' sounds like it has the potential to be a tricky topic, but it's actually dead simple. You take the best plants or animals and breed them together to get the best possible offspring. That's it.

Selective Breeding is Mating the Best Organisms to Get Good Offspring

Organisms are selectively bred to develop the best features according to what we want from them. This includes things like:

- Maximum yield of meat, milk, grain, etc. — this means that food production is as high as possible, which is very important for food security (see p.85).
- Good health and disease resistance.
- In animals, other qualities like temperament, speed, fertility, good mothering skills, etc.
- In plants, other qualities like attractive flowers, nice smell, etc.

This is the basic process involved in selective breeding:

1) The parent organisms with the best characteristics are selected, e.g. the largest sheep and rams — those with the highest meat yield.
2) They're bred with each other.
3) The best of the offspring are selected and bred.
4) This process is repeated over several generations to develop the desired traits, e.g. to produce sheep with very large meat yields.

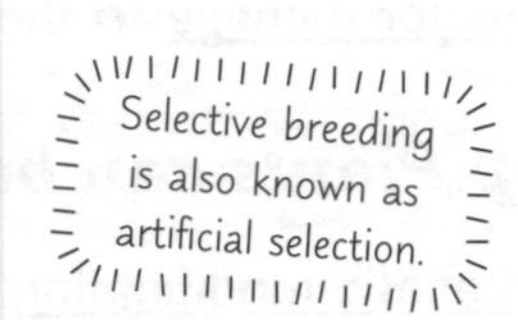

Selective breeding can also be used to combine two different desirable characteristics:

1) Tall wheat plants have a good grain yield but are easily damaged by wind and rain. Dwarf wheat plants can resist wind and rain but have a lower grain yield.
2) These two types of wheat plant were cross-bred, and the best resulting wheat plants were cross-bred again. This resulted in a new variety of wheat combining the good characteristics — dwarf wheat plants which could resist bad weather and had a high grain yield.

The Main Drawback is a Reduction in the Gene Pool

1) The main problem with selective breeding is that it reduces the gene pool — the number of different alleles (forms of a gene) in a population. This is because the farmer keeps breeding from the "best" animals or plants — which are all closely related. This is known as inbreeding.
2) Inbreeding can cause health problems because there's more chance of the organisms developing harmful genetic disorders when the gene pool is limited.
3) There can also be serious problems if a new disease appears, because there's not much variation in the population. All the stock are closely related to each other, so if one of them is going to be killed by a new disease, the others are also likely to succumb to it.

I use the same genes all the time too — they flatter my hips...

Selective breeding's not a new thing. People have been doing it for absolutely yonks. But the basic process has stayed the same — select the best individuals, let them reproduce, repeat over many generations, and voilà...

Q1 A farmer who grows green beans lives in an area that experiences a lot of drought. Explain how he could use selective breeding to improve the chances of his bean plants surviving the droughts. [3 marks]

Q2 Give two disadvantages of selectively breeding animals. [2 marks]

Genetic Engineering

You first met genetic engineering back on page 87. The next couple of pages give you loads more detail...

Vectors Can Be Used To Insert DNA Into Other Organisms

The basic idea behind genetic engineering is to move genes for desirable characteristics from one organism to another so that it has those characteristics too. The organism's genome is changed during the process. A vector is something that's used to transfer DNA into a cell. Plasmids (see p.12) are often used as vectors. They are small, circular molecules of DNA that can be transferred between bacteria.

Viruses can also be used as vectors.

Here's how the process of genetic engineering works:

1) The DNA you want to insert (the gene for the desired characteristic) is cut out with a restriction enzyme. Restriction enzymes recognise specific sequences of DNA and cut the DNA at these points.
2) The plasmid is then cut open using the same restriction enzyme.
3) This creates sticky ends on the DNA — short tails of unpaired bases that are complementary to each other (see p.15).
4) The plasmid and the DNA you're inserting are mixed together with ligase enzymes.
5) The ligases join the sticky ends of the two pieces of DNA together.
6) Plasmid vectors that contain the new DNA are inserted into other cells, e.g. bacteria, known as hosts. The host cells can now use the gene you inserted to produce the desired characteristic.
7) However, not all of the host cells will have been modified successfully, e.g. the vector might not have been transferred properly. So, the last stage is to select (identify) the individuals that have successfully received the desired gene (see below).

Desired gene
Sticky ends
Restriction enzymes cut the gene out and cut open the plasmid...
Sticky ends
Plasmid
...ligases join the two pieces of DNA together...
...and the plasmid containing the desired gene is inserted into the host cell.

Genetically engineered organisms can also be called genetically modified or transgenic organisms. Transgenic organisms always contain genes transferred from another species.

Antibiotic Resistance Markers Are Used to Select Cells with the New DNA

To find the host cells that do contain the new DNA, antibiotic resistance markers are used. Here's how they work:

1) A marker gene, which codes for antibiotic resistance, is inserted into the vector at the same time as the gene for the desired characteristic.
2) The host bacteria are grown on a special plate containing antibiotics (see p.96). Only the bacteria that contain the marker gene will be able to survive and reproduce (the antibiotics will kill the rest).

Agrobacterium Tumefaciens *is Used to Genetically Modify Plants*

Genetic engineering is used in agriculture to produce crops with desirable characteristics that increase yields (see p.87). To genetically modify plants, scientists often use a bacterium called *Agrobacterium tumefaciens*:

1) *Agrobacterium tumefaciens* invades plant cells and inserts its genes into the plant's DNA.
2) Once the *Agrobacterium tumefaciens* bacteria has been genetically modified to include a useful gene (e.g. the gene for herbicide resistance), it's allowed to infect the cells of the 'target' plant. The bacteria will insert their genes (including e.g. the herbicide-resistance gene) into the plant's DNA.

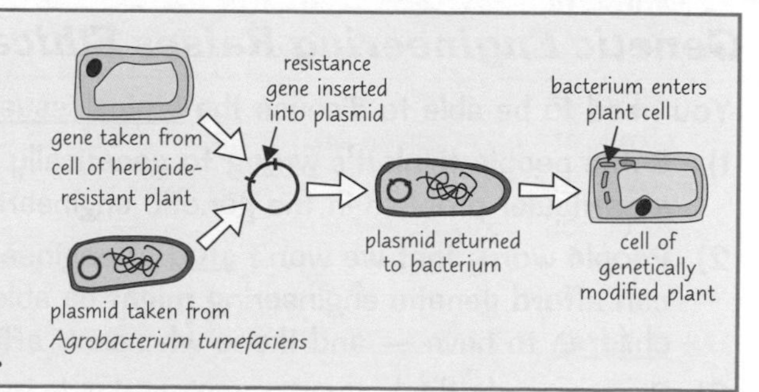

Using GM bacteria to make GM plants — genius...

Genetically engineer a bacterium, then use that to genetically engineer a plant — cunning.

Q1 What are antibiotic resistance markers used for in genetic engineering? [1 mark]

More on Genetic Engineering

Genetic engineering sounds great, and there are lots of benefits. But not everyone is happy with it being used.

Genetic Engineering Has Many Benefits...

As you saw on page 85, many people in the world today don't have enough food to eat. This mostly happens in developing countries — like those in Africa and parts of Asia. Genetic engineering could help:

1) Crops can be genetically modified to improve crop yields. For example:

See p.87 for more ways that genetic engineering can increase crop yields.

   1) Plants can be genetically modified to make them resistant to insect pests.
   2) There's a bacterium called *Bacillus thuringiensis* (Bt) which produces a toxin (poison) that kills many of the insect larvae that are harmful to crops.
   3) The gene for the Bt toxin is inserted into crops, like corn and cotton, which then produce the toxin in their stems and leaves — making them resistant to the insect pests.
   4) The toxin is specific to insect pests — it's harmless to humans, animals and other insects.
   5) A good thing about Bt crops is that farmers need to apply less pesticide (because the crops already have it built into them). This avoids the negative impacts of pesticide use (see p.86).
   6) There's a drawback to Bt crops though. There's a danger that insects might develop resistance to the toxin and no longer be killed by it.

2) Genetic engineering can also be used to combat certain deficiency diseases. For example:

   In some parts of the world, the population relies heavily on rice for food. In these areas, vitamin A deficiency can be a problem, because rice doesn't contain much of this vitamin, and other sources are scarce. Genetic engineering has allowed scientists to take a gene that controls beta-carotene production from carrot plants, and put it into rice plants. Humans can then change the beta-carotene into vitamin A. Problem solved.

...But It Also Comes With Risks

There are concerns about growing genetically modified crops...

1) Transplanted genes may get out into the environment. E.g. a herbicide resistance gene may be picked up by weeds, creating new 'superweeds'.
2) Another concern is that genetically modified crops could adversely affect food chains — or even human health.
3) Some people are against genetic engineering altogether. They worry that changing an organism's genes might create unforeseen problems — which would then get passed on to future generations. For example, the long-term effects of exposure to Bt crops (see above) aren't yet known.
4) Some people say that growing genetically modified crops will affect the number of weeds and flowers (and therefore wildlife) that usually live in and around the crops — reducing farmland biodiversity (number of species in an ecosystem).

People in developed countries, e.g. those in Europe, tend to be more concerned about the potential risks because food shortages are not as big an issue as in developing countries.

I say it's great.

Genetic Engineering Raises Ethical Issues

You need to be able to discuss the ethical issues surrounding genetic engineering too:

1) Some people think it's wrong to genetically engineer other organisms purely for human benefit. This is a particular problem in the genetic engineering of animals, especially if the animal suffers as a result.
2) People worry that we won't stop at engineering plants and animals. In the future, those who can afford genetic engineering might be able to decide the characteristics they want their children to have — and those who can't afford it may become a 'genetic underclass'.
3) Some people think genetic engineering is irresponsible when there's uncertainty about the consequences.

If only there was a gene to make revision easier...

Genetic engineering is a serious issue — its not just designer food. Make sure you can discuss both pros and cons.

Q1 Give two potential risks of growing genetically engineered crops. [2 marks]

Health and Disease

If you are feeling bright-eyed and bushy-tailed then you probably won't be for much longer — you're about to find out about lots of lovely diseases and all the nasties that can cause them. Mwah ha ha.

Organisms' Health Can be Affected by Disease

1) A healthy organism is one that is functioning just as it should be — both physically and mentally.
2) A disease is a condition that impairs the normal functioning of an organism. Both plants and animals can get diseases.
3) Most organisms will experience disease at some point.
4) There are many causes of disease. For example:
   - the organism may become infected by a pathogen (see below),
   - there may be a mutation in the organism's genes (see page 67),
   - the organism may be affected by environmental conditions, e.g. if a plant doesn't get enough light it won't grow properly (see page 66), or a human may be affected by issues such as poor diet or lack of exercise.

Diseases Can be Communicable or Non-Communicable

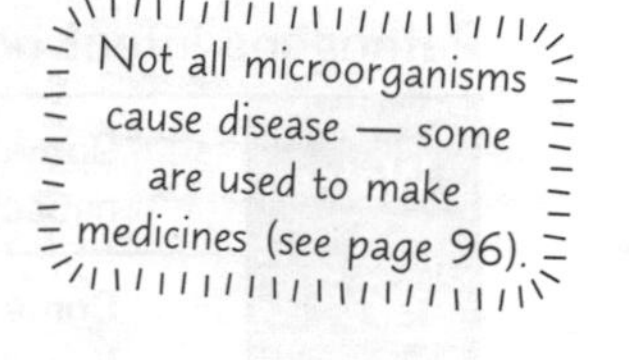

1) A pathogen is a type of microorganism (microbe) that causes disease. Types of pathogen include bacteria, viruses, protists and fungi (see next page).
2) A communicable disease is a disease that can spread between organisms. They are caused by pathogens infecting the organism, e.g. malaria is caused by a protist, and tobacco mosaic disease in plants is caused by a virus. Communicable diseases are also known as infectious diseases.
3) Non-communicable diseases cannot be passed from one organism to another, e.g. cardiovascular and respiratory diseases, cancers and diabetes. They generally last for a long time and progress slowly. They are often linked to unhealthy lifestyles (see page 102).

One Disease Can Lead to Another

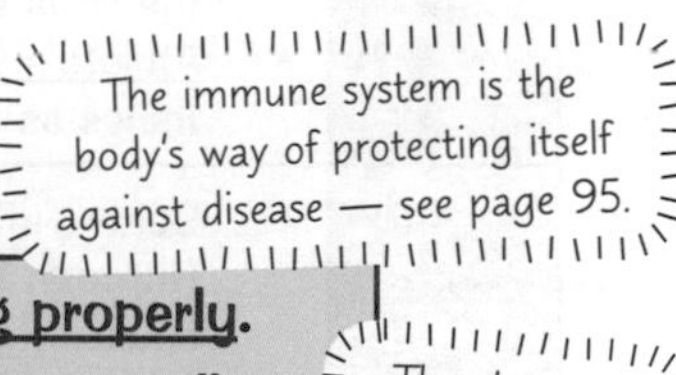

Sometimes having one disease can make it more likely that you will suffer from another disease. Here are two examples that you need to know about:

There's more about HIV on the next page.

1) HIV (human immunodeficiency virus) stops the immune system from working properly.
2) The bacteria that cause another communicable disease called tuberculosis are normally destroyed by the immune system before symptoms of the disease can develop.
3) But, if the tuberculosis bacteria infect someone with HIV, the bacteria are not destroyed by the immune system so the disease progresses very rapidly — this means people with HIV are much more likely to show symptoms of tuberculosis. It's also much more difficult for people with HIV to recover from tuberculosis.

1) HPV (human papillomavirus) is a virus that can infect the reproductive system. One way that it's transmitted is in body fluids (see next page), usually through sexual activity.
2) An infection by the virus doesn't always cause symptoms and often clears up on its own within a couple of months.
3) However, some HPV infections can cause cell changes resulting in the development of certain types of cancer. It's thought that nearly all cervical cancer cases result from HPV infections.

I have a communicable disease — it's telling me to go to bed...

Communicable diseases can be passed between people because they involve pathogens.

Q1 What is a non-communicable disease? [3 marks]

How Disease Spreads

Well, here are loads of ways you can catch diseases. As if I wasn't feeling paranoid enough already...

Communicable Diseases are Caused by Pathogens

Pathogens are microbes that cause communicable diseases (see previous page). There are four types:

1) BACTERIA — very small cells (about 1/100th the size of your body cells), which can reproduce rapidly. They make you feel ill by producing toxins (poisons) that damage your cells and tissues.
2) VIRUSES — these are not cells. They're really tiny, about 1/100th the size of a bacterium. They replicate themselves inside the infected organism's cells. These cells then burst, releasing the viruses.
3) PROTISTS — these are eukaryotic (see page 12) usually single-celled and vary in size. Protists that cause disease are often parasites (see page 61).
4) FUNGI — some fungi are single-celled while others have a body, which is made up of thread-like structures called hyphae. These hyphae can grow and penetrate human skin and the surface of plants, causing diseases. They can also produce spores, which can be spread to other plants and animals.

Once inside an organism, pathogens can rapidly multiply, e.g. *E.coli* can divide once every 20 minutes. As this happens, the infected organism will start to show symptoms of the disease.

Communicable Diseases are Transmitted in Different Ways

Pathogens infect both animals and plants and can spread in different ways. For example:

Water	• Some pathogens can be picked up by drinking or bathing in dirty water. E.g. cholera is a bacterial infection that causes diarrhoea and dehydration. It's spread via drinking water containing the diarrhoea of other sufferers.
Air	• Some pathogens are carried in the air. E.g. *Erysiphe graminis* is a fungus that causes barley powdery mildew. It makes white, fluffy patches appear on the leaves of barley plants. This affects the plant's ability to photosynthesise, which can decrease yields. It's spread by spores that are blown between plants by the wind. • Airborne pathogens can be carried in droplets produced when you cough or sneeze — so other people can breathe them in. E.g. the influenza virus that causes flu is spread this way.
Contact	• Some pathogens can be picked up by touching contaminated surfaces. E.g. tobacco mosaic disease affects many species of plants, e.g. tomatoes. It's caused by a virus called tobacco mosaic virus (TMV) that makes the leaves of plants mottled and discoloured. The discolouration means the plant can't photosynthesise as well, so the virus affects growth. It's spread when infected leaves rub against healthy leaves. • Athlete's foot is a fungus which makes skin itch and flake off. It's most commonly spread by touching the same things as an infected person, e.g. shower floors and towels.
Body fluids	• Some pathogens are spread by body fluids such as blood (e.g. by sharing needles to inject drugs), breast milk (through breast feeding) and semen (through sex). HIV is a virus spread by exchanging body fluids. It initially causes flu-like symptoms for a few weeks, but after that, the person doesn't usually experience any symptoms for several years. The virus enters the lymph nodes and attacks the immune cells. If the immune system isn't working properly, it can't cope with other infections (see previous page) or cancers. At this stage, the virus is known as late stage HIV, or AIDS.
Animal vectors	• Animals that spread disease are called vectors. E.g. malaria is caused by a protist. Part of the malarial protist's life cycle takes place inside a mosquito. Mosquitoes act as vectors — they pick up the malarial protist when they feed on an infected animal. Every time the mosquito feeds on another animal, it infects it by inserting the protist into the animal's blood vessels. Malaria causes repeating episodes of fever. It can be fatal.
Soil	• Some pathogens can live in the soil, so plants in the contaminated soil may be infected. E.g. the bacteria, *Agrobacterium tumefaciens*, that cause crown gall disease, are able to live freely in some soils and on the roots of some plants. If the bacteria enter a plant, they can cause growths or tumours called galls on roots, stems and branches. The galls can damage the plant tissue, restricting the flow of water through the plant. This causes the plant to become weaker and it may eventually die.
Food	• Some pathogens are picked up by eating contaminated food. E.g. *Salmonella* bacteria are found in some foods, e.g. raw meat. If these foods are kept too long or not cooked properly the bacteria can cause food poisoning.

You can use sampling techniques to estimate the number of organisms in a population that are infected with a disease. First you'd work out the mean number of infected individuals in some samples, then multiply this mean by the total number of individuals in the population.

Ahh...Ahh... Ahhhhh Chooooooo — urghh, this page is catching...

Pathogens are usually really small — you often need a microscope to see them — but they don't half get about...

Q1 Give three ways in which communicable diseases can be spread. [3 marks]

Reducing and Preventing the Spread of Disease

Aha, a page about what we can do to avoid catching communicable diseases. Things are definitely looking up.

Communicable Diseases Can Be Affected by Social and Economic Factors

1) The transmission of many communicable diseases increases when lots of people live crowded together in a small space because it's easier for pathogens to pass from one person to another, e.g. if people cough.
2) Poor diet can also increase the risk of infection because the immune system can be weakened by not getting the right nutrients.
3) The risk of infection increases where there is limited access to healthcare and health education too:

- Having access to healthcare means that people are more likely to be diagnosed and get the treatment they need to get better. This reduces the chance of them passing on the infection.
- Good education gives people better knowledge of how diseases are transmitted so they can avoid catching the infections in the first place, e.g. through safe-sex practices like using condoms to avoid getting HIV (see previous page).

The Spread of Disease Can Be Reduced or Prevented in Humans...

There are things that we can do to reduce, and even prevent, the spread of disease. For example:

1) Being hygienic — Using simple hygiene measures can prevent the spread of disease. For example, doing things like washing your hands thoroughly before preparing food or after you've sneezed can stop you infecting another person.
2) Destroying vectors — By getting rid of the organisms that spread disease, you can prevent the disease from being passed on. Vectors that are insects can be killed using insecticides or by destroying their habitat so that they can no longer breed.

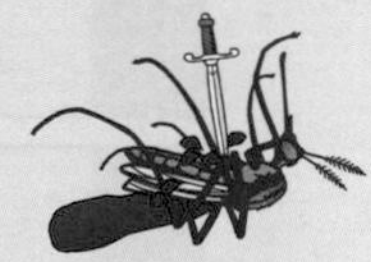

3) Isolating infected individuals — This prevents people with a communicable disease from passing it on.
4) Vaccination — Vaccinating people and animals against communicable diseases means that they can't develop the infection and then pass it on to someone else.

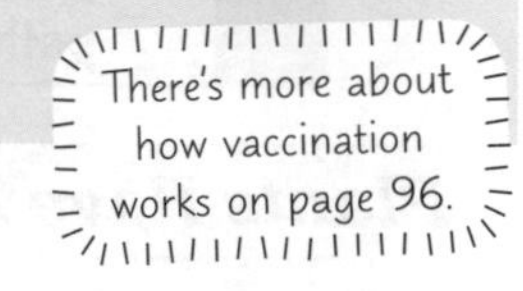

The early detection (and treatment) of a disease can be useful for limiting its spread. This can reduce the chance of the disease being passed on to others.

... And in Plants

The first step in reducing the spread of disease is identifying them — see next page.

Plants are a very important food source throughout the world. Plant diseases can reduce crop yield (see page 85) and the biodiversity of ecosystems, so preventing the spread of disease in plants is really important. Here are some ways that the spread of disease can be controlled:

1) Regulating movement of plant material — this makes sure that infected plants don't come into contact with healthy plants, e.g. plant nurseries are not allowed to sell plants which have crown gall disease.
2) Destroying infected plants — this stops them being sources of infection.
3) Crop rotation — many pathogens are specific to a particular plant. Changing the type of plants that are grown stops the pathogens becoming established in an area.
4) Chemical control — for example, fungicides can be used to kill fungal pathogens or used as a preventative method by coating the bulbs or seeds before they're planted.
5) Biological control — e.g. crown gall disease can be prevented by dipping roots of plants into a suspension of a similar bacterium before they are planted in infected soils. This bacteria doesn't infect the plants — instead, it produces an antibiotic (see p.96) that prevents *Agrobacterium tumefaciens* from reproducing.

The spread of disease — mouldy margarine...

You may be sick of diseases already (geddit?) but don't turn this page until you've got all the facts firmly fixed in your brain. You don't want to catch a disease — you might have to take a day off school. That'd be terrible.

Q1 Malaria is spread by mosquitoes which carry protists. The protists enter the bloodstream of animals when the mosquito feeds on them. Explain one way in which the spread of malaria could be reduced. [2 marks]

Detecting Plant Disease and Plant Defences

We are coming up with more and more advanced ways to detect plant diseases. And plants have some pretty nifty ways of defending themselves too. Together we are taking up the fight against those pesky pathogens.

Diseases Can be Detected in the Field and in the Lab

1) In the field, plant diseases are usually detected by observations. Scientists can recognise the symptoms of different plant diseases.

   Growths might indicate crown gall disease or mottling of leaves might mean that the plant has tobacco mosaic disease (see p.92).

   Sometimes a microscope is needed to observe smaller features, e.g. to distinguish between different types of fungi that look similar to the naked eye.

Plant diseases may also be identified by touch (e.g. a soft or squashy feeling may indicate rot) or by smell (e.g. some bacterial diseases have a particular smell).

2) Pathogens can also be identified in the lab. The ELISA test and the Polymerase Chain Reaction (PCR) are two methods that are commonly used:

ELISA test

- Antigens are unique molecules on the surface of cells. They can be detected using antibodies — proteins that bind to a specific antigen.
- Antigens from a pathogen will be present in a plant infected with that pathogen.
- In an ELISA test, antibodies for the pathogens' antigens are used. These antibodies have enzymes attached to them, which can react with a substrate causing a colour change.
- The antibodies are added to the sample being tested, and are then washed off — but, if the antibodies bind to antigens they will remain in the sample. If there's a colour change when the substrate is added, it demonstrates that the antigen (and so the pathogen) is present.

There's more on antigens and antibodies on the next page.

PCR

- You can see if the DNA of the pathogen is present in your plant sample.
- Parts of the DNA strand complementary (see page 15) to that of the pathogen are used as primers (a sort of template). Any DNA that matches is copied over and over again. If the pathogen is present, lots of its DNA will be made and this will show up on images of the DNA.

Plants Have Physical Defences Against Pathogens...

1) Most plant leaves and stems have a waxy cuticle, which acts as a waterproof barrier (see page 40). This barrier also stops pathogens entering the plant. The cuticle helps prevent water collecting on the leaf too, reducing the risk of infection by pathogens that are transferred in water.
2) Plant cells themselves are surrounded by cell walls made from cellulose. These form a physical barrier against pathogens that make it past the waxy cuticle.
3) If pathogens do make it past these defence mechanisms, it can trigger the cell to produce a substance called callose. This gets deposited between plant cell walls and cell membranes, to reinforce the cell wall.

...as Well as Chemical Ones

1) Plants produce antimicrobial chemicals which kill pathogens or inhibit their growth.

   - Mint plants and witch hazel produce antibacterial chemicals which kill bacteria.
   - Some plants produce chemicals called saponins. These are thought to destroy the cell membranes of fungi and other pathogens.

Antimicrobials are chemicals that act against microbes — e.g. antibiotics (see page 96).

2) Chemicals that plants use in self-defence are often used the basis for modern medicines — drugs are synthesised by chemists in labs, but the process often starts with a chemical extracted from a plant.
3) The genes responsible for producing some of these chemicals are also used in the genetic engineering of insect-resistant and disease-resistant crops (see page 87).

Imagine the hilarity when my Dad's sister married Mr Biotic...

Admit it — plants are cleverer than you thought. There's lots to learn here so keep going over it 'til it sticks.

Q1 Give two physical methods that plants use to defend themselves against pathogens. [2 marks]

The Human Immune System

Right, back to humans. Your body has some pretty neat features when it comes to fighting disease.

Your Body Has a Pretty Sophisticated Defence System

The human body has got features that stop a lot of nasties getting inside in the first place. These are non-specific defences — they aren't produced in response to a particular pathogen.

1) The skin acts as a barrier to pathogens. It also secretes antimicrobial substances which kill pathogens.
2) The whole respiratory tract (nasal passage, trachea and lungs) is lined with mucus and cilia (hair-like structures) and there are hairs in the nose. The mucus and hairs trap particles that could contain pathogens and the cilia waft the mucus up to the back of the throat where it can be swallowed.
3) Eyes produce (in tears) an enzyme called lysozyme which break down bacteria on the surface of the eye.
4) The stomach produces hydrochloric acid. This kills pathogens that make it that far from the mouth.
5) When you damage a blood vessel, platelets in the blood clump together to 'plug' the damaged area. This is known as blood clotting. Blood clots stop you losing too much blood and prevent microorganisms from entering the wound.

Platelets are tiny fragments of cells. They contain lots of different substances that are needed to help form the clot. They also have proteins on their surface which help them stick together and to the site of the wound.

Your Immune System Can Attack Pathogens

You can read more about what's in the blood in Topic B2 — see p.38.

1) If pathogens do make it into your body, your immune system kicks in to destroy them.
2) The most important part of your immune system is the white blood cells. They travel around in your blood and crawl into every part of you, constantly patrolling for pathogens. When they come across an invading pathogen they have three lines of attack:

1. Consuming Them

Some white blood cells (phagocytes) have a flexible membrane and contain lots of enzymes. This enables them to engulf foreign cells and digest them. This is called phagocytosis.

2. Producing Antibodies

1) Every invading pathogen has unique molecules (antigens) on its surface.
2) When your white blood cells come across a foreign antigen (i.e. one they don't recognise), they will start to produce proteins called antibodies to lock onto the invading cells. The antibodies produced are specific to that type of antigen — they won't lock on to any others.

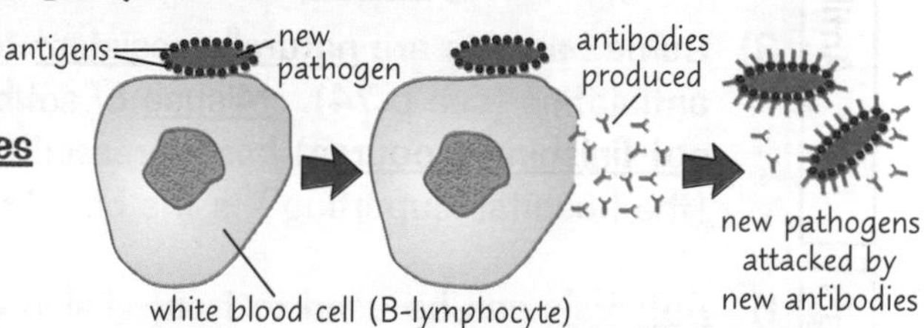

3) Antibodies are then produced rapidly and carried around the body to lock on to all similar pathogens.
4) The antibodies help the phagocytes find the pathogens, so they can engulf them.
5) Some white blood cells, called memory cells, stay around in the blood after the pathogen has been fought off. If the person is infected with the same pathogen again, the white blood cells will rapidly produce the antibodies to help destroy it — the person is naturally immune to that pathogen and won't get ill.

The white blood cells that produce antibodies are also known as B-lymphocytes.

3. Producing Antitoxins

These counteract toxins produced by the invading bacteria.

Fight disease — give your nose a blow with boxing gloves...

The body makes antibodies against the antigens on pathogens. There, don't say I never help you. Right, tea...

Q1 Describe the role of platelets in the defence of the body against pathogens. [2 marks]

Vaccines and Medicines

An ounce of prevention is worth a pound of cure. That's what my mum says, anyhow.

Vaccinations Stop You Getting Infections

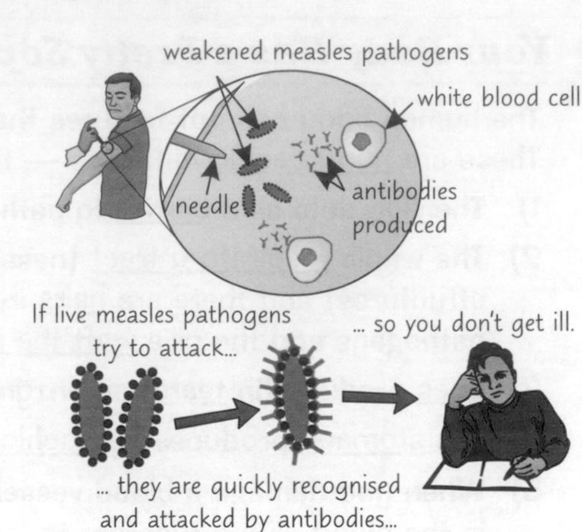

1) When you're infected with a new pathogen it can take your white blood cells a while to produce the antibodies to deal with it. In that time you can get very ill, or maybe even die.
2) To avoid this you can be vaccinated (immunised) against some diseases, e.g. polio or measles.
3) Vaccination involves injecting dead, inactive or weakened pathogens into the body. These carry antigens, so even though they're harmless they still trigger an immune response — your white blood cells produce antibodies to attack them.
4) Some of these white blood cells will remain in the blood as memory cells (see previous page) so if live pathogens of the same type ever appear, the antibodies to help destroy them will be produced immediately.

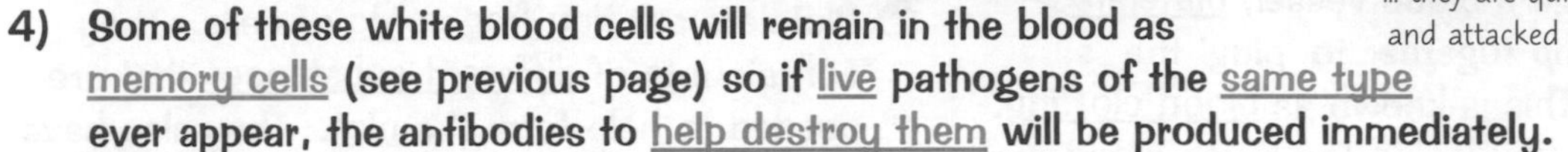

5) Big outbreaks of disease — called epidemics — can be prevented if a large percentage of the population is vaccinated. That way, even the people who aren't vaccinated are unlikely to catch the disease because there are fewer people able to pass it on. But if a significant number of people aren't vaccinated, the disease can spread quickly through them and lots of people will be ill at the same time.

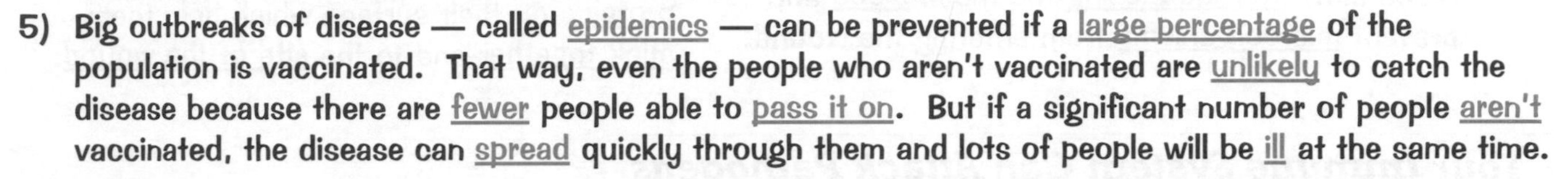

Medicines are Used to Treat Disease

1) Drugs are substances which alter the way the body works. Some drugs are medically useful, such as antibiotics (e.g. penicillin). But many drugs are dangerous if misused.
2) This is why you can buy some drugs over the counter at a pharmacy, but others are restricted so you can only get them on prescription — your doctor decides if you should have them.
3) You need to know about antibiotics, antivirals and antiseptics...

Antibiotics

1) Antibiotics are chemicals that kill bacteria without killing your own body cells. Many are produced naturally by fungi and other microbes, e.g. penicillin is made by a type of mould. Pharmaceutical companies can grow them on a large scale in a lab and extract the antibiotics.
2) They're very useful for clearing up bacterial infections that your body is having trouble with, however they don't kill viruses.
3) Some bacteria are naturally resistant to (not killed by) certain antibiotics (see p.74). Misuse of antibiotics (e.g. doctors overprescribing them or patients not finishing a course) has increased the rate of development of resistant strains. MRSA (the hospital 'superbug') is the best-known example of an antibiotic-resistant strain.

Remember, not all microbes are harmful. Many are helpful.

Antivirals

1) Antivirals can be used to treat viral infections. They are difficult to produce because viruses use the host cells to replicate — its hard to target the virus without damaging the cell.
2) Most antivirals don't kill the viruses but stop them from reproducing.

Antiseptics

1) Antiseptics are chemicals that destroy microorganisms or stop them growing.
2) Antiseptics are used outside the body to help to clean wounds and surfaces. They're used to prevent infection rather than treat it.
3) Plenty of household products contain antiseptics, e.g. bathroom cleaners.
4) Antiseptics are used in hospitals and surgeries to try to prevent the spread of infections like MRSA.

GCSEs are like antibiotics — you have to finish the course...

Kapow, down with you nasty pathogens — we will kill you all. Ahem, sorry. You best learn this lot.

Q1 Explain how vaccines containing dead pathogens can prevent people getting infections. [4 marks]

Investigating Antimicrobials

PRACTICAL

Time to get hands on — you can grow your own microbes to see how effective different antimicrobials are.

You Can do a Practical to Investigate Antimicrobials

You can test the action of antibiotics (or other antimicrobials, e.g. antiseptics) by growing cultures of microorganisms:

1) Pour hot, sterilised agar jelly into a sterile Petri dish (a shallow round plastic dish).
2) When the jelly's cooled and set, inoculating loops (wire loops) can be used to transfer microorganisms to the culture medium. Alternatively, a sterile dropping pipette and spreader can be used to get an even covering of bacteria.
3) Then take three discs of filter paper — soak one disc in an antibiotic (disc A) and another in a different antibiotic (disc B). The third disc (disc C) is a control disc (see below) — it should be soaked in sterile water.
4) Place the discs on the jelly using sterile forceps and tape the lid onto the dish (to prevent contamination by other microbes). The antibiotic will diffuse (soak) into the agar jelly.
   Leave some space between the discs and don't forget to label them on the bottom of the dish so you know which one is which.
5) Leave the dish for 48 hours at 25 °C. The bacteria will multiply and grow into a 'lawn' covering the jelly.
6) Anywhere the bacteria can't grow is called a 'clear zone'. The more effective the antibiotic is against the bacteria, the larger the clear zone around the paper disc will be — see next page.
7) Using a control disc means that you can be sure that any difference between the growth of the bacteria around the control disc and around the antibiotic discs is due to the effect of the antibiotic alone (and not something weird in the paper, for example).
8) You can carry out the same experiment as above using other antimicrobials.

The jelly is a culture medium — it contains the carbohydrates, minerals, proteins and vitamins that microorganisms need to grow.

No clear zone around an antibiotic disc could mean that the bacteria are resistant to it — see page 74.

You need to control all other variables, such as temperature (e.g. don't leave one side of the dish near a radiator), disc size, etc.

In the lab at school, cultures of microorganisms are kept at about 25 °C because harmful pathogens aren't likely to grow at this temperature. In industrial conditions, cultures are incubated at higher temperatures so that they can grow a lot faster. (Not too high though, or the enzymes in the microorganisms could be denatured — see p.18.)

Aseptic Techniques Make Sure the Culture Doesn't Get Contaminated

Contamination by unwanted microorganisms will affect your results and can potentially result in the growth of pathogens. To avoid this:

1) Regularly disinfect work surfaces. (Alcohol works best but can be dangerous because it's flammable.)
2) Sterilise all glassware and other equipment, such as forceps, before and after use, e.g. in an autoclave (a machine which steams equipment at high pressure). The prepared agar jelly should also be put through the autoclave.
3) If an inoculating loop is used to transfer the bacteria to the culture medium, it should be sterilised first by passing it through a hot flame.
4) Work near a Bunsen flame. Hot air rises, so microbes in the air should be drawn away from the culture.
5) Briefly flame the neck of the glass container of bacteria just after it's opened and just before it's closed — this causes air to move out of the container, preventing unwanted microbes from falling in.

Agar — my favourite jelly flavour after raspberry...

You really don't want to grow microbes that make you ill — that's partly why it's so important to work aseptically.

Q1 Why is it important to work near a Bunsen flame when preparing cultures of microorganisms? [2 marks]

PRACTICAL Comparing Antimicrobials

Once you've done all that boring practical stuff, like growing bacterial colonies and using fire, you get to do the really fun stuff — a lovely bit of maths. Woo. Here's how you can compare your clear zones...

Calculate the Sizes of the Clear Zones to Compare Results

You can compare the effectiveness of different antibiotics (or antiseptics) on bacteria by looking at the relative sizes of the clear zones. Remember, the larger the clear zone around a disc, the more effective the antibiotic is against the bacteria.

You can do this by eye if there are large differences in size. But to get more accurate results it's a good idea to calculate the area of the clear zones using their diameter (the distance across).

Don't open the Petri dish to measure the clear zones — they should be visible through the bottom of the dish.

When you calculate the area of the clear zone you should include the area of the disc.

To calculate the area of a clear zone, you need to use this equation:

This is the equation for the area of a circle. You're likely to use the units cm^2 or mm^2.

$$\text{Area} = \pi r^2$$

r is the radius of the clear zone — it's equal to half the diameter.

π is just a number. You should have a button for it on your calculator. If not, just use the value 3.14.

EXAMPLE: The diagram below shows the clear zones produced by antibiotics A and B. Use the areas of the clear zones to compare the effectiveness of the antibiotics.

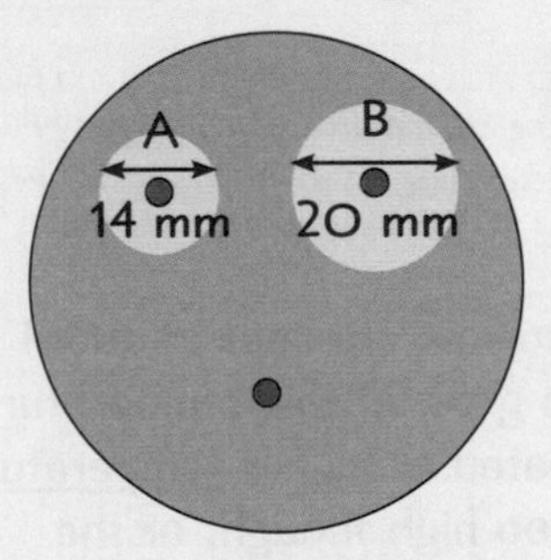

1) Divide the diameter of zone A by two to find the radius. — Radius of A = 14 ÷ 2 = 7 mm
2) Stick the radius value into the equation area = πr^2. — Area of A = $\pi \times 7^2 = 154\ mm^2$
3) Repeat steps 1 and 2 for zone B. — Radius of B = 20 ÷ 2 = 10 mm. Area of B = $\pi \times 10^2 = 314\ mm^2$
4) Compare the sizes of the areas. $314\ mm^2$ is just over twice $154\ mm^2$, so you could say that: **The clear zone of antibiotic B is roughly twice the size of the clear zone of antibiotic A, so antibiotic B is more effective than antibiotic A.**

My brother's football socks create a clear zone...

Bacteria might be the perfect pets. You don't have to walk them, they won't get lonely and they hardly cost anything to feed. But whatever you do, do not feed them after midnight. Oh, and it's probably a good idea if you learn how to calculate the area of a clear zone for your exams. Just a thought.

Q1 A researcher was investigating the effect of three different antiseptics on the growth of bacteria. The diagram on the right shows the results.

a) Which antiseptic was most effective against the bacteria? [1 mark]

b) Calculate the size of the clear zone for Antiseptic C. Give your answer in mm^2. [2 marks]

c) Describe a control that could have been used for this investigation. [1 mark]

d) Explain why a control should be used. [1 mark]

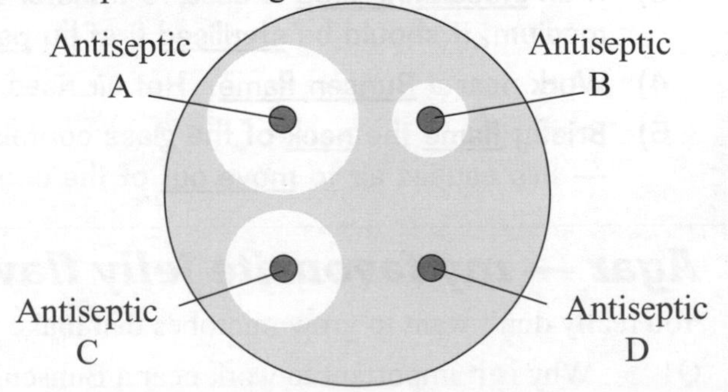

Developing New Medicines

You can't just get a random drug and give it to a poor unsuspecting person. That's unethical and thankfully there are laws against it. No, you've got to go through a rigorous testing process that starts with a computer...

New Drugs are Tested First in Pre-Clinical Trials in a Laboratory

New drugs developed to treat any kind of disease need to be thoroughly tested before they can be used to make sure they're safe and that they work. New drugs first go through pre-clinical trials, which usually involve computer simulations, testing on human cells and tissues, and finally testing on animals:

Computer models are often used first of all — these simulate a human's response to a drug, so you don't need to test on live animals at this stage. They can identify promising drugs to be tested in the next stage, but it's not as accurate as actually seeing the effect on a live organism.

→ The drugs are then developed further by testing on human tissues. However, you can't use human tissue to test drugs that affect whole/multiple body systems, e.g. testing a drug for blood pressure must be done on a whole animal, i.e. one that has an intact circulatory system.

→ The last step is to develop and test the drug using animals. The law in Britain states that any new drug must be tested on two different live mammals. Some people think it's cruel to test on animals, but others believe this is the safest way to make sure a drug isn't dangerous before it's given to humans.

Drugs are Then Tested on Humans in Clinical Trials

After the drug has been tested on animals, it's tested on humans — this is known as a clinical trial.

1) First, the drug is tested for safety on healthy volunteers. This is to make sure it doesn't have any harmful side effects when the body is working normally. Sick people are likely to be more vulnerable to any damage the drug could do, which is why the drug isn't tested on them yet.
2) If the results of the tests on healthy volunteers are good, the drugs can be tested on people suffering from the illness. These are tests for both safety and effectiveness.
3) Human drug trials usually last a very long time, but it's important that they do. In some cases it takes a while for a drug to have the effect it was designed for, e.g. treating cancer. It's also important to find out if a drug has any side effects which may only appear after a long time.
4) There are usually two groups of patients in clinical trials. One is given the new drug, the other is given a placebo (a substance that looks like the real drug but doesn't do anything). This is done so scientists can see the actual difference the drug makes — it allows for the placebo effect (when the patient expects the treatment to work and so feels better, even though the treatment isn't doing anything).
5) In some trials where patients are seriously ill placebos aren't used because it's unethical not to allow all patients to get the potential benefits of the new drug.
6) Scientists sometimes test new drugs against the best existing treatment rather than a placebo. This tells them how well the new drug compares to what we already have.

Clinical trials are blind — the patient in the study doesn't know whether they're getting the drug or the placebo. In fact, they're often double blind — neither the patient nor the scientist knows until all the results have been gathered. This is so the doctors monitoring the patients and analysing the results aren't subconsciously influenced by their knowledge.

Double Blindman's Buff — now that's got to be fun...

A trial in London in March 2006 left six men seriously ill after a new anti-inflammatory drug caused 'completely unanticipated' effects. But then, if nobody ever took part in trials, there would never be any new drugs.

Q1 a) What is a placebo? [1 mark]

b) Explain why placebos are used in clinical trials. [2 marks]

Monoclonal Antibodies

Right, onto something new now — monoclonal antibodies. Antibodies (see page 95) aren't only used by our immune systems — scientists have engineered them for lots of new uses. Intrigued — read on...

Monoclonal Antibodies are Identical Antibodies

1) Antibodies are produced by B-lymphocytes — a type of white blood cell (see page 95).
2) Monoclonal antibodies are produced from lots of clones of a single white blood cell. This means all the antibodies are identical and will only target one specific protein antigen.
3) However, you can't just grab the lymphocyte that made the antibody and grow more — lymphocytes don't divide very easily.
4) Tumour cells, on the other hand, don't produce antibodies but divide lots — so they can be grown really easily.
5) It's possible to fuse a mouse B-lymphocyte with a tumour cell to create a cell called a hybridoma.
6) Hybridoma cells can be cloned to get lots of identical cells. These can all divide really quickly to produce the same antibodies (monoclonal antibodies). These can be collected and purified.
7) You can make monoclonal antibodies that bind to anything you want, e.g. an antigen that's only found on the surface of one type of cell. Monoclonal antibodies are really useful because they will only bind to (target) this molecule — this means you can use them to target a specific cell or chemical in the body.

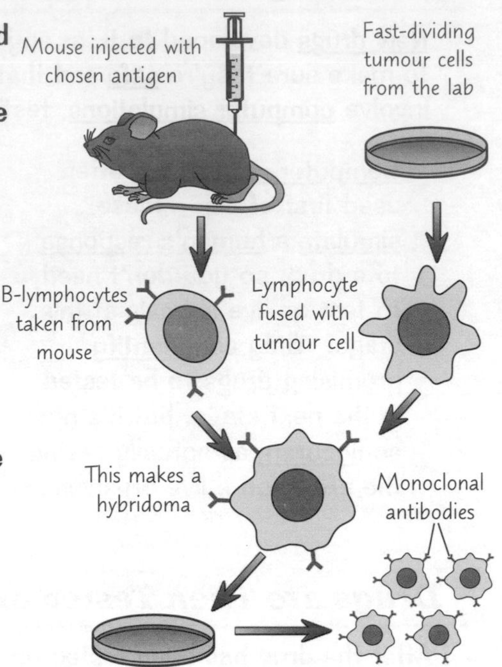

Monoclonal Antibodies Are Used In Pregnancy Tests

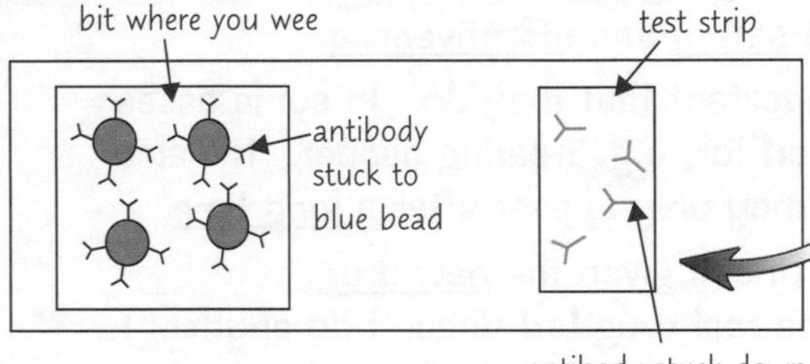

If you're pregnant:

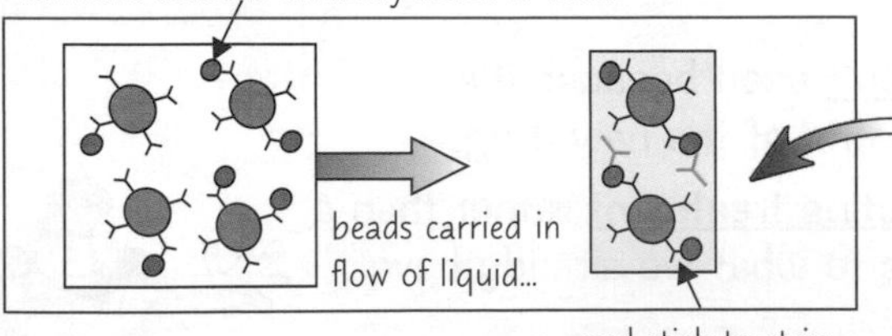

If you're not pregnant:

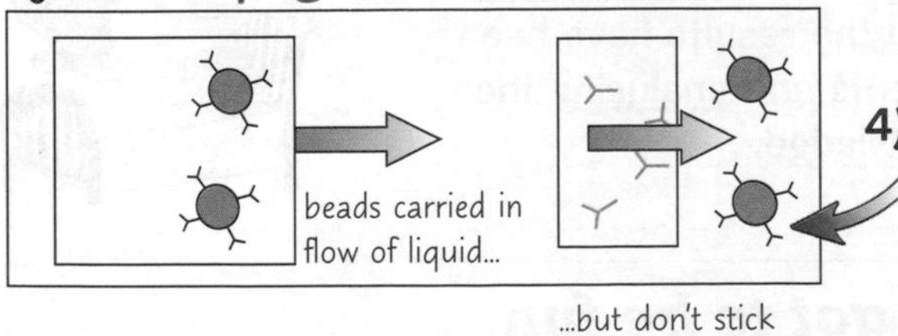

A hormone is found in the urine of women only when they are pregnant. Pregnancy testing sticks detect this hormone. Here's how they work:

1) The bit of the stick you wee on has some antibodies to the hormone, with blue beads attached.
2) The test strip (the bit of the stick that turns blue if you're pregnant) has some more antibodies to the hormone stuck onto it (so that they can't move).
3) If you're pregnant and you wee on the stick:
   - The hormone binds to the antibodies on the blue beads.
   - The urine moves up the stick, carrying the hormone and the beads.
   - The beads and hormone bind to the antibodies on the strip.
   - So the blue beads get stuck on the strip, turning it blue.
4) If you're not pregnant and you wee on the stick, the urine still moves up the stick, carrying the blue beads. But there's nothing to stick the blue beads onto the test strip, so it doesn't go blue.

The one time when you can write "wee on a stick" in an exam...

There's more on monoclonal antibodies coming up next, but don't move on until you understand this page.

Q1 Describe how monoclonal antibodies are produced. [3 marks]

More on Monoclonal Antibodies

Because monoclonal antibodies can be produced to target a specific chemical or cell, they have loads of uses. For example, they can be used to detect and to treat some forms of cancer.

You Can Make Monoclonal Antibodies That Stick to Cancer Cells

1) Different cells in the body have different antigens on their cell surface. So you can make monoclonal antibodies that will bind to specific cells in the body (e.g. just liver cells).
2) Cancer cells have antigens on their cell membranes that aren't found on normal body cells. They're called tumour markers.
3) However, as cancer cells are produced by the body their antigens aren't recognised as 'foreign' by the body's immune system. This means that they're not attacked by the white blood cells in the immune response (see page 95).
4) In the lab, you can make monoclonal antibodies that will bind to these tumour markers. They can be used to help diagnose and treat cancer.

Monoclonal Antibodies Can Be Used To Diagnose Cancer...

Prostate cancer is one type of cancer that can be detected using monoclonal antibodies. Here's how its done:

1) First, the antibodies are labelled with a radioactive element.
2) Then, the labelled antibodies are given to a patient through a drip. They go into the blood and are carried around the body.
3) When the antibodies come into contact with the cancer cells they bind to the tumour markers.
4) A picture of the patient's body is taken using a special camera that detects radioactivity. Anywhere there are cancer cells will show up as a bright spot.
5) Doctors can see exactly where the cancer is, what size it is, and find out if it is spreading beyond the prostate gland.

...and to Target Drugs to Cancer Cells

1) An anti-cancer drug is attached to monoclonal antibodies. This might be a radioactive substance or a toxic drug which stops cancer cells growing and dividing.
2) The antibodies are given to the patient through a drip.
3) The antibodies target specific cells (the cancer cells) because they only bind to the tumour markers.
4) The drug kills the cancer cells but doesn't kill any normal body cells near the tumour.
5) Other cancer treatments, such as radiotherapy and chemotherapy, can affect normal body cells as well as killing cancer cells.
6) So the side effects of an antibody-based drug are lower than for radiotherapy or chemotherapy.

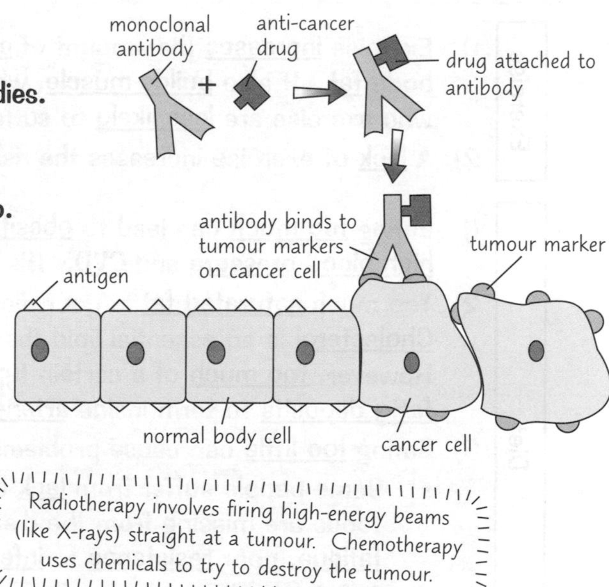

Radiotherapy involves firing high-energy beams (like X-rays) straight at a tumour. Chemotherapy uses chemicals to try to destroy the tumour.

Bonoclonal antibodies — used to detect Irish rock bands...

Monoclonal antibodies are really useful for finding stuff. Imagine having a horde of trained fireflies to search for your lost keys, or phone, or remote control. Instead of you having to search under everything, you just release the fireflies and wait for them to cluster around your lost stuff, in a big obvious glowing mass. Genius.

Q1 What is a tumour marker? [1 mark]

Q2 Describe how prostate cancer can be detected using monoclonal antibodies. [4 marks]

Non-Communicable Diseases

You may remember non-communicable diseases from page 91. Well, here's a bit more about them...

Lots of Factors Interact to Cause Non-Communicable Diseases

1) All diseases have risk factors — things that increase a person's chance of getting that disease. Risk factors are often aspects of a person's lifestyle (e.g. how much exercise they do). They can also be the presence of certain substances in the environment (e.g. air pollution can contribute to the symptoms of asthma) or a genetic predisposition for a disease (e.g. inheriting particular mutated alleles increases your risk of developing coronary heart disease).
2) Many non-communicable diseases (e.g. many types of cancer, cardiovascular disease (CVD) (diseases of the heart or blood vessels, see p.36-37), some lung diseases, liver diseases, and some nutrition-related diseases, e.g. type 2 diabetes, see p.53) are caused by several different risk factors interacting with each other rather than one factor alone. For example:

Normally, when cells have divided enough times to make enough new cells, they stop. But if there's a mutation in a gene that controls cell division, the cells can grow out of control. The cells keep on dividing by mitosis to make more and more cells, which form a tumour. Cancer is a tumour that invades surrounding tissue.

Sometimes you can inherit faulty genes that make you more susceptible to cancer. The genes alone don't mean you will get cancer but the chance is increased if you have other risk factors too, such as poor diet, high alcohol consumption and smoking (see below and next page).

Loads of things are known to be risk factors for cancer, e.g. HPV (see p.91), UV exposure, radiation, etc.

3) Risk factors are identified by scientists looking for correlations in data, but correlation doesn't always equal cause (see p.10). Sometimes a risk factor is linked to another factor, and it's this other factor that actually causes the disease. For example, a lack of exercise and a high fat diet are heavily linked to an increased chance of CVD, but they can't cause it directly. It's the resulting high blood pressure and high 'bad' cholesterol levels (see below) that can actually cause it.
4) There are some examples where scientists have found evidence to support a risk factor being a cause of a disease though, e.g. the fact that smoking can cause lung disease and lung cancer (see next page).

Lifestyle Factors Can Increase the Risk of Non-Communicable Diseases

Exercise

1) Exercise increases the amount of energy used by the body and decreases the amount of stored body fat. It also builds muscle, which helps to boost your metabolic rate (see p.46). So people who exercise are less likely to suffer from health problems such as obesity (see below) and CVD.
2) A lack of exercise increases the risk of CVD because it increases blood pressure.

Diet

1) Eating too much can lead to obesity. Obesity is linked to type 2 diabetes, high blood pressure and CVD. It's also a risk factor for some cancers.
2) Too much saturated fat in your diet can increase your blood cholesterol level. Cholesterol is an essential lipid that your body produces and needs to function properly. However, too much of a certain type of cholesterol (known as 'bad' or LDL cholesterol) can cause fatty deposits to form inside arteries, which can lead to coronary heart disease (see p.104).
3) Eating too little can cause problems too:
   - Some people suffer from lack of food. The effects of malnutrition vary depending on what foods are missing from the diet. But problems commonly include slow growth (in children), fatigue, poor resistance to infection, and irregular periods in women.
   - Deficiency diseases are caused by a lack of vitamins or minerals. E.g. a lack of vitamin C can cause scurvy, a deficiency disease that causes problems with the skin, joints and gums.

Obesity is defined as being >20% over the maximum recommended body mass.

People whose diet is badly out of balance are said to be malnourished.

Best put down that cake and go for a run...

You might be asked to interpret data about risk factors. Remember, correlation doesn't necessarily mean cause.

Q1 Explain how exercising can reduce the risk of obesity. [2 marks]

More on Non-Communicable Diseases

Unfortunately, you're not finished with risk factors for non-communicable diseases yet. Here are some more...

Alcohol and Smoking Can Also Lead to Non-Communicable Diseases

Alcohol

1) Alcohol is poisonous. It's broken down by enzymes in the liver and some of the products are toxic. If you drink too much alcohol over a long period of time these toxic products can cause the death of liver cells, forming scar tissue that stops blood reaching the liver — this is called cirrhosis.
2) Drinking too much alcohol increases blood pressure which can lead to CVD.
3) Many cancers including those of the mouth, throat, bowels and liver have all been linked to alcohol consumption because the toxic products damage DNA and cause cells to divide faster than normal.

Smoking

Burning cigarettes produce nicotine, which is what makes smoking addictive. They also produce carbon monoxide, tar, and particulates — which can all cause illness and other problems. E.g:

1) CVD — carbon monoxide reduces the oxygen carrying capacity of the blood. If the cardiac muscle doesn't receive enough oxygen it can lead to a heart attack (see next page). Nicotine increases heart rate. The heart contracts more often increasing blood pressure, which also increases the risk of CVD.
2) Lung, throat, mouth and oesophageal cancer — tar from cigarette smoke is full of toxic chemicals, some of which are carcinogens (cause cancer). Carcinogens make mutations in the DNA more likely, which can lead to uncontrolled cell division (see previous page).
3) Lung diseases, such as chronic bronchitis — cigarette smoke can cause inflammation of the lining of the bronchi and bronchioles (tubes in the lungs), which can result in permanent damage. Symptoms of chronic bronchitis include a persistent cough and breathing problems.
4) Smoking when pregnant can cause lots of health problems for the unborn baby.

Lifestyle Factors Cause Different Trends

Global

Non-communicable diseases are more common in developed countries, where people generally have a higher income, than in developing countries. However, these diseases are now becoming much more common in developing countries too. Different lifestyle factors contribute to these trends, but a lot of it is to do with income. For example:

- Lack of exercise and higher alcohol consumption are associated with higher income.
- Smoking varies massively between countries, but smoking-related deaths are more common in poorer countries.
- In both developed and developing countries, obesity is associated with higher incomes as people are able to afford lots of high-fat food. However, obesity is now associated with lower incomes too, as people are eating cheaper, less healthy foods.

National

Non-communicable diseases are the biggest cause of death in the UK.
However, there are differences across the country. For example:

- People from deprived areas are much more likely to smoke, have a poor diet, and not take part in physical activity than those who are better off financially. This means that the incidence of heart disease, obesity, type 2 diabetes, and cancers is higher in those areas. People from deprived areas are also more likely to suffer from alcohol-related disorders.

Local

Individual lifestyle choices affect the incidence of non-communicable diseases at the local level — if you choose to smoke, drink, not take part in exercise or have a poor diet, then the risk increases.

Too many exams are a risk factor for stress...

Trends in non-communicable diseases are often to do with income, because it can have a big effect on lifestyle.

Q1 Give two non-communicable diseases that excessive alcohol consumption is a risk factor for. [2 marks]

Treating Cardiovascular Disease

Cardiovascular disease is a big, big problem in the UK. The good news is there are lots of ways to treat it.

Cardiovascular Disease Affects The Heart and Blood Vessels

See p.36-37 for more on the heart and blood vessels.

Cardiovascular disease (CVD) are diseases to do with your heart and blood vessels. E.g.

1) High blood pressure and lots of LDL cholesterol can lead to the build up of fatty deposits inside arteries, narrowing them. Over time the fatty deposits harden, forming atheromas. CORONARY HEART DISEASE is when the coronary arteries have lots of atheromas in them, which restricts blood flow to the heart.
2) Sometimes bits of atheromas can break off or damage the blood vessel, causing a blood clot. Complete blockage of an artery by atheromas or blood clots can lead to a HEART ATTACK, where part of the cardiac muscle is deprived of oxygen. If the blockage occurs in the brain, it can cause a STROKE.

There are Different Ways of Treating CVD

See pages 102-103 for more about risk factors for CVD.

Healthy Lifestyle

1) Making changes to your lifestyle can reduce the risk of CVD, even if you've already had problems, e.g. a heart attack. People at risk of CVD are encouraged to eat a healthy diet that is low in saturated fat, exercise regularly and stop smoking.
2) Lifestyle changes can also help other forms of treatment (see below) be more effective.

Drugs

Sometimes drugs are needed to help control the effects of CVD. For example:

1) Statins can reduce the amount of cholesterol present in the bloodstream. This slows down the rate of fatty deposits forming, reducing the risk of CVD. However, statins can sometimes cause negative side effects, e.g. aching muscles. Some of these side effects can be serious, e.g. kidney failure, liver damage and memory problems.
2) Anticoagulants are drugs which make blood clots less likely to form. However, this can cause excessive bleeding if the person is hurt in an accident.
3) Antihypertensives reduce blood pressure. This reduces the risk of atheromas and blood clots forming. Their side effects can include headaches or fainting.

Some antihypertensives reduce blood pressure by widening the blood vessels, some decrease the strength of the heartbeat and some reduce the blood volume.

Surgical Procedures

If the heart or blood vessels are too badly damaged then surgery may be needed.

1) Stents are tubes that are inserted inside arteries. They keep them open, making sure blood can pass through to the cardiac muscle. Stents are a way of lowering the risk of a heart attack in people with coronary heart disease. But over time, the artery can narrow again as stents can irritate the artery and make scar tissue grow. The patient also has to take drugs to stop blood clotting on the stent.
2) If part of a blood vessel is blocked, a piece of healthy vessel taken from elsewhere can be used to bypass the blocked section. This is known as coronary bypass surgery.
3) The whole heart can be replaced with a donor heart. However, the new heart does not always start pumping properly. The new heart can also be rejected because the body's immune system recognises it as 'foreign'. Drugs have to be taken to prevent this from happening, and these can have side effects, e.g. making you more vulnerable to infections.

normal artery

deposits of fat build up

space in centre of artery shrinks, so it's harder for blood to pass through

stent pushes artery wall out, squashing fatty deposit

more space in the centre of the artery

Heart surgery is a major procedure and, as with all surgeries, there is risk of bleeding, clots and infection.

Look after yerselves me hearties...

...and make sure you're aware of the drawbacks as well as the advantages for the above ways of treating CVD.

Q1 Anticoagulants make blood clots less likely. Give a disadvantage of their use in treating CVD. [1 mark]

Stem Cells in Medicine

Stem cells could be the next big thing in medicine — imagine being able to grow a new body part from your own supply of cells. Maybe I could even grow a new brain to help me with all this revision...

Stem Cells May Be Able to Cure Many Diseases

You may remember from page 29 that stem cells are found in both embryos and adults. They have the potential to be really useful in treating some medical conditions because of their ability to differentiate into different cell types.

1) Medicine already uses adult stem cells to cure some diseases:

Leukaemia is a cancer of the blood or bone marrow. It's been successfully treated using stem cell technology. Bone marrow transplants can be used to replace the faulty bone marrow in patients suffering from leukaemia. Bone marrow contains stem cells that can become specialised to form any type of blood cell. The stem cells in the transplanted bone marrow produce healthy blood cells.

2) Scientists can also extract stem cells from very early human embryos and grow them.

Embryos are created in a laboratory using *in vitro* fertilisation (IVF) — egg cells are fertilised by sperm outside the womb (see p.48). Once the embryos are approximately 4 to 5 days old, stem cells are removed from them and the rest of the embryo is destroyed.

3) These embryonic stem cells could be used to replace faulty cells in sick people — you could make beating heart muscle cells for people with heart disease, insulin-producing cells for people with diabetes, nerve cells for people paralysed by spinal injuries, and so on.

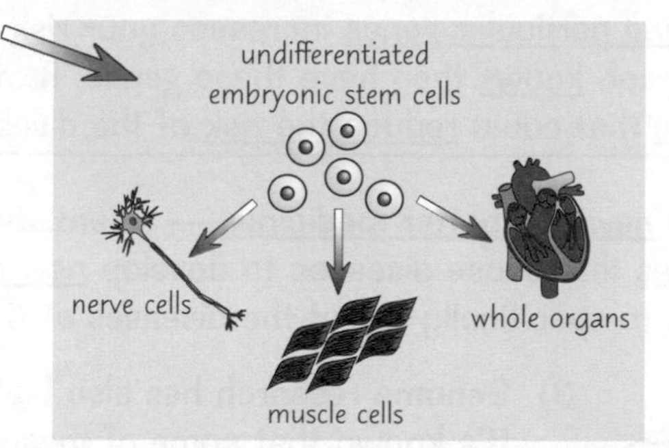

4) To get cultures of one specific type of cell, researchers try to control the differentiation of the stem cells by changing the environment they're growing in. So far, it's still a bit hit and miss — lots more research is needed.

5) There are concerns that transplanting tissues and organs grown from embryonic stem cells or from donor stem cells may lead to rejection because the patient's immune system recognises the cells as foreign and attacks them (see page 95). However, if a patient needs a stem cell transplant and their own adult stem cells can be used (from elsewhere in their body) it's thought that there'll be less risk of rejection.

Some People Are Against Stem Cell Research

1) Some people are against stem cell research because they feel that human embryos shouldn't be used for experiments since each one is a potential human life. Others think that curing patients who already exist and who are suffering is more important than the rights of embryos.
2) Sometimes unwanted embryos from fertility clinics are used for research. One fairly convincing argument in favour of stem cell research is that if these embryos weren't used by scientists they would probably just be destroyed. Campaigners for the rights of embryos generally want this banned too.
3) As the use of stem cells is controversial, governments often make laws about how they can be used for research and medicine. Around the world, there are now 'stocks' of stem cells that scientists can use for their research. Some countries (e.g. the USA) won't fund research to make new stem cell stocks, but in the UK it's allowed as long as it follows strict guidelines.

But florists cell stems, and nobody complains about that...

The potential of stem cells is huge — but it's early days yet. There's still lots of work to be done getting stem cells to behave as we want them. And you've got lots of work to be doing too — this page isn't going to learn itself.

Q1 a) Tissues can be grown from donor stem cells or embryonic stem cells and transplanted into a patient. Explain why these tissues can be rejected by the patient. [1 mark]

b) How could the risk of rejection be reduced? [1 mark]

Q2 Give one reason why some people are against stem cell research. [1 mark]

Using Genome Research in Medicine

Wow. Science is amazing — this page is all about how scientists might be able to use genes to predict diseases and provide us with new and better drugs. How cool is that. Alright, maybe I should get out more...

The Human Genome Project Identified All Our Genes

1) Human DNA is made up of about 25 000 genes.
2) The Human Genome Project (HGP) was a 13 year long project that identified all of the genes found in human DNA (the human genome).
3) Understanding the human genome is an important tool for science and medicine — we can use the information to identify genes that are involved in disease.

Genome Research Can Help Us To Predict and Treat Disease...

1) Predict and prevent diseases — many common diseases like cancers and heart disease are caused by the interaction of different genes as well as lifestyle factors (see pages 102-103). If doctors knew what genes predisposed people to what diseases, we could all get individually tailored advice on the best diet and lifestyle to avoid our likely problems.

   Inheriting particular genes increases your risk of developing certain cancers. If a person knows they have these genes, it might help them to make choices that could reduce the risk of the disease developing (see page 102).

   Doctors could also check us regularly to ensure early treatment if we do develop the diseases we're susceptible to.

2) Develop new and better medicines — scientists can use information about the genes that cause diseases to develop new medicines. The new medicines are able to specifically target the diseases at the molecular level.

3) Genome research has also highlighted common genetic variations between people. It's known that some of these variations make some drugs less effective, e.g. some asthma drugs are less effective for people with a particular mutation. Scientists can use this knowledge to design new drugs that are tailored to people with these variations.

... But There are Risks with Using Gene Technology in Medicine

1) Increased stress — if someone knew from an early age that they're susceptible to a nasty brain disease, they could panic every time they get a headache (even if they never get the disease).
2) Gene-ism — people with genetic problems could come under pressure not to have children.
3) Discrimination by employers and insurers — life insurance could become impossible to get (or blummin' expensive at least) if you have any genetic likelihood of serious disease. And employers may discriminate against people who are genetically likely to get a disease.
4) Unfair health system — creating specific drugs for different people will increase costs for companies that develop the drugs. So the new drugs will be more expensive, which could lead to a two-tier health service — only wealthier people could afford these new drugs.
5) Practical risks — some people worry that we may do more harm than good by using gene technology. We don't know what effects there may be in future generations.

New medicines coming soon — in skinny, bootcut, hipster...

These new medicines are only possibilities — some may happen soon, some will take ages, and others might not happen at all. You must know the benefits and the risks. No problem — you were going to learn it all anyway.

Q1 Type 2 diabetes is caused by a combination of genetic and lifestyle factors. Explain how our understanding of the human genome may help doctors prevent more cases of type 2 diabetes. [2 marks]

Revision Questions for Topic B6

Wow, that was a massive topic. It's time to put yourself to the test and find out how much you really know.

- Try these questions and tick off each one when you get it right.
- When you've done all the questions under a heading and are completely happy with it, tick it off.

Investigating Distribution and Abundance (p.77-80)

1) What would you use a sweep net for?
2) Describe how you would use a quadrat to compare the distribution of dandelions in two areas.
3) Give two abiotic factors that can affect the distribution of organisms.
4) Describe how you can estimate the percentage cover of an organism in a quadrat.

Ecosystems, Maintaining Biodiversity and Environmental Change (p.81-84)

5) Give three human activities which reduce the amount of land available to other organisms.
6) Describe how preventing the introduction of harmful species can help protect biodiversity.
7) Explain why maintaining biodiversity by setting up conservation schemes can be challenging.
8) How could a change in the availability of water cause the distribution of organisms to change?

Food Security, Increasing Yields and Genetic Engineering (p.85-90)

9) List five factors that affect the level of food security.
10) Explain how biological controls can increase agricultural yields.
11) Give three examples of how crops could be genetically modified to increase yields.
12) What is selective breeding?
13) In genetic engineering, what is a vector?
14) Describe two ethical issues that genetic engineering raises.

Health and Disease (p.91-95)

15) What is a communicable disease?
16) Explain how the tobacco mosaic virus is transmitted between plants.
17) Give three ways that the spread of disease in plants can be controlled.
18) Give one chemical method of defence used by plants.
19) Explain how the production of antibodies helps the body defend itself against disease.

Treating Disease and the Development of Medicines (p.96-101)

20) What are antiseptics?
21) Describe an experiment you could do to investigate the effectiveness of different antibiotics.
22) Give the formula you need to calculate the area of a clear zone in a bacterial lawn.
23) Give three things that can happen when a drug is at the pre-clinical testing stage of development.
24) Why does a pregnancy test strip turn blue when you wee on it if you're pregnant?
25) Explain how monoclonal antibodies can be used to treat cancer.

Non-Communicable Diseases and Advances in Medicine (p.102-106)

26) Give three health problems that are linked to eating too much.
27) Describe a global trend in the incidence of non-communicable diseases.
28) Describe the risks of using surgical procedures to treat cardiovascular disease.
29) Why do stem cells have the potential to be useful in the treatment of disease?
30) Give three potential risks of using gene technology in medicine.

Safety, Ethics and Sampling

- Topic B7 covers practical skills you'll need to know about for your course (including 15% of your exams).
- You're required to do at least 8 practical activities (experiments). These are covered in Topics B1-B6 earlier in the book and they're highlighted with practical stamps like this one. PRACTICAL
- The following pages of this topic cover some extra bits and bobs you need to know about practical work. First up, safety in the lab...

Make Sure You're Working Safely in the Lab

1) Before you start any experiment, make sure you know about any safety precautions to do with your method or the chemicals you're using. You need to follow any instructions that your teacher gives you carefully. The chemicals you're using may be hazardous — for example, they might be flammable (catch fire easily), or they might irritate or burn your skin if it comes into contact with them.
2) Make sure that you're wearing sensible clothing when you're in the lab (e.g. open shoes won't protect your feet from spillages). When you're doing an experiment, you should wear a lab coat to protect your skin and clothing. Depending on the experiment, you may need to also wear safety goggles and gloves.
3) You also need to be aware of general safety in the lab, e.g. keep anything flammable away from lit Bunsen burners, don't directly touch any hot equipment, handle glassware carefully so it doesn't break, etc.

You Need to Think About Ethical Issues In Your Experiments

1) Any organisms involved in your investigations need to be treated safely and ethically.
2) Animals need to be treated humanely — they should be handled carefully and any wild animals captured for studying (e.g. during an investigation of the distribution of an organism) should be returned to their original habitat. Any animals kept in the lab should also be cared for in a humane way, e.g. they should not be kept in overcrowded conditions.
3) If you're carrying out an experiment involving other students (e.g. investigating the effect of caffeine on reaction time), they should not be forced to participate against their will or feel pressured to take part.

Organisms Should Be Sampled At Random Sites in an Area

1) It's generally not possible to count every single organism in an area. So if you're interested in the distribution of an organism in an area, or its population size, you need to take samples of the population in the area you're interested in.
2) You can use quadrats or transects to take population samples — see pages 78 and 80.
3) If you only take samples from one part of an area, your results will be biased — they may not give an accurate representation of the whole area.
4) To make sure that your sampling isn't biased, it needs to be random. This means you need to use a method of choosing sampling sites in which every site has an equal chance of being chosen. For example:

If you're looking at plant species in a field...

1) Divide the field into a grid.
2) Label the grid along the bottom and up the side with numbers or letters.
3) Use a random number generator (e.g. on a computer or calculator) to select coordinates, e.g. 2,4; 7,3.
4) Take your samples at these coordinates.

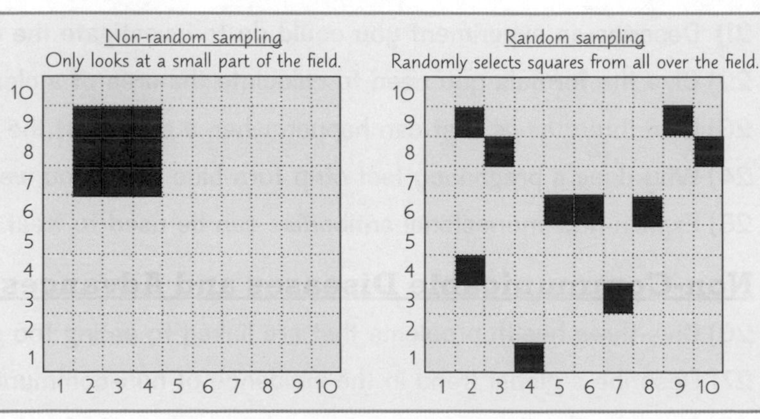

There's a single birch in my garden — it's a random sapling...

Have a good think about safety, ethics and bias before you start any experimental work — it's all important stuff.

Measuring Substances

Get your lab coats on, it's time to find out about the skills you'll need in experiments...

Use the Right Apparatus to Take Accurate Readings

1) Length

1) Length can be measured in different units (e.g. mm, cm, m). Smaller units have a higher degree of accuracy. For example, it's more accurate to measure the length of a potato cylinder to the nearest mm than the nearest cm.
2) You'll need to decide on the appropriate level of accuracy for your experiment. For example, the length of a leaf would be better measured in millimetres, but the length of a transect line would be better measured in metres.
3) It is also important to choose the right equipment when measuring length — a ruler would probably be best for small things, but a metre rule or tape measure would be better for larger distances.

2) Area

In biology, you might need to measure the area of something (e.g. part of a habitat, a living thing). Living things are usually quite complex shapes, but you can make their area easier to work out by comparing them to a simpler shape and working out the area of that (e.g. clear zones in bacterial lawns are roughly circular — see p.98). To find the area of something:

1) First, you'll need to take accurate measurements of its dimensions.

> If you want to measure the area of a field (see p.78) that is rectangular, you'll need to use a tape measure or a trundle wheel to measure the length and width of the field. Record your readings in metres.

2) Then you can calculate its area.

> Area of a rectangle = length × width.
> So, if your field is 30 m by 55 m, the area would be 30 × 55 = 1650 m^2.

Don't forget the units of area are always something squared, e.g. mm^2.

Here are some examples of other area formulas that may come in useful:

- Area of a triangle = ½ × base × height
- Area of a circle = πr^2

3) Mass

To weigh a solid, start by putting the container you are weighing your substance into on a balance. Set the balance to exactly zero and then weigh out the correct amount of your substance. Easy peasy.

4) Time

1) If your experiment involves timing something (e.g. how long a reaction takes to happen) or taking measurements at regular intervals, it's probably best to use a stopwatch.
2) Using a stopwatch that measures to the nearest 0.1 s will make your results more accurate.
3) Always make sure you start and stop the stopwatch at exactly the right time. For example, if you're investigating the rate of a reaction, you should start timing at the exact moment you mix the reagents and start the reaction.
4) It's a good idea to get the same person to do the timing so the results are as precise as possible.

5) Temperature

You can use a thermometer to measure the temperature of a solution. Make sure that the bulb of the thermometer is completely submerged in the solution and that you wait for the temperature to stabilise before you take your initial reading. Read off the scale on the thermometer at eye level to make sure your reading is correct.

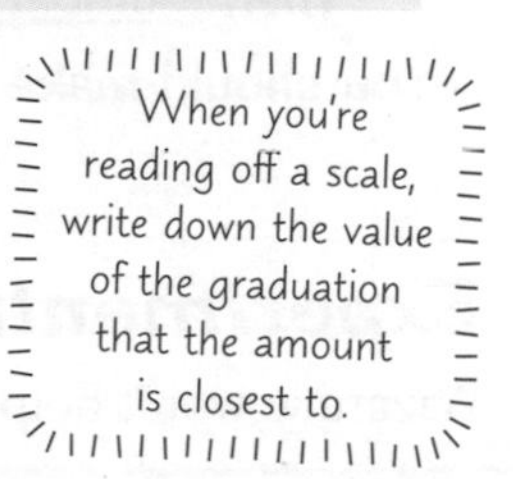

Measuring Substances

6) Volume of a Liquid

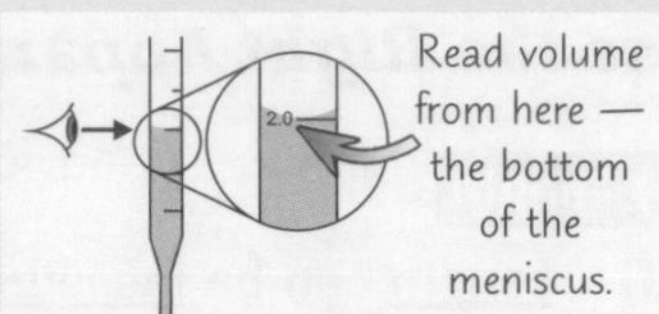

There's more than one way to measure the volume of a liquid. Whichever method you use, always read the volume from the bottom of the meniscus (the curved upper surface of the liquid) when it's at eye level.

- Using a pipette — Pipettes are used to suck up and transfer volumes of liquid between containers. Dropping pipettes are used to transfer drops of liquid. Graduated pipettes are used to transfer accurate volumes. A pipette filler is attached to the end of a graduated pipette, to control the amount of liquid being drawn up.
- Using a measuring cylinder — Measuring cylinders come in all different sizes. Make sure you choose one that's the right size for the measurement you want to make. It's no good using a huge 1 dm³ cylinder to measure out 2 cm³ of a liquid — the graduations will be too big, and you'll end up with massive errors. It'd be much better to use one that measures up to 10 cm³.

7) Volume of a Gas

1) To accurately measure the volume of gas, you should use a gas syringe.
2) Alternatively, you can use an upturned measuring cylinder filled with water. The gas will displace the water so you can read the volume off the scale — this method is shown on page 19.

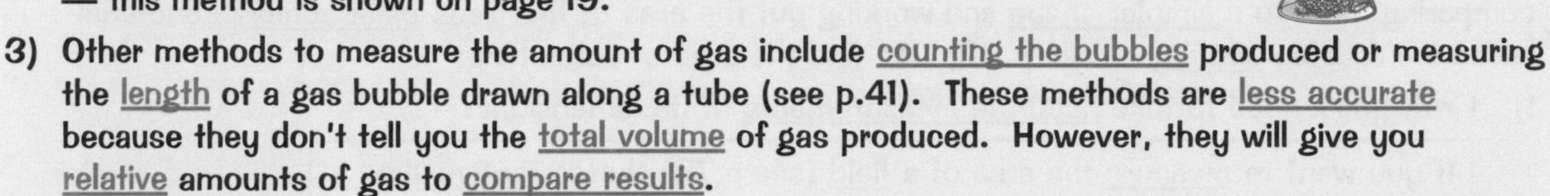

3) Other methods to measure the amount of gas include counting the bubbles produced or measuring the length of a gas bubble drawn along a tube (see p.41). These methods are less accurate because they don't tell you the total volume of gas produced. However, they will give you relative amounts of gas to compare results.
4) When you're measuring a gas, you need to make sure that the equipment is set up so that none of the gas can escape, otherwise your results won't be accurate.

8) pH

The method you should use to measure pH depends on what your experiment is.

1) Indicators are dyes that change colour depending on whether they're in an acid or an alkali. You use them by adding a couple of drops of the indicator to the solution you're interested in. Universal indicator is a mixture of indicators that changes colour gradually as pH changes. It's useful for estimating the pH of a solution based on its colour.
2) Indicator paper is useful if you don't want to colour the entire solution that you're testing. It changes colour depending on the pH of the solution it touches. You can also hold a piece of damp indicator paper in a gas sample to test its pH.
3) pH meters have a digital display that gives an accurate value for the pH of a solution.

Blue litmus paper turns red in acidic conditions and red litmus paper turns blue in alkaline conditions.

You Should be Able to Measure Your Pulse

For experiments that involve finding your heart rate, e.g. investigating the effect of exercise on heart rate (see p.20), you need to know how to measure your pulse. Here's how to do it:

1) Find your pulse in your wrist by placing your index and middle fingers where the base of your thumb meets your forearm.
2) Count the number of beats in 15 seconds — get a friend to measure the time with a stopwatch. Then multiply by four to get the number of beats per minute.

You should make sure you practise measuring your pulse before you have to do it for real in the experiment.

Experimentus apparatus...

Wizardry won't help you here, unfortunately. It's best you just get your head down and learn this stuff.

Heating Substances and Drawing Observations

Some more useful biology skills for you now — this time, it's all about heating things up and drawing stuff.

Bunsen Burners Have a Naked Flame

Bunsen burners are good for heating things quickly. But you need to make sure you're using them safely:

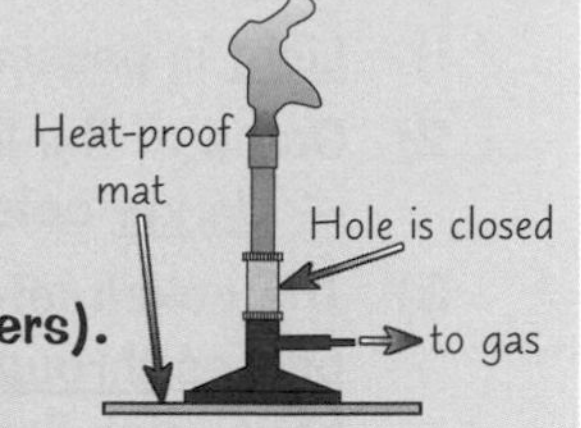

- You should always use a Bunsen burner on a heat-proof mat.
- If your Bunsen burner is alight but not heating anything, make sure you close the hole so that the flame becomes yellow and clearly visible.
- Use the blue flame to heat things. If you're heating a vessel in the flame, hold it at the top (e.g. with tongs) and point the opening away from yourself (and others).
- If you're heating something over the flame (e.g. a beaker of water), you should put a tripod and gauze over the Bunsen burner before you light it, and place the vessel on this.

The Temperature of Electric Water Baths and Electric Heaters Can Be Set

1) A water bath is a container filled with water that can be heated to a specific temperature. A simple water bath can be made by heating a beaker of water over a Bunsen burner and monitoring the temperature with a thermometer. However, it is difficult to keep the temperature of the water constant.
2) An electric water bath will monitor and adjust the temperature for you. Here's how you use one:
   - Set the temperature on the water bath, and allow the water to heat up.
   - To make sure it's reached the right temperature, use a thermometer.
   - Place the boiling tube containing your substance in the water bath using test tube holders. The level of the water outside the boiling tube should be just above the level of the substance inside the boiling tube.
   - The substance will then be warmed to the same temperature as the water. As the substance in the boiling tube is surrounded by water, the heating is very even.

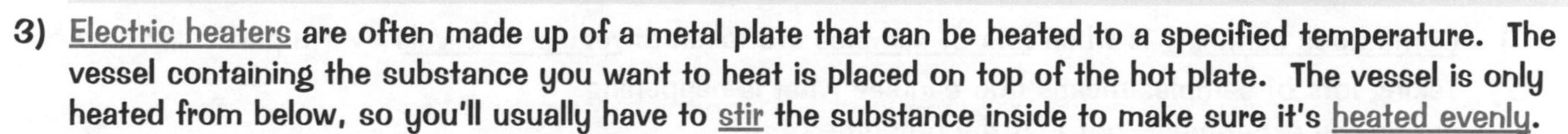

3) Electric heaters are often made up of a metal plate that can be heated to a specified temperature. The vessel containing the substance you want to heat is placed on top of the hot plate. The vessel is only heated from below, so you'll usually have to stir the substance inside to make sure it's heated evenly.

Draw Your Observations Neatly with a Pencil

1) You should draw what you see under the microscope using a pencil with a sharp point.
2) Make sure your drawing takes up at least half of the space available and that it is drawn with clear, unbroken lines.
3) Your drawing should not include any colouring or shading.
4) If you are drawing cells, the subcellular structures should be drawn in proportion.
5) Remember to include a title of what you were observing and write down the magnification that it was observed under.
6) You should also label the important features of your drawing (e.g. nucleus, chloroplasts), using straight lines. Make sure that none of these lines cross each other because this can make them hard to read.

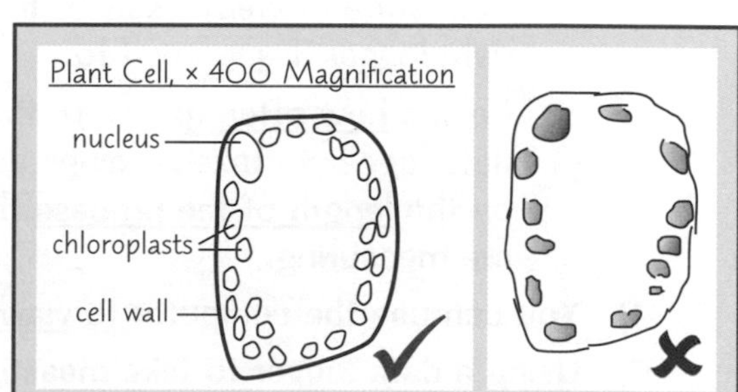

Electric water bath, lots of bubbles and a good book — suits me...

Ah, Bunsen burners — always make me feel like a real scientist. You've got to be on guard when there's fire about though. Using electric water baths or hot plates can be a safer way to go — but there's still the potential for scalds if you're not careful. At least you can always do some nice drawings if dealing with hazards gets too much.

Colorimetry and Continuous Sampling

OK, last stop on this whirlwind tour of practical skills. Colorimetry is used for measuring colour and continuous sampling is used to measure whatever you want... continuously. Hold onto your hats, here comes the fun...

Colorimeters Measure the Intensity of Colour

Colorimeters are machines that measure colour. They work like this:

1) Light is passed through a solution.
2) Some of the light is absorbed by the solution — darker colours absorb more light than lighter colours.
3) The colorimeter measures the amount of light that passes through the solution and uses this to work out how much light was absorbed.

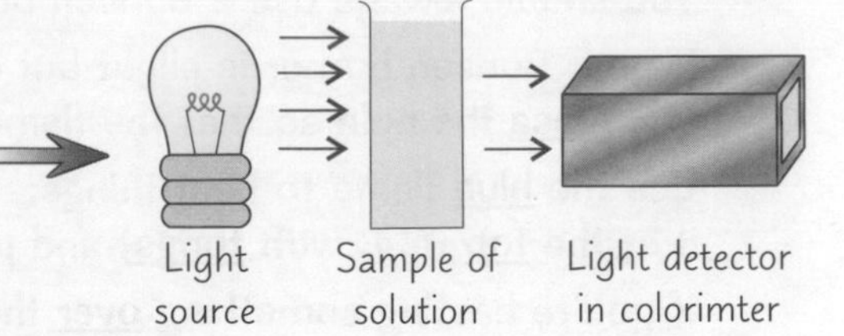

4) A reading of absorbance is given (the amount of light absorbed). The higher the absorbance, the darker the colour of the solution.
5) You can use the absorbance value for a particular colour to determine a colour change. For example:

- If you are investigating the rate at which amylase breaks down starch into maltose (see page 19), you may want to know the exact point at which all the starch has been broken down.
- This is shown in the experiment by the colour change from blue-black to browny-orange.
- If you measure the absorbance value with a colorimeter for pure maltose (browny-orange colour), you can compare the absorbance readings for other samples taken during the experiment to this to determine when exactly that colour change takes place.
- If you have a data logger (see below) you can take continuous samples of the changing absorbance of a solution during a reaction.

Data Loggers can be Used to Take Continuous Samples

1) Continuous sampling is when lots of samples are taken at regular intervals over a particular time period.
2) Taking lots of samples means you can see what is happening during the experiment, not just the outcome of it.
3) Using a data logger connected to a computer is an example of continuous sampling. If you're going to use a data logger in one of your experiments, you'll need to:
   - Decide what you are measuring and what type of data logger you will need, e.g. temperature, pH.
   - Connect an external sensor to the data logger if you need to.
   - Decide how often you want the data logger to take readings depending on the length of the process that you are measuring.

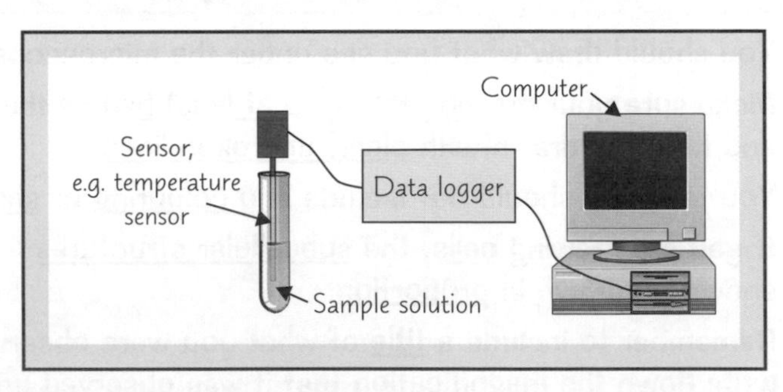

4) You can use the computer to view the data and to process it (draw graphs, calculate averages, etc.).
5) Using a data logger to take measurements can improve the accuracy of your results because you can take a large sample size.

When revising, I find continuous samples of chocolate help...

Colorimetry and data logging are two useful ways of improving your experiment by getting a bit of equipment to take readings with a higher degree of accuracy than you or I ever could — that's modern technology for you. Aaaand that's the end of Practical Skills, folks. Go forth, and science like you've never scienced before...

Answers

p.12 — Cells and Microscopy

Q1 It provides a selective barrier to control what goes in and out of the cell ***[1 mark]***. It contains receptor molecules that are used for cell communication ***[1 mark]***.

p.13 — Light Microscopy

Q1 Place a drop of mountant/water on the slide ***[1 mark]***. Use tweezers to place the specimen on the mountant ***[1 mark]***. Add a drop of stain ***[1 mark]***. Carefully apply a cover slip over the specimen ***[1 mark]***.

p.14 — More on Light Microscopy

Q1 total magnification = eyepiece lens magnification × objective lens magnification
$8 \times 15 = 120$
so the total magnification is ×120
[1 mark].

p.15 — DNA

Q1 It's a large, complex molecule made up of nucleotides (monomers) joined together in a long chain ***[1 mark]***.

Q2 a) G ***[1 mark]***

b) Each base forms cross links to a base on the opposite strand ***[1 mark]***. This keeps the two DNA strands wound tightly together ***[1 mark]***.

p.16 — Protein Synthesis

Q1 The order of bases in a gene determines the order of amino acids in a protein ***[1 mark]***. Each gene contains a different order of bases which means that it codes for particular protein ***[1 mark]***.

Q2 A single DNA strand is used as a template to make the mRNA ***[1 mark]***. Base pairing means that the mRNA strand that forms is complementary to the DNA strand ***[1 mark]***.

Q3 Amino acids that match the triplet code ***[1 mark]*** on the mRNA ***[1 mark]*** are joined together in the cytoplasm to make a protein ***[1 mark]***.

p.17 — Enzymes

Q1 C ***[1 mark]***

Q2 Enzymes have an active site ***[1 mark]***, which the substrate has to fit into in order for the reaction to be catalysed ***[1 mark]***. This means that enzymes usually only work with one substrate so they are very specific ***[1 mark]***.

p.18 — More on Enzymes

Q1 The enzyme's activity may slow down/stop ***[1 mark]*** because the enzyme may be irreversibly denatured ***[1 mark]***. A pH higher than pH 4 will interfere with the bonds holding the enzyme together ***[1 mark]***. This may change the shape of the active site ***[1 mark]*** so the substrate can no longer fit ***[1 mark]***.

p.19 — Investigating Enzyme Activity

Q1 $33 \div 60 = 0.55$ cm^3/second ***[1 mark]***

p.20 — Respiration

Q1 glucose + oxygen → carbon dioxide + water ***[1 mark for correct reactants, 1 mark for correct products]***

p.21 — Anaerobic Respiration

Q1 Ethanol and carbon dioxide ***[1 mark]***.

Q2 E.g. aerobic respiration produces much more ATP than anaerobic respiration ***[1 mark]***.

p.22 — Respiration Experiments

Q1 A flask with boiled/dead beans ***[1 mark]***.

p.23 — Biological Molecules

Q1 a) (simple) sugars ***[1 mark]***

b) amino acids ***[1 mark]***

Q2 E.g. so that energy can be transferred from their breakdown during respiration ***[1 mark]***.

p.24 — Testing for Biological Molecules

Q1 Protein is present in the sample ***[1 mark]***.

p.25 — Photosynthesis

Q1 Photosynthesis produces glucose ***[1 mark]***, which is used to make larger, complex molecules that make up the mass of the plant's living material/the plant's biomass ***[1 mark]***.

p.26 — The Rate of Photosynthesis

Q1 Initially, as the temperature increases, the rate of photosynthesis increases ***[1 mark]*** because the enzymes needed for photosynthesis work faster at higher temperatures ***[1 mark]***. However, if the temperature gets too hot, the enzymes start to denature ***[1 mark]*** so the rate of photosynthesis decreases dramatically beyond this point ***[1 mark]***.

p.28 — The Cell Cycle and Mitosis

Q1 When the cell divides during mitosis, the two new cells will contain identical DNA ***[1 mark]***.

Q2 Mitosis is when a cell reproduces itself by splitting to form two identical offspring ***[1 mark]***.

p.29 — Cell Differentiation and Stem Cells

Q1 Differentiation is the process by which a cell changes to become specialised for its job ***[1 mark]***.

p.30 — Diffusion and Active Transport

Q1 a) The net movement of particles from an area of higher concentration to an area of lower concentration ***[1 mark]***.

b) The movement of particles across a membrane against a concentration gradient/from an area of lower to an area of higher concentration ***[1 mark]*** using ATP released during respiration ***[1 mark]***.

p.31 — Osmosis

Q1 Osmosis is the net movement of water molecules across a partially permeable membrane from a region of higher water concentration to a region of lower water concentration / Osmosis is the diffusion of water molecules across a partially permeable membrane down a water potential gradient (i.e. from an area of higher water potential to an area of lower water potential) ***[1 mark]***.

Q2 E.g. the piece of carrot will shrivel and become floppy ***[1 mark]***. This is because the cells become flaccid/lose water as a result of osmosis ***[1 mark]***.

p.32 — Investigating Osmosis

Q1 $$\text{percentage change} = \frac{11.4 - 13.3}{13.3} \times 100$$
$= -14.3\%$
[2 marks for correct answer, 1 mark for correct answer without minus sign]

p.33 — Exchanging Substances

Q1 surface area = $5 \times 5 \times 6 = 150$ cm^2
volume = $5 \times 5 \times 5 = 125$ cm^3
surface area : volume ratio
= 150 : 125
= 6 : 5 ***[1 mark]***

p.34 — Exchange Surfaces

Q1 It means that substances only have to travel a short distance ***[1 mark]***.

p.35 — More on Exchange Surfaces

Q1 Any three from: leaves are broad, so there's a large surface area for diffusion. / Leaves are thin, which means gases only have to travel a short distance. / There are air spaces inside the leaf, which let carbon dioxide and oxygen move easily between cells. / Air spaces inside the leaf increase the surface area for gas exchange. / The lower surface is full of little holes called stomata, which let carbon dioxide and oxygen diffuse in and out ***[1 mark for each correct answer, up to 3 marks]***.

Q2 Each branch of a plant's roots is covered in millions of root hair cells ***[1 mark]***, which gives the plant a big surface area for absorbing water and mineral ions from the soil ***[1 mark]***.

p.36 — The Circulatory System

Q1 the right ventricle ***[1 mark]***

p.37 — The Blood Vessels

Q1 They have a big lumen to help the blood flow despite the low pressure ***[1 mark]*** and they have valves to keep the blood flowing in the right direction ***[1 mark]***.

Q2 E.g. networks of capillaries carry blood to every cell in the body to exchange substances with them ***[1 mark]***. They have permeable walls, so that substances can easily diffuse in and out of them ***[1 mark]***. Their walls are only one cell thick, which increases the rate of diffusion ***[1 mark]***.

p.38 — The Blood

Q1 E.g. red blood cells have a large surface area to volume ratio for absorbing oxygen ***[1 mark]***. They don't have a nucleus, which allows more room for carrying oxygen ***[1 mark]***. They contain haemoglobin, which can combine with oxygen in the lungs and release it in body tissues ***[1 mark]***.

p.39 — Plant Transport Systems and Transpiration

Q1 Water evaporates and diffuses from a plant's surface, creating a slight shortage of water in the leaf ***[1 mark]***. This draws more water up from the rest of the plant through the xylem vessels to replace it ***[1 mark]***. This in turn means more water is drawn up from the roots ***[1 mark]***.

p.40 — More on Transpiration

Q1 guard cells ***[1 mark]***

Q2 In low light conditions, the stomata begin to close ***[1 mark]***. This means that very little water can escape and the rate of transpiration decreases ***[1 mark]***.

Q3 As it gets warmer, the rate of transpiration increases ***[1 mark]*** because when it's warm the water particles have more energy to evaporate and diffuse out of the stomata ***[1 mark]***.

p.41 — Investigating Transpiration

Q1 Any two from: e.g. air humidity / light intensity / air movement ***[2 marks]***.

p.43 — The Nervous System

Q1 brain ***[1 mark]***, spinal cord ***[1 mark]***

p.44 — The Eye

Q1 It refracts light into the eye ***[1 mark]***.

Q2 The lens may be the wrong shape ***[1 mark]***. / The eyeball may be too short ***[1 mark]***.

p.45 — The Brain

Q1 a) E.g. it is involved in maintaining body temperature at the normal level / it produces hormones that control the pituitary gland ***[1 mark]***.

b) E.g. it controls unconscious activities / it controls breathing / it controls heart rate ***[1 mark]***.

c) E.g. it is responsible for muscle coordination ***[1 mark]***.

p.46 — Hormones and Negative Feedback Systems

Q1 Endocrine glands secrete hormones ***[1 mark]***. These act as chemical messengers ***[1 mark]*** and travel in the bloodstream ***[1 mark]*** to target cells / organs ***[1 mark]***. These have receptors so they can respond to the hormone ***[1 mark]***.

p.47 — Hormones in Reproduction

Q1 LH stimulates the release of an egg/ ovulation ***[1 mark]***. It also indirectly stimulates progesterone production ***[1 mark]***.

p.48 — Hormones for Fertility and Contraception

Q1 The hormones FSH and LH ***[1 mark]*** can be injected by women with naturally low FSH levels ***[1 mark]*** to stimulate ovulation ***[1 mark]***.

p.49 — More on Contraception

Q1 E.g. oral contraceptives can have unpleasant side-effects ***[1 mark]***. / She might find it difficult to remember to take a pill every day ***[1 mark]***.

Q2 Any two from: e.g. IUDs are more effective. / IUDs are longer acting. / There's less chance of IUDs not working as they are intended ***[1 mark for each correct answer, up to 2 marks]***.

p.50 — Plant Growth Hormones

Q1 a root ***[1 mark]***

p.51 — Uses of Plant Hormones

Q1 E.g. stimulates seed germination ***[1 mark]***, stimulates stem growth ***[1 mark]***, stimulates flowering ***[1 mark]***.

p.52 — Homeostasis

Q1 Less blood flows near the surface of the skin ***[1 mark]*** because blood vessels near the surface constrict (vasoconstriction) ***[1 mark]***. This means less energy is transferred to the surroundings, which helps keep the person warm ***[1 mark]***.

p.53 — Controlling Blood Sugar Level

Q1 In type 1 diabetes, the person produces little or no insulin ***[1 mark]***, whereas in type 2 diabetes, the person still produces insulin but they are resistant to it/don't respond properly to it ***[1 mark]***.

p.54 — Controlling Water Content

Q1 The cell may burst/lysis may occur ***[1 mark]*** as there will be a net movement of water into the cell by osmosis ***[1 mark]***.

p.55 — More on Controlling Water Content

Q1 ADH helps to control the water content of the blood ***[1 mark]*** as it affects the permeability of the nephrons/kidney tubules ***[1 mark]***, which determines how much water is reabsorbed back into the blood ***[1 mark]***.

Q2 When it's hot more sweat may be produced ***[1 mark]***. Sweat causes water to be lost from the body ***[1 mark]***. When the brain detects the fall in the water content of the blood, it triggers feelings of thirst ***[1 mark]***.

p.57 — The Carbon Cycle

Q1 E.g. not as much CO_2 in the air is being used for photosynthesis ***[1 mark]***. Microorganisms involved in the decomposition of the dead trees release CO_2 into the atmosphere through respiration ***[1 mark]***.

p.58 — The Nitrogen Cycle and the Water Cycle

Q1 Decomposers turn proteins in dead leaves into ammonia, which goes on to form ammonium ions ***[1 mark]***. Then nitrifying bacteria turn the ammonium ions into nitrates ***[1 mark]***.

p.59 — Decomposition

Q1 Any two from: e.g. make sure that plenty of oxygen can get in to the waste. / Keep the compost bin in a warm place. / Make sure that the waste is moist but not too wet ***[1 mark for each correct answer, up to 2 marks]***.

p.60 — Ecosystems and Interactions Between Organisms

Q1 All the organisms (different species) living in a habitat ***[1 mark]***.

Q2 Any two from: e.g. temperature / moisture level / light intensity / pH of the soil ***[1 mark for each correct answer, up to 2 marks]***.

p.61 — More On Interactions Between Organisms

Q1 Mutualism ***[1 mark]*** as the relationship benefits both the cow and the microorganisms ***[1 mark]***.

p.62 — Food Chains and Food Webs

Q1 a) hawk / ladybird ***[1 mark]***

b) producers ***[1 mark]***

c) E.g. the number of hawks might increase because there will be more mice for them to eat ***[1 mark]***. The amount of wheat might decrease because more will be eaten by the mice ***[1 mark]***. The number of aphids might decrease because they would be competing with more mice for food ***[1 mark]***. The number of humans might decrease because they would be competing with more mice for food ***[1 mark]***.

p.63 — Pyramids of Biomass and Number

Q1 The mass of living material at that stage of the food chain/at that trophic level ***[1 mark]***.

Q2 B, because the bar for the producer is smaller than for the primary consumer ***[1 mark]*** and just one tree/large plant may feed many consumers ***[1 mark]***.

p.64 — Biomass Transfer

Q1 Any two from: respiration / excretion / egestion ***[1 mark for each correct answer, up to 2 marks]***

Q2 $110 \div 995 \times 100 = 11\%$ ***[1 mark]***

p.66 — Genes and Variation

Q1 Your height is partly influenced by your genome because your genes control how tall you can grow ***[1 mark]***. But your height will also be affected by environmental factors, such as your diet, because if you don't take in enough food you won't be able to grow as tall ***[1 mark]***.

p.67 — Genetic Variants

Q1 A gene mutation alters the base sequence of DNA in a gene ***[1 mark]***, which may affect the order of amino acids in the chain ***[1 mark]***. This may lead to changes in the protein produced, leading to a possible change in phenotype ***[1 mark]***.

p.68 — Sexual Reproduction and Meiosis

Q1 During fertilisation, a male gamete fuses with a female gamete to form a fertilised egg ***[1 mark]***. The gametes need to be haploid so that the fertilised egg ends up with the diploid number of chromosomes, and not twice as many ***[1 mark]***.

Q2 When the cell divides, some of the father's chromosomes and some of the mother's chromosomes go into each new cell ***[1 mark]***. The mixing up of the chromosomes/genes creates genetic variation ***[1 mark]***.

p.69 — Comparing Asexual and Sexual Reproduction

Q1 E.g. reproducing asexually can produce lots of offspring very quickly so the strawberry plant could spread quickly ***[1 mark]***. It also means that the strawberry plant can take advantage of good conditions for growth without needing a mate ***[1 mark]***. However, asexual reproduction produces genetically identical organisms ***[1 mark]***. This means that if environmental conditions change, making it difficult for the strawberry plant to survive, the whole population of strawberry plants could be affected ***[1 mark]***.

p.70 — Genetic Diagrams

Q1 a) E.g.

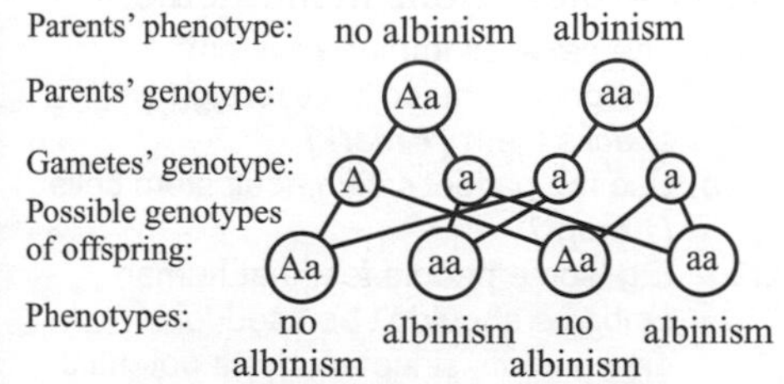

[1 mark for correctly identifying the parents' genotypes, 1 mark for correctly completing a genetic diagram.]

b) 50% ***[1 mark]***

p.71 — Sex Chromosomes and The Work of Mendel

Q1 E.g.

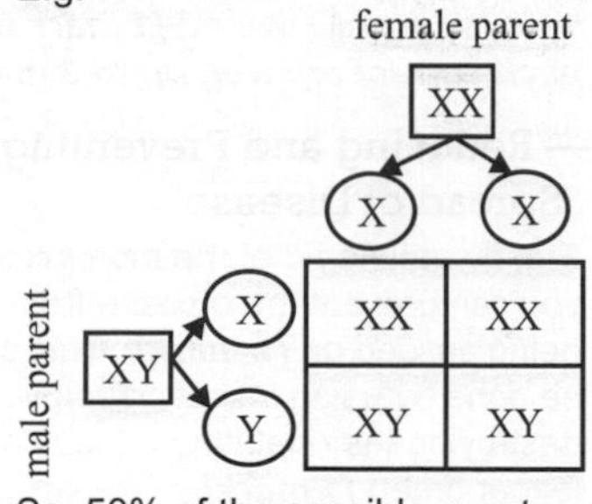

So, 50% of the possible genotypes are XX (girls) and 50% are XY (boys) so the probability of the baby being a boy or girl is equal.
[1 mark for correctly identifying the parents' gametes, 1 mark for correctly completing the diagram]

p.72 — Classification

Q1 An artificial classification system sorts organisms into groups depending on their observable features ***[1 mark]***, whereas a natural classification system sorts organisms into groups based on their evolutionary relationships/common ancestors and common structural features ***[1 mark]***.

p.73 — Evolution and Natural Selection

Q1 Some of the musk oxen may have had a gene variant/allele which gave them thicker fur ***[1 mark]***. Those musk oxen would have been more likely to survive and reproduce ***[1 mark]*** and so pass on their gene variants/alleles for thicker fur ***[1 mark]***. This process of natural selection may have continued over many generations, leading to all musk oxen having thick fur ***[1 mark]***.

p.74 — Evidence for Evolution

Q1 D ***[1 mark]***

Q2 Fossils can show what organisms that lived a long time ago looked like ***[1 mark]***. Arranging them in chronological/date order shows how organisms gradually changed/developed ***[1 mark]***.

p.75 — Darwin and Wallace

Q1 E.g. observations by Wallace provided evidence to help support the theory ***[1 mark]***.

p.77 — Investigating Distribution and Abundance

Q1 E.g. the student could use a pitfall trap in each area of woodland ***[1 mark]***. Each trap could be set up and left overnight ***[1 mark]***. The next day, insects present in the traps could be counted and the student could compare what was found in the two traps ***[1 mark]***.

p.78 — More on Investigating Distribution and Abundance

Q1 Population size = (number in first sample × number in second sample) ÷ number in second sample previously marked
= (22 × 26) ÷ 4
= 143 crabs ***[2 marks for correct answer, otherwise 1 mark for correct working]***

p.79 — Using Keys and Factors Affecting Distribution

Q1 Any two from: e.g. air temperature / sand temperature / sand moisture level / sand pH ***[1 mark for each correct answer, up to 2 marks]***.

p.80 — Using Transects

Q1 E.g. mark out a line/transect across the field using a tape measure ***[1 mark]***. Place a quadrat at the start of the line and count and record the organisms you find in the quadrat ***[1 mark]***. Then place your quadrat at the next sampling point on the transect and count and record the organisms you find in the quadrat ***[1 mark]***. The second sampling point could be at an interval along the line (e.g. every 2 metres) or directly after the first quadrat ***[1 mark]***. Carry on sampling until you reach the end of your transect ***[1 mark]***.

p.81 — Human Impacts on Ecosystems

Q1 E.g. the building of houses on a meadow would involve destruction of the habitats provided by the meadow ***[1 mark]***. This is likely to reduce the number of species that can live in the area, therefore reducing biodiversity ***[1 mark]***.

p.82 — More Human Impacts on Ecosystems

Q1 E.g. individual plants grown in the botanical gardens could be reintroduced into the wild ***[1 mark]***. By reintroducing plants into the protected habitat areas it's more likely that they'll survive as the habitat is protected from damage ***[1 mark]***.

p.83 — Maintaining Biodiversity

Q1 E.g. undiscovered plant species may contain new medicinal chemicals ***[1 mark]***. If these plants are allowed to become extinct we could miss out on valuable medicines ***[1 mark]***.

p.84 — Impacts of Environmental Change

Q1 E.g. some species may become more widely distributed, e.g. species that need warmer temperatures may spread further as the conditions they thrive in exist over a wider area ***[1 mark]***. Other species may become less widely distributed, e.g. species that need cooler temperatures may have smaller ranges as the conditions they thrive in exist over a smaller area ***[1 mark]***.

p.85 — Food Security

Q1 E.g. a pathogen such as a bacterium, fungus or virus could result in the loss of crops ***[1 mark]*** and could lead to widespread famine reducing the level of food security ***[1 mark]***.

p.86 — Ways of Increasing Agricultural Yields

Q1 a) Mean yield = (30 + 28 + 32 + 35) ÷ 4 = 31 tonnes per hectare ***[2 marks for correct answer, otherwise 1 mark for correct working]***.

b) Year 5 yield = 35 × 1.06 = 37 tonnes per hectare ***[2 marks for correct answer, otherwise 1 mark for correct working]***.

p.87 — More Ways of Increasing Agricultural Yields

Q1 a) Hydroponics is where plants are grown in nutrient solutions (water and fertilisers) rather than soil ***[1 mark]***. They can be supported and have their roots dangling into the nutrient solution or they can be planted in a growth medium ***[1 mark]***.

b) E.g. in areas where it's difficult or impossible to grow plants in soil (such as places with harsh climates or barren soil) ***[1 mark]***.

p.88 — Selective Breeding

Q1 He should choose the bean plants that are best at surviving the drought ***[1 mark]*** and let them reproduce ***[1 mark]***. He should then continue this process over several generations ***[1 mark]***.

Q2 E.g. it reduces the gene pool which can lead to health problems developing, such as genetic disorders ***[1 mark]***. It means that if a new disease appears, the whole population could be affected because there's not much variation between individuals ***[1 mark]***.

p.89 — Genetic Engineering

Q1 They are used to identify which host cells have taken up the vector/new DNA ***[1 mark]***.

p.90 — More on Genetic Engineering

Q1 Any two from: e.g. transplanted genes may get out into the environment creating 'superweeds'. / Genetically engineered crops could adversely affect food chains/human health. / Genetically engineered crops could create unforeseen problems, which would then be passed on to future generations. / Genetically engineered crops might affect the number of weeds and flowers that live in and around the crops, reducing biodiversity ***[1 mark for each correct answer, up to 2 marks]***.

p.91 — Health and Disease

Q1 A non-communicable disease is one that cannot be passed from one organism to another ***[1 mark]***. They generally last for a long time and progress slowly ***[1 mark]***. They are often linked to unhealthy lifestyles ***[1 mark]***.

p.92 — How Disease Spreads

Q1 Any three from: e.g. in water / by air / by contact / in body fluids / by animal vectors / in soil / in food ***[1 mark for each correct answer, up to 3 marks]***.

p.93 — Reducing and Preventing the Spread of Disease

Q1 E.g. by getting rid of the mosquitoes you can prevent the disease from being passed on ***[1 mark]***. This could be done by using insecticides/by destroying their habitat so they can no longer breed ***[1 mark]***.

p.94 — Detecting Plant Disease and Plant Defences

Q1 Any two from: e.g. most plant stems and leaves have a waxy cuticle, which acts as a barrier to stop pathogens entering. / Having a waxy cuticle helps prevent water collecting on the leaf, which reduces the risk of infection by pathogens that are transferred in water. / Plant cells are surrounded by cell walls made from cellulose, which form a physical barrier against pathogens. / Pathogens can trigger the production of callose, which is deposited between cell walls and membranes to reinforce the cell wall ***[1 mark for each correct answer, up to 2 marks]***.

p.95 — The Human Immune System

Q1 When you damage a blood vessel, platelets clump together forming a blood clot ***[1 mark]***. This prevents microorganisms from entering the wound ***[1 mark]***.

p.96 — Vaccines and Medicines

Q1 The antigens on the dead pathogens in the vaccine trigger an immune response ***[1 mark]*** so your white blood cells produce antibodies to attack the pathogens ***[1 mark]***. Some of the white blood cells remain as memory cells in the blood ***[1 mark]*** so if the same pathogens appear, the antibodies to help destroy them can be produced immediately ***[1 mark]***.

p.97 — Investigating Antimicrobials

Q1 Hot air rises, so microbes in the air should be drawn away from the culture ***[1 mark]*** preventing contamination by unwanted microorganisms ***[1 mark]***.

p.98 — Comparing Antimicrobials

Q1 a) A ***[1 mark]***

b) diameter = 13 mm
radius = 13 ÷ 2 = 6.5 mm ***[1 mark]***
$\pi r^2 = \pi \times 6.5^2 = 132.7...$
$= 133\ mm^2$ ***[1 mark]***

c) E.g. a disc soaked in sterile water ***[1 mark]***.

d) To show that any difference in the growth of the bacteria is only due to the effect of the antiseptic ***[1 mark]***.

p.99 — Developing New Medicines

Q1 a) A substance that looks like the real drug but doesn't do anything ***[1 mark]***.

b) So scientists can see the actual difference the drug makes ***[1 mark]***. It allows for the placebo effect, where the patient expects the treatment to work and so feels better, even though the treatment isn't doing anything ***[1 mark]***.

p.100 — Monoclonal Antibodies

Q1 B-lymphocytes/white blood cells from mice are fused with tumour cells to make hybridomas ***[1 mark]***. The hybridomas are cloned to produce lots of identical cells ***[1 mark]***. These divide quickly and produce the monoclonal antibodies ***[1 mark]***.

p.101 — More on Monoclonal Antibodies

Q1 An antigen on the surface of a cancer cell that isn't found on normal body cells ***[1 mark]***.

Q2 The antibodies are labelled with a radioactive element and given to the patient through a drip ***[1 mark]***. When the antibodies come into contact with the cancer cells they bind to the tumour markers ***[1 mark]***. A picture of the patient's body is taken with a camera that detects radioactivity ***[1 mark]***. The cancer cells will show up as a bright spot on the image ***[1 mark]***.

p.102 — Non-Communicable Diseases

Q1 Exercise increases the amount of energy used by the body and decreases the amount of stored body fat ***[1 mark]***. It also builds muscle so it helps to boost your metabolic rate ***[1 mark]***.

p.103 — More on Non-Communicable Diseases

Q1 Any two from: e.g. cirrhosis / cardiovascular disease / cancers (e.g. mouth, throat, bowel, liver) ***[1 mark for each correct answer, up to 2 marks]***.

p.104 — Treating Cardiovascular Disease

Q1 E.g. they can cause excessive bleeding if the person taking them is hurt in an accident ***[1 mark]***.

p.105 — Stem Cells in Medicine

Q1 a) The patient's immune system recognises the cells as foreign and attacks them ***[1 mark]***.

b) Use the patient's own adult stem cells ***[1 mark]***.

Q2 E.g. some people feel that human embryos shouldn't be used for experiments since each is a potential human life ***[1 mark]***.

p.106 — Using Genome Research in Medicine

Q1 If doctors know which genes predispose people to type 2 diabetes ***[1 mark]***, they could provide individually tailored advice on the best diet and lifestyle to reduce the risk of type 2 diabetes developing ***[1 mark]***.

Index

Index